Quality Management

(Principles and Techniques)

3rd Edition

Geoff Vorley MSc, MIQA

Associate Lecturer with Surrey University
Founding Director of Quality Management & Training Ltd.

Quality Management & Training (Publications) Limited
P O Box No 172
Guildford
Surrey
GU4 7GS
Telephone/Fax: 01483 453511/2
E_Mail: Brenda@qmt.cableol.co.uk

Quality Management &Training (Publications) Limited
P O Box No 172 : Guildford : Surrey : GU4 7GS

First Published Whitehall Publications Ltd 1991
2nd Edition Nexus Business Communications Ltd 1993
3rd Edition Quality Management & Training (Publications) Ltd 1996

British Library Cataloguing in publications data

A catalogue record for this book is available from the British Library

ISBN 0 9528391 0 5

Printed and Bound in Great Britain by Biddles Limited,
Woodbridge Park Estate : Woodbridge Road : Guildford Surrey : GU1 1DA

A237

Quality Assurance Management

Table of Contents

Introduction to the book

There are an enormous number of different approaches that can be adopted in achieving that elusive objective "quality." It is a never ending quest with a whole variety of methods and techniques, some complimentary, some conflicting (examination of the Quality Philosophy section will show that even influential individuals cannot agree as to what the correct approach is). The objective of this book is to give a rounded view of the various systems, techniques and approaches available, providing the opportunity to evaluate all these different approaches and to select the most suitable for a particular set of circumstances.

There can be no one solution or approach to achieving quality because it can never ever be completely achieved. There will always be new advances and improvements. A friend and colleague once said *"You know, this Quality Assurance thing's OK, but I'll give it a year or three and something else will come along!"* That statement was made some 22 years ago, which makes the statement approximately 20 years out, with time the statement will become even more inaccurate. There are representations of Egyptian masons measuring the sizes of blocks of stone to build the Pyramids - so Quality Control (assurance) was undertaken in those days. With technology and the general public demanding ever higher quality and performance standards, then Quality Assurance will need to be in place. It may be in a different guise - Total Quality Management etc. but nevertheless just as essential today as it was in the past and will be in the future. It is because of the changes that have taken place that it has become necessary to up date, expand and reprint this book.

The book has been split into three basic sections:

Part A:
A general Introduction to Quality Assurance, discussing where historically quality assurance has been and a view on what the future direction could be. An interpretation of key quality definitions is also provided, to help cut through some of the jargon associated with Quality Assurance.

Quality Assurance Management System (QAMS), the systems or QAMS model approach to QA, including what QAMSs are available and appropriate. How these QAMSs are interpreted, implemented and monitored (Audited) in particular organisations. Not only manufacturing organisations but service and software.

Part B:
Motivation for Quality, an examination of Quality Philosophy and the various approaches suggested by influential individuals.

Total Quality Management, describing what TQM is, the approach and means of introduction and implementation, including the various techniques associated with TQM.

Part C:
A general section including such topics as:

Purchasing Control, how suppliers can be selected, controlled and their performance (service, cost and delivery) improved.
Statistical Quality Control, some of the methods that can be used to control and improve process performance.
Cost of Quality, how the Quality Department can make an active contribution towards the profitability of an organisation.
Computer Aided Quality Assurance, how the computer can be used in the quality environment and what the advantages and disadvantages are.
Law and Quality Assurance; Criminal and Civil Law, Product Liability and the implication of these various directives on the Quality Department and organisations.

The book was intended to be written in a way that hopefully makes the various techniques and approaches to Quality Assurance self explanatory. However, if the reader has any problems with the contents or has a quality problem or issue that they would like to discuss further, please do not hesitate in contacting me. I can be contacted via the publishers - I welcome the opportunity to discuss quality issues.

The book has been written by Geoff Vorley, with contributions from Mary Brightman, John Lewis and Fred Tickle.

PART A

Introduction to Quality Assurance

Traditional Quality Control

In the days when a craftsman saw the whole job through from start to finish, quality was synonymous with craftsmanship. The craftsman would see the job through from start to finish, ensuring quality at every stage. With the advent of Taylorism, Fordism, Work Study and the division of labour, firstly between 'Planners' and 'Doers', and secondly between tasks themselves, de-skilling. This led, on the one hand, to a loss of personal involvement and a sense of pride in one's work and a need for planning and coordination on the other. This resulted in the formation of centralised inspection departments and quality being controlled by filtering out defective work during inspection stages. It was reactive and detection orientated. It also tended to suggest that quality problems were related to the manufacturing process whereas studies on the origin of quality problems have shown that up to 60% of quality problems are design faults. If the traditional approach to controlling quality with the emphasis on the monitoring manufacturing or production process is employed, the best that can be achieved is to make the product perfectly wrong! Clearly there was a need to extend control of quality into other areas that could have an impact on the quality of the product or service.

Quality and Survival

Today, as never before, society is virtually totally dependent on technology and quality failures frequently have catastrophic consequences. Only 20% of our food is 'organic'. The balance of chemicals used in food production is extremely fine and we frequently hear of breakdowns in the system causing alarming outbreaks of food poisoning. Air traffic control depends totally on computers which can reach the point of overload. Currently 80% of the water authorities are failing to supply water which meets the required standards. Many treatments and cures for illnesses are totally dependant on technology. It is only in recent years that the long term damage to our environment has been realised. It can be seen from the above that it is not just the immediate customer or user who is at risk, we all are. More than at any other time in history we are relying on the correct and continuing operation of technological systems. How then do we ensure that everything that we design, make and service can be relied upon to operate every time it is required to do so?

Quality Sells

Why do people buy our products and services? Well there are a number of reasons of which price is often the major and most important reason. However there are other reasons which can sometimes be even more important; features, range of service, reliability, or quality. In order of importance, typically the sequence could be:

1. Price
2. Features of the product or range of services offered (possibly grade)
3. Reliability or Quality

How could a supplier sell more?

Spend more on advertising? - Well it is suggested that all advertising does is replace those customers which have been lost through poor quality of product or service.

Reduce the price?
Yes, get into a price war - examination of the graph opposite suggests that this option is possible but there can be serious consequences. If you are Company C then a price reduction is of advantage. This company can afford to reduce the market selling price below the

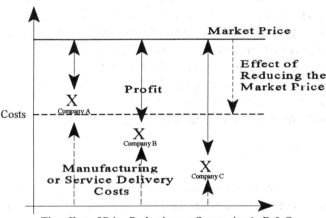

The effect of Price Reduction on Companies A, B & C

Figure 1 Price Reduction

manufacturing or service delivery costs of its competitors. Possibly making Company A's position untenable. However, Company A has problems its costs are too high to allow the company to embark on such a strategy. So much depends on the organisations market position as to whether such a price war is appropriate.

Increase the range? Improve the grade of the product or service? Yes, improvement to the product or service will affect the marketability of the product. The competition will obviously be doing the same and what becomes a new or novel feature soon becomes what the customer naturally expects as standard. Also, these enhancements may merely move the product or service into a different market sector.

Improve the quality or reliability of the service? Reduce costs and improve the customers perception that this is a quality product or service. Advertising can improve the customers perception that this is a quality product but advertising is very expensive and is not always appropriate. Advertising, as stated previously may only replace customers lost through poor quality. Consider this - It has been stated that if the customers perception is that the product or service is of a better quality than the competitors. Then the customer will pay up to 30% more for that product or service. Would you pay 30% more for a better quality product or service? Think about some recent purchases; coffee, stereo, garage services and consider if you have paid more.

All these issues need to be considered when attempting to grow and development a business. And determining a strategy for price, advertising, grade of service etc. is essential. One element of this strategy is where to place the greater emphasis. Which strategy requires the greater effort? Which will provide the best return on investment? More advertising, a price war or a quality improvement initiative?

Quality Assurance

The complexities in technology and integration of designs have made total quality control by inspection alone unsuitable. Inspection can only determine the quality of an item in the as-made condition. To ensure reliability, which is the time-dependant dimension of quality, it is necessary to build-in quality at every stage. In recent years a new approach towards achieving quality and reliability has been evolving known as the systems approach to Quality Assurance. Since every stage of the product or service cycle is a potential source of failure we need to consider just what could go wrong at each stage. Quality is the degree to which this is successfully achieved for each of the above functions. It follows therefore, that quality achievement must be planned. This implies the examination of each stage of the process and careful consideration of the potential deviations and the methods and techniques necessary to prevent the occurrence of defective work. Quality Assurance is pro-active rather than reactive.

Quality Standards

During the 1970's and '80's standards and specifications have been emerging to provide either guides or even contractual requirements for Quality Systems.

In particular, the Ministry of Defence can require contractors to install and maintain quality systems in accordance with the Allied Quality Assurance Publications (590 SERIES), depending on the content of the contract (see section Quality Assurance Management System Standards). BS EN ISO9000 provides a similar set of specifications for industry in general. For each of the above there is provision for independent assessment to monitor compliance with the respective standards.

System Review and Evaluation

Since the emphasis of Quality Assurance is that a properly designed and maintained system will result in the design and manufacture of quality products, it is essential that a regular programme of system checks is carried out. The actual observation and collection of facts about the operation of the system procedures is called a QUALITY AUDIT. The findings of such audits are reported to Senior Management for consideration and corrective action where necessary.

Quality Motivation

In spite of all the above attempts to organise for Quality Assurance in a systematic way, if the employee attitude is wrong then efforts on coordinating the systems will have only limited success. Fostering a responsible attitude by everyone towards doing "it right first time" is the most effective means there is of assuring quality. For this reason many organisations have been looking for a number of years at various ways of motivating and involving employees in the quality of their work. There are numerous approaches that can be employed; Philip C. Crosby's - Zero Defects, W. Edwards Deming - 14 Points, A. V. Feigenbaum - Total Quality Control, K. Ishikawa - Quality Circles and Joseph M. Juran - Breakthrough and Control.

The above approaches have been employed with varying degrees of success, depending on a number of factors not least of which is the culture, systems and structure of the organisation.

Total Quality Management

Total Quality Management is the synthesis of the organisational, technical and cultural elements of a company. It is a "hearts and minds" philosophy which recognises that company culture (customs and practice) affects behaviour which in turn affects quality. It is not merely the performance of the product with regard to conformance to specification, reliability or even customer satisfaction, but the performance of every activity in the organisation. To this end every subsystem or function in the organisation is seen to have internal customers and suppliers as well as external customers and suppliers. Take the Purchasing Department. Who are the Purchasing Department's customers? Who are the Purchasing Department's suppliers? Well, its customers may include the production or process units who need raw materials and equipment supplied to specification, on time and to a price. In this sense the Purchasing Department is the supplier to the production or processing units. The suppliers to the Purchasing Department might be the outside suppliers or contractors who provide the material and services; the Goods Receiving Department with information regarding quality and on time delivery; the process units with information regarding quality and conformance to specification; the Training Department who supply training services and facilities; the Computer Department who supplies computing facilities for planning and scheduling. Thus, the organisation becomes a chain or network of suppliers and customers. The principle underlying this approach is that every function or department is required to identify its immediate customers and is accountable for identifying the needs of those customers and ensuring the quality of service required by them. This in turn means that the function or department must ensure that its suppliers understand what is required and provide it.

From the above it follows that every function or department must operate its own quality assurance system and employ appropriate quality control techniques. In some departments this may mean the application of various techniques such as Statistical Quality Control, in others it may be Failure Mode and Effects Analysis or Cause and Effect Diagrams to solve problems. In other words Total Quality Management embraces all known techniques and methodologies to create a management climate that encourages and inspires every member of the organisation to have conscientious commitment to quality.

Quality Definitions

In common with many Management subjects Quality Assurance has its own jargon. To assist in understanding some of the jargon this section has been provided to expand and explain some of the quality terminology. The British Standard definition can be found in BS4778 (ISO8402).

Quality: The totality of features and characteristics of a product or service that bear on its ability to satisfy stated or implied needs - In simple terms this means Fitness for Purpose or, 'to satisfy a given need'. Needs covers more than mere function. Even if aesthetics is included in function there are many other factors to be considered. For example, the method of distribution, initial and running costs, user awareness or knowledge, other possible uses including reasonable misuse.

Grade: An indicator of category or rank related to features or characteristics that cover different sets of needs for products or services intended for the same functional use.

Table 1 Quality v Grade

Quality v Grade: **Table 1** opposite describes the difference between quality and grade. Both high grade (gold) or low grade (plastic) pens can be of high quality, if they meet the customer's expectations. Equally the pens can be low quality if they fail to meet the required customer standard. Another example of the misunderstanding of the difference between quality and

Grade	Quality	
	Good	Bad
High Grade	Gold pen that works perfectly	Gold pen that is unreliable
Low Grade	Ordinary plastic pen that writes smoothly	Ordinary plastic pen that doesn't write smoothly

grade is where - A carpenter once said "This quality thing is all well and good but I perform work on Board Rooms finished with Oak panelling. I also fit out shops - down to a price - possibly using plastic fixtures and fittings. Now if quality means that the board room finish has to be put into shop fitting then that will put me out of business. No one will be able to afford my work". Here the carpenter confused quality and grade although the board room is a high grade job both jobs need to achieve the correct quality, finished on time and to the agreed price.

Quality Assurance: All those planned and systematic actions necessary to provide adequate confidence that a product or service will satisfy given requirements for quality.

Inspection: Activities such as measuring, examining, testing, gauging one or more characteristics of a product or service and comparing these with specified requirements to determine conformity.

Specification: The document that prescribes the requirements with which the product or service has to conform.

Quality Control: The operational techniques and activities that are used to fulfil requirements for quality.

In other words quality control is the regulation of individual activities that are performed to ensure the process performs reliably and consistently for quality. This control is not confined to manufacturing processes but extends to design processes, service processes etc. In fact any process that can effect the quality of the product or service provided.

11

Figure 2 describes *a typical process* listing the activities from Customer Requirements, through Project Control & Development, Purchase of materials and Process Control to Delivery and subsequent Service Support.

The left hand side of **Figure 2** indicates *some of the quality control methods* that would be appropriate for regulating each stage. For example in the Project and Development stage the quality control methodology could include implementation of specification control, project planning, failure mode and effects analysis, project review and other quality control methods such as design validation and verification. Note that there are a series of dots under each suggested quality control method. The dots are to indicate that the list is not complete; there are numerous other quality control methods that can be employed. In fact the action of designing the Quality Assurance System requires review and determination of which of the multitude of Quality Control methods are appropriate for each process stage.

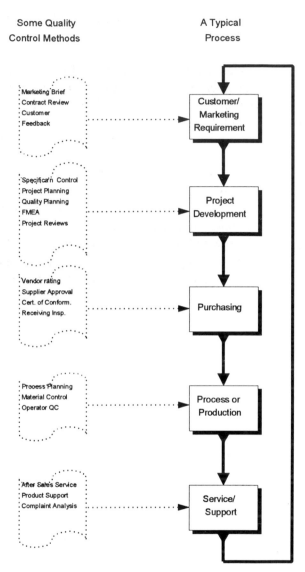

Figure 2 Quality Controlling a Process

Not shown in **Figure 2** are the other support activities that go to make up the complete Quality Assurance System - activities such as training, audit, feedback and control, data collection.

How the appropriate Quality Controls could be determined and implemented needs to be established i.e.:

a)   Determine the quality objectives for each process stage. E.g. One of the aims may be to ensure that the customer requirements are completely understood by the completion of a marketing brief and contract review.

b)   Institute a programme and plan to achieve the objectives. E.g. For a marketing brief and contract review to be completed, a planned and programmed introduction of how to complete a marketing brief and contract review will be necessary (training, procedures etc.).

c)   Establish the quality control systems for each stage in the process. E.g. For the marketing brief and contract review - checks will be necessary on the completeness and accuracy of the brief and review.

d)   Review and evaluate the implementation of the applied quality controls. E.g. For the marketing brief and contract review an audit will be necessary to confirm that the documents are being produced as per the procedures.

Listed below are some appropriate International and British Standards:

Table 2

Standard	Title & Remarks
ISO8402/ BS4778	Quality Vocabulary
BS4891	Guide to Quality Assurance
ISO9000-1	A Quality Management and Quality Assurance Standard - Guide to selection and use
ISO9000-2	A Quality Management and Quality Assurance Standard - Guide to the application of ISO9001, 2 & 3
ISO9000-3	A Quality Assurance Management System Standard - Guide to application of ISO9001 to Software
ISO9000-4	A Quality Assurance Management System Standard - Guide to dependability programme management
ISO9001, 2 & 3	Quality System - Model for Quality Assurance
ISO9004-1	Quality Management & Quality Standards - Guidelines
ISO9004-2	Quality Management & Quality System Elements - Guidelines for Service Organisations
ISO9004-3	Quality Management & Quality System Elements - Guidelines for Processed Materials
ISO9004-4	Quality Management & Quality System Elements - Guidelines for Quality Improvement
BS ISO10005	Quality Plans
BS ISO10007	Configuration Management
BS ISO10013	Developing Quality Manuals
ISO10011 BS EN 30011	Quality Systems Auditing
ISO10012-1 BS EN30012-1	Quality Assurance Requirements for Measuring Equipment
BS5760	Reliability of constructed or manufactured products, systems, equipment and components
BS6143	Cost of Quality
BS7373	Specification - Guide to the Preparation of Specifications
BS7850	Total Quality Management

Quality Assurance Management System Standards

A Model for a Quality Assurance Management System

A Quality Assurance Management System (QAMS) standard is a model that management can employ to give guidance to the selection of appropriate quality assurance controls. It is possible to apply a QAMS to most key areas and processes and in most stages of supply of the product or service. This is to ensure that the process of providing the product or service has been fully quality assured. The aim of a QAMS standard is primarily to prevent non-conformity or customer problems and to achieve customer satisfaction by concentrating on the product or service process. The objective of this type of standard is the minimisation of risk and cost and the maximisation of benefits that the organisation can obtain from achieving the required quality requirements.

Table 3 shows the risks and costs the organisation can be exposed to if the company does not introduce a QAMS. The diagram also shows the risks and costs the customer is exposed to if the customer buys from a company which does not have a QAMS.

Table 3 Risk/Cost/Benefits

Factor	For the Company	For the Customer
Risk	The risk of an adverse effect on image or reputation, the loss of market, possible liabilities, customer complaints, waste of resources.	Dissatisfaction with the goods or service, availability, general loss of confidence in the product or service.
Cost	The cost of rework, scrap, replacement, lost production, warranty and field repair, cost of change.	Operating costs, maintenance costs, total life costs, down time, repair costs and disposal costs.
Benefit	Increased profit and market share - satisfied customers.	Reduced costs, customer satisfaction, fitness use purpose, confidence.

What is a QAMS?

In order to regulate a process, (whether the process is an aircraft control system, a manufacturing sequence or a design and development process), it is necessary to have some formal method of control and feedback, otherwise the system may become unstable or go out of control.

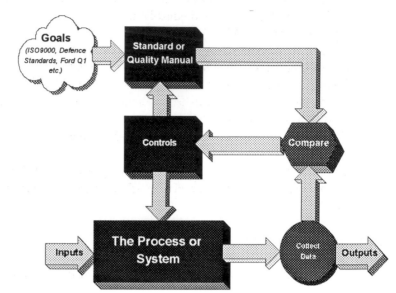

Figure 3 A Control System

A simple control system is described in the diagram (**Figure 3**). There is an *input* to the system (possibly data or raw materials). The *process* then manipulates the data or material, providing an *output* in terms of an acceptable or unacceptable finished product. If the process consists of data manipulation, the output could be a report - controls are necessary to avoid the production of an inaccurate report.

There will be a *goal* which could be costs, quantity, delivery targets or the QAMS model - ISO9000? This goal will need interpretation into a *Standard* or possibly the *Quality Manual*.

There will be a feedback mechanism to control the process allowing timely action to be taken to avoid failure to achieve the goal. This could involve *collection of data* regarding the performance of the process and a *comparison* with the goal, possibly by performing an audit. If the comparison indicates an unacceptable trend *controls,* as described in the Quality System or Quality Manual, may need to be updated or improved.

Why do organisations need a QAMS?

There are a number of reasons why organisations embark on the implementation of a QAMS:

a)   The organisation may consider themselves to be leaders in their own particular field and wish to retain and consolidate their position by the introduction and application of a QAMS.

b)   The organisation will have competitors, these competitors will not be stationary and the competitors may be actively pursuing the introduction of a QAMS.

c)   Often customers are demanding the introduction of a QAMS as part of their purchasing policy or as part of the contractual agreement. (We only buy from firms of assessed capability!).

d)   The introduction and application of a QAMS saves time and money.

The application of a Quality Assurance Management System (QAMS) may help to provide a goal for system control and to maintain the achievement of quality at each stage in the process.

Comparison of various QAMS Standards

There are numerous QAMS standards available; **Table 4** describes a few.

Table 4

Standards Body	Guide to selection and use of the QAMS standard	Specification for a QAMS for design, production, installation and servicing	Specification for a QAMS for production and installation	Specification for a QAMS for final inspection and test	Guide to quality management and quality system elements
ISO	ISO9000-1	ISO9001	ISO9002	ISO9003	ISO9004-1
CEN	EN9000-1	EN9001	EN9002	EN9003	EN9004-1
British Standards Institute	BS EN ISO9000-1 Formally BS5750 Pt0 Section 0.1	BS EN ISO9001 Formally BS5750 Pt1	BS EN ISO9002 Formally BS5750 Pt2	BS EN ISO9003 Formally BS5750 Pt3	BS EN ISO9004-1 Formally BS5750 Pt0 Section 0.2
United States	ANSI/ASQC Q90-1987	ANSI/ASQC Q91-1987	ANSI/ASQC Q92-1987	ANSI/ASQC Q93-1987	ANSI/ASQC Q94-1987
NATO	590 Series	591 Formally AQAP 1	592 Formally AQAP 4	593 Formally AQAP 9	594

The most commonly accepted QAMS model is the ISO9000 series, (which is exactly the same as the BS5750 series).

Historically, ISO9000 originated with the American Military Standards which arrived from across the Atlantic with NATO to become the Defence Standards 05-21 series. Later these standards evolved into the Allied Quality Assurance Publications (AQAP) series. (See **Figure 4**).

In the meantime civilian organisations considered these standards to be of value and developed their own, namely BS5750 (1979), which has been updated to BS5750 (1987). In 1994 the ISO9000 was revised and updated.

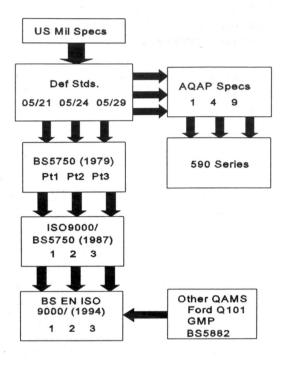

Figure 4 Evolution of ISO9000

At this point some digression is necessary to explain the workings of BSI and ISO organisations.

The ISO (International Organisation for Standardisation) is a worldwide federation of national standard's bodies. The work of preparing International Standards is normally carried out through ISO technical committees. Draft International Standards (DIS) adopted by the technical committees are circulated to the member bodies for approval before their acceptance as International Standards by the ISO Council. Preparation and revision of ISO9000 series of standards are the responsibility of ISO Technical Committee TC176. In 1990 ISO/TC176 adopted a strategy for revision of the ISO9000 series originally published in 1987. In terms of the ISO this is the first revision and is dated the 1994 version. In this revision there is no major change in the architecture of the standards ISO9001, ISO9002, ISO9003 and ISO9004.

The major changes to ISO9000 are now explained, for more details refer to the section Interpretation of ISO9001 requirements.

The 1994 revision is very significant and is aimed at providing clarification of various requirements, especially in the light of experience in applying the standard to non-manufacturing organisations.

ISO9002 is now entitled 'Quality Systems - Model for quality assurance in production, installation and *servicing.*' It has always been questionable why servicing was omitted from ISO9002. This has now been corrected by including it as a requirement of ISO9002. Thus, there are now 19 requirements to ISO9002.

There have been some changes to Definitions - The term 'product' has been defined to include 'service', 'hardware', 'processed material', 'software', or combination of these. However, it precludes the application of the standard to waste material. This would depend upon the scope of registration.

The Numbering of requirements has also changed - One inconsistency in the ISO9000 series that sometimes causes confusion is the numbering of the requirements. Since Design Control only appears in ISO9001, paragraph numbering from 4.4 on, differs in ISO9002 and ISO9003. I.e., 4.4 in ISO9001 it is Design Control and in ISO9002 it is Document Control. In the new revision, this anomaly has been eliminated by standardising on the requirement numbering in line with ISO9001. In other words, requirement 4.4 is Design Control in all three standards. However, in ISO9002 and ISO9003 under this requirement is the statement "This is not a requirement for this standard." Thus Document Control will become 4.5 in ISO9002 and ISO9003 and subsequent requirements will be renumbered accordingly.

The Defence Standards (AQAPs) have now incorporated ISO9000 as the basis of the defence QAMS standard. The latest defence standards are the 5/90 series and are very similar to ISO9000, with the addition of a number of supplements to the ISO9000 paragraph headings. (The additional requirements include the right to review suppliers systems and have, unusually, extended the requirements for calibration). These American and NATO military standards and civilian standards are used for contractual requirements for the Purchasing Department to apply to prospective suppliers in controlling the quality assurance systems they must apply. Thus hopefully ensuring that the product or services supplied will, in all respects, meet the customers' requirements.

All of this has meant that originally BS5750 was a purchasing standard and possibly because of this there were a number of omissions. For example marketing, motivation, economics, product safety and product liability were not addressed. Subsequently

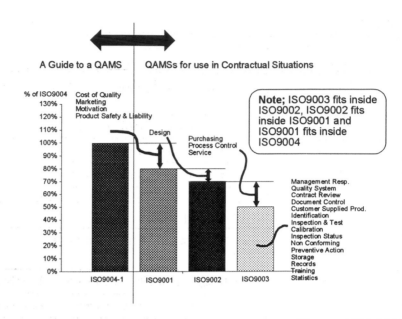

A Guide to a QAMS   QAMSs for use in Contractual Situations

Note; ISO9003 fits inside ISO9002, ISO9002 fits inside ISO9001 and ISO9001 fits inside ISO9004

Figure 5 ISO9000

these omissions were addressed with the publication of ISO9004-1 or BS5750 Part 0 section 0.2. Although ISO9004 is meant to be aimed at the organisation's own internal quality assurance systems and ISO9001 at its suppliers it would appear that most organisations have decided to choose ISO9001 as the model for their own quality assurance system, possibly with a view to up grading to ISO9004 at some later stage. **Figure 5** shows how ISO9003 fits inside ISO9002 and how ISO9002 fits inside ISO9001 etc. The list adjacent to ISO9003 show the contents of ISO9003. The list above ISO9003 shows the additional requirement for the standard to be the same as ISO9002. Similarly the list above ISO9002 shows the additional requirements for the standard to be the same as ISO9001.

Other Quality Assurance Publications

Some of the publications in **Table 5** have not been included with the previous list of standards as they may be considered specialist.

Table 5

Issuing Organisation and Identification	Remarks
ISO9000-1	Quality Management & Quality Assurance Standard - Part 1: Guide to the selection and use.
ISO9000-2	A guide to the interpretation of ISO9001, 2, & 3.
BS5882	A QAMS for the Construction of Nuclear Power Stations.
ISO9000-3	A QAMS for the design, development, supply and maintenance of software.
ISO9000-4	Quality Management And Quality Assurance Standard. A guide to dependability programme management.
ISO9004-1	Quality Management & Quality System Elements. Replaces BS5750 part 4 section 0.2 .
ISO9004-2	Quality Management & Quality System Elements. Guidelines for Services.
ISO9004-3	Quality Management & Quality System Elements. Guidelines for Processed Materials.
ISO9004-4	Quality Management & Quality System Elements. Guidelines for Quality Improvement.
Department of Health and Social Security; Guide to Good Manufacturing Practice	Similar to ISO9001 but includes issues such as sterility and product recall.
QS 9000	An interpretation of ISO9000 for the Automotive Industry Includes additional requirements such as Quality Control Planning, Failure Mode and Effects Analysis, Statistical Quality Control, Measure System Analysis. (See section Supplier Quality Assurance).
Ford Q101	A QAMS which Ford require their suppliers to meet. Covers issues such as Quality Planning, Failure Mode and Effects Analysis, Statistical Quality Control and Packaging requirements - A different approach from ISO9001. (See section Supplier Quality Assurance) - Now replaced by QS 9000.
Motorola Six Sigma	The use of statistical techniques to reduce variation. Specifically how to improve measuring and controlling these variations. With a view to parameter selection and measurement. Analysis of the results to enable definition of the optimisation method and finally control the process for quality. (See section Statistical Quality Control).

Instead of using one of the above nationally recognised QA standards an organisation could develop its own QAMS - possibly because it felt that the available QAMS did not *fit* or was not appropriate for the organisation. However, there are certain problems associated with this approach.

o   Can agreement be reached with all parties concerned as to the content of such a QAMS standard?

o   Resources may be devoted to the development of such a QAMS standard only to find that it is very similar to an already existing standard.

It is possible to interpret ISO9001 series for most industries.   An interpretation of ISO9001 follows describing an approach that may be adopted in meeting the requirements of ISO9001. Where appropriate, at the end of some of the ISO9001 paragraph sections a typical procedure has been provided.   These procedures outline an approach and sequence which has been frequently used successfully, as the basis of various organisations documented quality system.

Interpretation of ISO9001 requirements

Management Responsibility:

Quality policy - it is essential that the management define and document their policy, showing clear objectives and commitment to quality. In conjunction with this policy it is of obvious importance that this policy and objectives are understood, implemented and maintained at all levels within the organisation.

In practice this may mean writing a Quality Policy Statement (usually half a page) which is signed by the Managing Director or Chief Executive. **Figure 6** is such a typical quality policy statement.

Quality Policy Statement

As the leading chilled foods producer our company has built up a reputation with retailers and consumers at home and abroad for high quality products.

To maintain and enhance this reputation, a Quality Assurance System has been introduced based on the requirements of ISO9001.

The Quality Manual provides written quality practices for all aspects of managing the business and compliance is mandatory for all employees.

The quality system will be reviewed on a regular basis by the Quality Manager for compliance with ISO9001 and this Quality Assurance Manual. The results of these reviews shall be issued to the Directors of the company.

Signed: Managing Director

Figure 6 A typical Quality Policy Statement

Organisation - It may be appropriate in certain circumstances to appoint someone with the responsibility and authority to monitor the Quality Control arrangements. In particular, this person would need to have the organisational freedom and the authority to:

a. Take action to prevent the occurrence of any quality problems with the product or service.
b. Identify and record any known or possible quality problems with the product or service.
c. Organise solutions to any quality problems.
d. Verify that these solutions have been fully implemented and are effective.

e.   To control any further processes, delivery or installation of non-conforming products or services, until the quality deficiency or unsatisfactory condition has been corrected.

The appointment of a Quality Manager, with a direct line of responsibility to the Board of Directors, could assist with achieving some of the above objectives. However, this person need not necessarily be a full time Quality Manager thus there is a need for someone with Executive Responsibility for quality which implies that there is a need to have someone on the Board with responsibility for quality (not necessarily solely). This will not preclude Q-Support schemes.

The organisation will need to identify and provide adequately trained personnel to assist in the verification activities. These verification activities could include review of product design, inspection and test during production, installation and service. The ISO9001 standard also mentions resources. This is now wider than the limited phrase Verification resources and personnel. This potentially means not just personnel but the resources applied to quality are reviewed, adequate etc.

Management Review - Quality performance should not be static and improvements need to be continually made. A review of the current quality performance can give an indication as to what areas require improvement. This review could involve a minuted meeting discussing such topics as: Internal Audit reports, Supplier Performance, Customer complaints, Quality policy and objectives etc. (See Corrective Action).

Guidelines for Management Responsibility

In the main this requirement for Management Responsibility only requires a procedure for Management Review, the remainder of this requirement can be usually be covered by a policy statement, job descriptions and an organisation chart.

Management Review

On a twice yearly basis the Managing Director holds a Management Review with the Quality Manager and others as appropriate. During this meeting the following items are reviewed:

a)   Results of the internal audits
b)   Customer complaints (both of customers and from customers)
c)   Suppliers' quality
d)   Rework and concessions
e)   Training needs for the organisation

24

f)   Results of customer or assessment body audits

g)   Review of the Quality Manual (including Quality Policy, Responsibilities & any changes)

h)   Quality improvement suggestions

i)   Any Quality Performance Indicators as appropriate

j)   Resource requirements

Minutes of the meeting are recorded together with any agreed corrective and preventive actions taken to avoid recurrence and timescales. The minutes are issued to those in attendance and others as required.

NOTE: The above list is not comprehensive but should be covered as a minimum.

Quality System:

Having determined the need for a Quality Assurance System then there is a need to document the system. This ensures that all the necessary requirements have been addressed and the QAMS is agreed, available and understood by all personnel who have an effect on the quality performance of the organisation. (See section Quality Assurance Manual).

The standard refers to a Quality Manual and Quality Planning. Where Quality Manuals tend to be organisation specific Quality Plans tend to be project specific.

It is necessary to define and document how the requirements of quality are to be met. As mentioned a Quality Plan tends to be a project, contract or product specific document which defines the Quality Assurance tasks to ensure that specific customer requirements and time scales are met. It enables the identification of preventive activities to provide early warning of any possible problems occurring or becoming major. Quality Planning is used to anticipating any possible project or product risk areas so that the appropriate action can be taken to eliminate or mitigate any such difficulties. A Quality Plan differs from a Quality Manual and Quality Programme. A Quality Manual is project or product independent and a Quality Programme which usually describes the implementation of the Quality Manual.

Guidelines for Quality System

The only procedure that should be required to address this requirement of the standard is Quality Planning and the section Quality Planning can be used as a guide. Also, see section Quality Manual.

Contract Review:

It is necessary to examine the tender[1], contract and order (customer requirements) to ensure that the customer's needs and expectations can be fully met and that any quality assurance requirements have not been overlooked. A review of the contract may provide adequate information regarding the customer requirements. Often understanding of the customer requirements needs to start at a much earlier stage, probably at the enquiry or tender stage.

---

[1]   With the inclusion of tenders, procedures may need to be extended to include control of tender generation.

Figure 7 shows a typical sequence that may be followed when controlling the process *"Bidding to Winning."* The process starts with the customer's requirements and ends with an accepted order. Included in the diagram are the use of standard formats for tenders and quotations. The diagram shows the typical reviews or approvals that may be appropriate at each stage.

The review could take the form of completion of a check list, which ensures that all key aspects of the customer requirements have been identified and addressed. Contained in the following procedure for Contract Review are a typical series of contract review questions. Due to the importance of this activity it is critical that records of contract review are maintained. It is worth noting that Contract Review also applies to orders, even when not written.

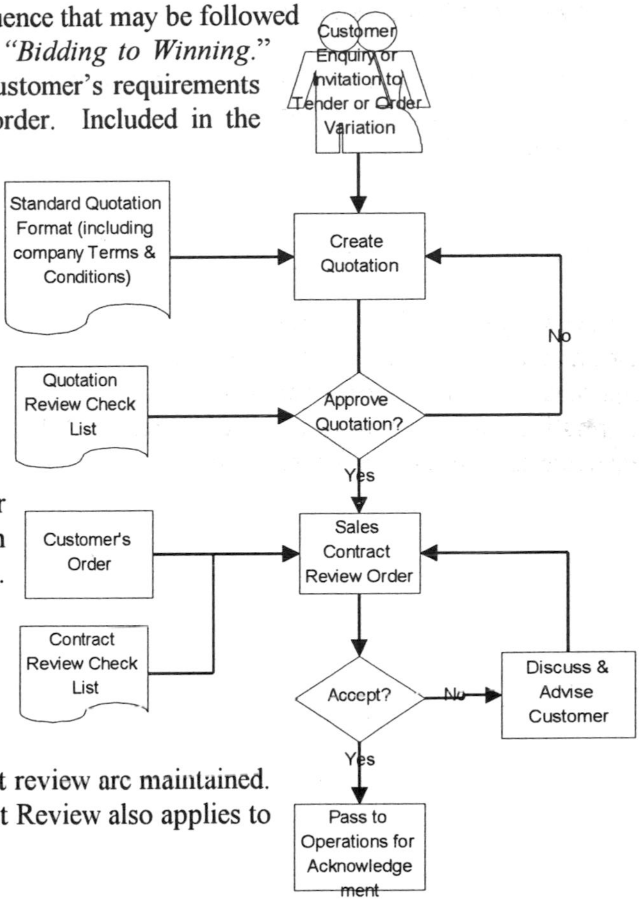

Figure 7 Contract Review

Guidelines for Contract Review

1. **Review of customer enquiries/specifications, quotations and orders**

    a. Review of customer enquiries/specifications.

        On receipt of a customer enquiry or specification: when the enquiry is special (e.g. away from the standard price list) the Salesperson concerned completes an enquiry form/check list detailing the customer's requirements. (See Appendix A).

        On completion of the enquiry form the form is signed by the reviewer and where appropriate submitted to the Manager for approval. If the enquiry is acceptable to the supplier and the customer's requirements are understood, a quotation is raised on the basis of the information contained within the enquiry form.

b. Approval of quotations

On raising a written quotation, the Salesperson, Technical Administrator or other appropriate person concerned reviews the quotation against an appropriate relevant check list. (See Appendix A) The quotation is then provided to the customer.

c. Approval of orders

On receipt of a customer order - the order is then reviewed against the relevant check list (See Appendix A) by the Salesperson or Technical Administrator. On completion of the review, which may involve drawing up an initial project plan (in the case of large orders), the order is then stamped and signed *"contract review - accepted"*. The order is then entered into the computer system via a series of screen prompts.

If rejected the customer is advised.

NOTE: All these actions require checks for Quality Assurance requirements and may require frequent and lengthy discussions with the customer in order to establish that both parties are satisfied with regard to what is to be supplied.

d. Should there be any subsequent amendments to the contract the above procedure will be repeated and the contract updated accordingly.

Appendix A

General Check list for reviewing customers enquiries, quotations and orders[2]

Customer Order - Check List		
Customer Number	Order Number	Date
Customer Name	Customer Address	
Product/Services Defined?		
Training Defined?		
Customer Contractual Requirements Defined?		
Prices Correct?		
Delivery Times Acceptance?		
Client Financial Health Acceptable?		
Supplier's Terms & Conditions accepted by Client?		
Client Terms & Conditions acceptable?		
Legal Consideration Acceptable?		
Any special Quality Assurance requirements (e.g. special customer tests)?		
Signed	Checked	Approved

---

[2] It is unlikely that this check list would be completed, it is for reference purposes, when conducting a Contract Review.

Design Control:

Controlling the design of any product or service is fundamental in ensuring that all quality requirements and considerations have been adequately addressed. It is worth considering that no amount of control in manufacture or installation will correct a design which is inherently wrong, at best all the manufacturer can achieve is to make something which is perfectly wrong, (meets the drawing but fails to meet the customer requirements).

So having gained a complete understanding of the customer requirements and specification, the next stage is to ensure that the designed solution will fulfil the customer expectations. Note, the design specification is not only useful for design purposes, it can also be easily rewritten into a test specification.

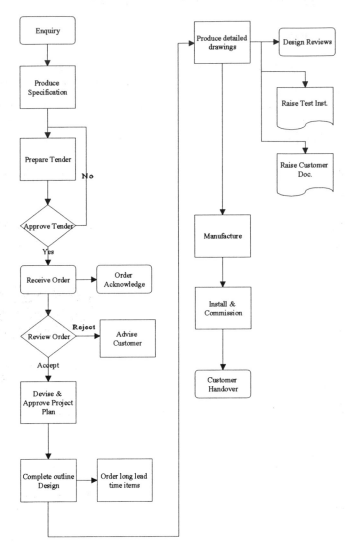

Figure 8 Project Plan Flow Diagram

Design and development planning - To ensure that the responsibilities and tasks for each development activity have been identified plans can be compiled (sometimes known as Pert charts) which describe references and indicate time scales for the various activities. These plans can include identification of personnel responsible for particular quality tasks in the design and development programme, such as design and safety reviews, trials and tests,

project audits (see section Auditing). **Figure 8** shows a typical project plan f
from receipt of the Invitation To Tender (ITT) or enquiry through to hando

The stages can include:

Understanding of customer requirements - possibly by the creation of a product's
specification. It is often the case that the customer does not know exactly what he wants
and it may be necessary for the supplier to draw up their own specification for approval
by the customer. However, prior to the release of this specification to the customer an
internal review may be necessary to check the proposals and quotation.

Acceptance of the order necessitates an investigation similar to the stages described in the
section Contract Review.

Design Input - At the beginning of any project it is essential that all the relevant
information is agreed, available and understood. The type of information required could
include:
Design and
Development
Plans, Functional
Specifications,
Customer,
Contractual,
Statutory and
Safety
Requirements,
budgets and
costings. It may
be appropriate to
review these
design inputs to
confirm the
information is
complete,
accurate and
adequate to safeguard the customer and user of the product or service.

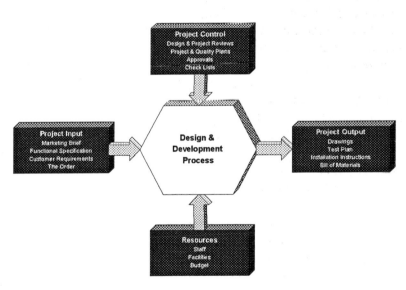

Figure 9 Design & Development Control

Design Output - The output from the design and development process needs to be
documented and reviewed. This review is to confirm that the design output meets all the
expectations of the customer. These expectations would have been detailed during the

31

the safe and correct use and function of the product. The design output ought to define the checks and tests that need to be carried out during manufacture, installation, commissioning, and possibly at regular intervals throughout the life of the product. The Design Output could include: reports, results of tests, trials and analysis (e.g. safety analysis), drawings, bills of materials, costs, process instructions, test instructions, operation and maintenance manuals etc.

Design Validation & Verification

Definitions: Verification - establishment of truth or correctness
              Validation - ratification or confirmation

The design output (drawings, test results, trials etc.) needs to be checked, validated and verified to confirm that the design output is not only accurate and reliable but also fulfils the criteria for the design input, namely meets original specifications. This may be achieved by a number of ways; holding design reviews (see **Table 6**), undertaking tests or demonstrations, proving, verifying and validating the appropriateness of the design. Verification may be performed by completing alternative calculations (doing the calculations in a different way) and having all key documentation, design decisions, calculations etc. checked and approved by competent personnel. **Figure 9** shows typically what may be included in design input, design output and design verification.

Table 6 A Typical Agenda of a Design Review Meeting

Design/Project Review Minutes		
Project Name:	Project Number:	Project Manager:
Distribution:		Date:
Items		Remarks
1 Specification: 1.1 Mechanical Specification 1.2 Electrical Specification 1.3 Services & Support Specification (Training, Technical etc.) 1.4 Any amendments to specification? 1.5 Will performance still be as defined?		
2 Target dates: What is the status of the following (are they still on target)? 2.1 Design 2.2 Purchasing 2.3 Release for production 2.4 Installation & Commissioning		
3 Design/Project review: 3.1 Safety factors/requirements (Failure Mode and Effects Analysis) 3.2 Drawing; GA, Detail 3.3 Calculations		
4 Status of documentation: 4.1 Inspection & Test Instructions 4.2 Project & Quality Plan completed 4.3 Installation & Commissioning Instructions 4.4 Operating, service and maintenance manuals (Spares List)		
5 Approvals: 5.1 Customer Approval 5.2 Third Party Approval		
6 Commercial aspects: 6.1 Is the project within budget, if not what are proposed actions? 6.2 Is the project within time scale, if not what are proposed actions? 6.3 Invoice & Payment Received		
7 Any other business?:		

Although reference is made to documents, approval is required for other types of data and information. **Table 7** shows the various activities that may require approval and the nominated persons that can perform the creation and approval function.

The first two columns show the typical activities that will require verification. Adjacent to each activity are *named* individuals who can create the documentation and an independent person who can approve or check the output.

Table 7 Verification Activities

VERIFICATION			
Activity	Remarks	Author	Approver
Calculations	Evidence of any calculation checking is recorded on the calculation sheet showing who performed the check and the date. (See Calculation Check List).	Draughtsman	Chief Engineer
Drawings	Detail drawings show the date, the originator, title, drawing number and are then independently checked.	Draughtsman	Design Engineer
Specifications	Specifications written by the Designer are checked and approved.	Draughtsman	Design Engineer
Operating Manuals	Operating Manuals written by the Designer are approved. Manuals written or obtained from the manufacturers or other external sources are approved by the Designer or Design Manager. (See document Check List).	Draughtsman	Design Engineer
Subcontractors	Designs produced at subcontractors or by contractors are reviewed and approved.	Subcontractors	Design Engineer

This next table shows a typical check list that can be used to help in the checking process. See section Document Inspection.

Table 8 Typical Calculation Check List

Calculation Check List	
Description	**Response**
Check for document control purposes e.g. title, number, issue number and date, originator etc.	
Calculation objectives stated.	
Methodology correct e.g. formulae or sequence etc. *Reference to text book solutions may be appropriate.*	
Definition of terms available and correct.	
Statement of constants and variables e.g. P=pressure (variable) g=9.81 m/s².	
Data accurate and correctly entered.	
Arithmetic correct e.g. 2+1=3.	
Units constant e.g. Imperial*metric.	

Note 1:   The questions are meant as a guide and in certain circumstances may not be applicable. Completion of this check would not absolve the author of the responsibility for the quality of the calculations.

Note 2:   This form would not normally be completed. However, the facility to record the approver's response is provided.

Installation & Commissioning - This stage can include the compilation of an installation & commissioning plan and instructions. These instructions can include (but are not limited to): all of the various checks and tests that will need to be performed, the expected or target figure and tolerances, the records of tests that will need to be retained and the handover certificate that is to be provided.

Document & Data Control

Document Approval and Issue - It is often the case with projects of any size that a certain amount of documentation will be generated. Sometimes it is necessary for documentation to be controlled, for both its issue and for any changes that may occur at some later date. There are numerous types of documents that require control both of their issue and change (sometimes known as configuration control). These documents may include: the original specification, drawings, test specifications, software, forms, procedures, manuals etc. Note the word *"software or drawing"* is interchangeable with the word *"document"*. Documents like these will need to be reviewed and approved for their completeness and accuracy prior to being issued. This means that documents which are under the change control system will need to carry the following information: Document title and number, an author, an approver, issue date and number, page of pages and a circulation list. **Figure 10** shows document creation to issue stages. Having created the document, it will require checking or approving. Typically a document check list could consist of:

    a.   Is the document accurate?
    b.   Is the document complete?
    c.   Is the document in the correct format?
    d.   Is the document issue status correct?

It is very important to remember at this stage that checking or approving documentation does not move responsibility for the document from the author to the checker. This responsibility still remains firmly with the author. The checker is only assisting the owner of the document.

Having accepted the document, the document will require registering. **Table 9** shows a typical drawing or document register. The left-hand column would contain the drawing

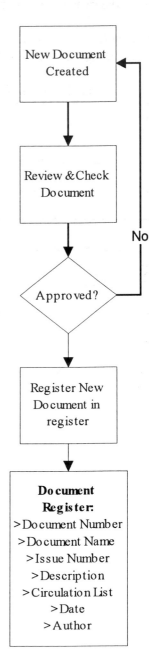

Figure 10 Drawing Creation Control

36

numbers and as new issues were created the columns to the right would be completed by adding the issue level and circulation date i.e. Issue A, Issue B etc.

At the bottom of the table is space to list names or titles of people on the circulation list and to the right of the name the date of transmittal of the drawing.

Table 9 Typical Drawing Register

Drawing Number	Issue Number							
	A	B	C	D	E	F	G	H
Circulation List								

If at some later stage the document undergoes change, procedures may be necessary that control approval of the change, control of the issue and circulation of the new documentation and implementation of the change.

A typical drawing or document control sequence from creation to issue and subsequently change control (should the drawing require updating) is detailed in **Figure 10** and **Figure 11**. The first stage is to raise a document change note; this note is necessary to detail the content of the change and to record the reasons for change control. It may also be necessary to detail the effects of change on fit and function and the implication of change on such items as stores stock, work in the field, service, maintenance manuals etc. In the case of software the analysis of the effects and implications of change is important, as a small change to the software in one place could have significant effect on the performance of the software elsewhere. Having agreed and completed the modification, the modification itself requires approval to confirm that the change meets the original objectives. The register can now be updated and the document circulated.

Purchasing

In industry today it is unlikely that any organisation will process raw material into a completed finished product. It is more likely that purchased items or sub-assemblies will be obtained for re-processing or assembly into the finished item. These sub-assemblies or purchased items need to be controlled as they can have significant effect on the finished product's ability to meet the quality requirements.

Assessment of Suppliers - It is important that the selection of suppliers is on the basis of the supplier's ability to meet the quality requirements. For this reason suppliers may be assessed to confirm their ability to meet the customer requirements. Assessment could take the form of a formal external audit (See Audit). Alternatively, the assessment could take the form of reviewing and accepting a

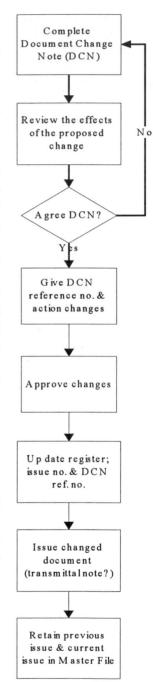

Figure 11 Control of Drawing Changes

38

satisfactorily completed quality assurance questionnaire from the supplier. Another method of assessment is confirming that the supplier has a quality assurance system of assessed capability (by a recognised assessment body). Records could be maintained for the supplier's performance in the form of an approved suppliers list and Vendor Rating. (See section Supplier Quality Assurance).

Purchasing Data - Purchasing documents need to accurately describe the product or service to be ordered and include identification of any key requirements which, if not met, could have an adverse effect on quality. The purchasing data could also include instructions regarding certificates of conformity or any tests or inspections the supplier must perform. A review of the purchasing data must be obtained prior to issue. This review usually takes the form of an authorising signature on the purchasing document.

Guidelines for Purchasing Control

1. General Procedures

For the purposes of this Manual, a 'supplier' is defined as a company providing services to the organisation's specified requirements. Suppliers also include any manufacturer or stockist of proprietary equipment or products.

Suppliers must be selected which have a sound financial base, the required background, capacity and capability. Suppliers will be chosen from the approved suppliers list where ever possible. Exceptions to using preferred suppliers can be made providing the following criteria have been met:

a. The material or service to be purchased will not significantly affect the quality standard required by the organisation.

b. The Quality Manager, or nominated deputy, approves the supplier.

2. Supplier Assessment & Evaluation

Suppliers should have established and effective quality control procedures based on ISO9000 or other appropriate standards. Not withstanding this, the organisation should reserve the right to carry out its own assessment of the supplier's Quality Assurance system which may be by the use of the supplier questionnaire or by an assessment visit to the supplier. An example of such a questionnaire can be found at the end of this section on Purchasing Control.

a.   **New Supplier Selection**

If a new supplier is to be selected or used, i.e. a supplier not on the approved supplier list, then the new supplier can be added to the approved list provided that the new supplier:

i.   Has established and effective quality control procedures based on ISO9000 or other appropriate standards. If possible confirmed by an independent body.

or

ii.   Can satisfactorily complete the supplier's questionnaire.

or

iii. The supplier is found to be satisfactory when assessed.

On satisfactory completion of one or more of the above the new supplier is added to the approved list at level 2.

3.   **Purchase Data**

The suppliers must be provided with complete and comprehensive documentation which details the standards to be achieved. Any modifications to the Purchase Order are agreed with the supplier and the documentation amended as appropriate.

The Buyer must also develop and foster relationships with the supplier aimed at reinforcing their appreciation of the need for effective Quality Assurance. Purchase orders must contain the following information:

a) Supplier's name and address
b) Order Number
c) Date
d) Some reference to standard terms and conditions
e) The appropriate inspection level
f) Destination address
g) Invoice address
h) Description of supply
i) Quantity
j) Delivery date required
k) Actual/estimated cost (on organisation's copy)

NOTE: Purchase orders will include the following Inspection Levels:

Inspection Level 1 -   Normal inspection by Goods Inwards Staff as per the Goods Receiving Instruction in Section 10 of the Quality Manual

Inspection Level 2 -   As Inspection Level 1 but supplied with a Certificate of Conformity

Inspection Level 3 -   Inspection as Level 2 but with full electrical and other safety tests (or checks as specified by the Purchase Order originator)

Three copies of the purchase order are produced, one master and two copies which are clearly identified. The Authorised Buyer then reviews the order for the above and signs to provide evidence that the buyer has authorised the order.

4.   Verification of the Purchased Product

The suppliers must understand that all supplies must be to the specified standards and that any deviation from the standard can only be permitted after formal agreement with the purchasing organisation. Where it is a requirement of the contract or order reasonable access shall be provided for the Customer to verify compliance of the product at source.

5.   Supplier Performance Evaluation

A record of acceptable suppliers and its products or services is maintained by the Quality Manager and held by the Buyer and Accounts. This record will be supplemented by notes of the results of any supplier appraisal gained by questionnaires and/or assessment visits, delivery monitoring and any customer feedback.

The suppliers' performance shall be monitored during the Management Review every six months by examination of the reject and concession notes. The goods inwards checking person annotates the delivery note with any problems found with the delivered goods, such as damaged packaging, damaged goods, incorrect goods etc. A reject note is raised on the basis of this information. (See sections "Inspection and Test" and "Control of Substandard Product and Work"). Dependent upon the frequency and category of rejection and concession, the suppliers shall either remain on the approved list or be removed.

Removal or addition of suppliers to these lists is discussed during the Management Review and the lists updated accordingly and re-issued.

Table 10 Typical example for Approved Suppliers List

Approved Suppliers List			
Name	Address	Blank or Specific	Vendor Rating

Typical Example of a Supplier Assessment Questionnaire[3]

Supplier's Name and Address

No.	Question	YES/NO/DETAILS
1	Is the Supplier's quality system of assessed capability by a recognised body? If yes please give details and ignore questions 3 to 17.	
2	Does the Supplier have: i) A person with written responsibility for Quality Assurance? If yes please give details ii) A person with responsibility for inspection? If yes please give details	Name: Title: Name: Title:
3	Does the Supplier have a Quality Assurance Manual?	
4	Does the Supplier assess the organisation's Orders for completeness, accuracy and viability?	
5	Does the Supplier further subcontract the organisation's work?	
6	Does the Supplier identify work throughout the process?	
7	Does the Supplier identify the inspection status of work throughout the process?	
8	Does the Supplier provide any written instructions describing how the work is to be performed? Please give details.	
9	Does the Supplier inspect incoming material?	
10	Does the Supplier perform any in-process and final test and inspection of completed work? If so what form does this take?	

---

[3]   Although very popular these questionnaires are of limited value.

No.	Question	YES/NO/DETAILS
11	Does the Supplier calibrate measuring and test equipment?	
12	Does the Supplier perform any Quality Assurance Audits? If so, what type?	
13	Does the Supplier keep records of the results of: Receipt inspection and test? In-process inspection and test? Final inspection and test? Quality Audits (Product/System)? Calibration?	
14	Does the Supplier train any personnel performing an inspection activity?	
15	Does the Supplier have scrap or reject labels?	
16	Does the Supplier have a written procedure for dealing with remedial action that may be necessary as a result of supplies being rejected by the organisation?	
17	Does the Supplier arrange for goods sent to the organisation to be packaged?	
18	Is there any additional information that may be relevant? If so please provide details below:	
Signed:	Position in Company:	Date:

Customer Supplied Product

It may be that on occasions the customer supplies material or products which need to be processed and then returned to the purchaser (Free Issue Material - FIM). Procedures need to be established and maintained to ensure that any FIM is controlled and looked after in the same manner as the organisation's own material. The security industry this takes on a more important aspect as there will be a need to properly safeguard and secure data and information (including electronic) supplied by the customer. This data may be of a commercially sensitive nature or pose a security (defence) risk.

Product Identification and Traceability

Material requires identification so that the wrong material is not used or the wrong part processed. This identification may need to extend throughout the process.

Traceability: The extent to which traceability is required is largely based on: the industry type (medical, food etc.), the customer requirements (aerospace industry) or a statutory requirement. The requirement for traceable material may, on occasion, extend to purchasing material which has undergone certain tests and inspections to ensure its suitability (e.g. Cast Certificates for raw material). In these cases it may also be appropriate to identify this material throughout the process to ensure traceability is maintained. **Figure 12** shows traceability of an item from the raw material production and laboratory tests (certification), through to manufacture and test (final test certificate). It may be necessary to extend this traceability into the field, particularly for items which are safety critical and may be re-called (medical industry). The level of identification could include test specification number, date of test, batch identification etc. The records may include the eventual destination of the item.

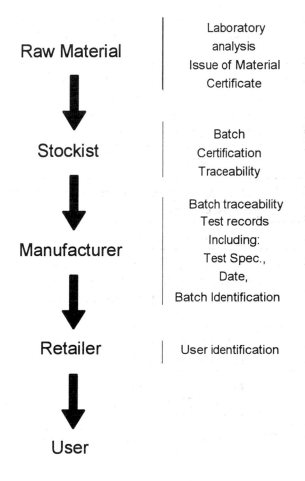

Figure 12 Traceability

Process Control

Controls need to be applied to the processes or tasks to ensure that all the methods are clearly specified and procedures followed. Such controls may include a documented work instruction, this work instruction will usually define:

- o   The process stages and the sequence.
- o   The features that need to be controlled.
- o   How the controls are going to be maintained.
- o   What the specified requirements are, i.e. the tolerances or standards to be achieved.
- o   The records that will be maintained, indicating successful completion of the process.
- o   The equipment that will be used, what environmental conditions are necessary and any other special standards or codes of practice. It may include any other criteria for workmanship by objective or subjective standards.

A typical format for a process planning sheet that can be used for describing the process control procedures is shown in **Table 11**.

Table 11 A Process Planning Sheet

Stage	Process Description	Work Instruction or Codes of Practice	Specification	Equipment	Records

Inspection and Testing

Receiving Inspection and Testing - All organisations, to some degree, perform Goods Receiving Inspection (GRI). It may be a full dimensional and physical assessment of the delivered materials ability to meet the purchasing specification or check on quantity, correct identification, condition or damage and documentation. Some decision by the organisation is needed to determine the necessary level of GRI. (See section Supplier Quality Assurance).

In-process Inspection & Test - It can be more efficient to ensure compliance in the intermediate stages of the process rather than waiting until the service or product has been completed.

Final Inspection and Test - Having completed the product or service, checks need to be performed to confirm the compliance.

A typical format of an Inspection and Test Plan for Final Inspection of a cereal packet is shown in **Table 12**.

Table 12 Typical Inspection and Test Plan

#	Inspection or Test Description	Inspection Instructions	Feature	Performance Criteria	Measuring Equipment	Recording Method
1	Printing	Description on how the test will be performed; method, sequence, responsibilities etc.	Clarity, Colours	Visual, Visual	Description of the gauges, measuring equipment, fixtures, machines etc.	Attribute Charts
2	Outer package		Peel strength, Material, Sizes, Strength, Thickness, Durability, Hygiene and sterility	$5N \pm 0.1N$, Chemical, $mm \pm mm$, $5N \pm 0.1N$, $mm \pm mm$, $5N \pm 0.1N$, Bug count		Variable charts, Attribute Chart, Variable Chart, Variable Chart, Variable Chart, Variable Chart, Attribute Chart
3	Inner package		Peel strength, Material, Sizes, Strength, Thickness, Durability, Hygiene and sterility	$5N \pm 0.1N$, Chemical, $mm \pm mm$, $5N \pm 0.1N$, $mm \pm mm$, $5N \pm 0.1N$, Bug count		Variable charts, Attribute Chart, Variable Chart, Variable Chart, Variable Chart, Variable Chart, Attribute Chart
	It could be that this table also includes checks on the package contents					

Calibration

When tests are performed, it is essential that the measuring or test equipment used is accurate, otherwise inaccurate results and wrong judgements can be made, e.g. faulty work could be inadvertently passed. The following list describes the key requirements of a calibration system.

o   Identify all measuring equipment with a unique identification e.g. serial number and its calibration status. See **Table 13**.

Table 13 Calibration Labelling

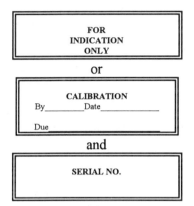

o   Establish the frequency with which the measuring equipment needs to be checked. E.g. for a set of weighing scales this could be every 6 months.

o   Define procedures that describe the calibration system (measuring equipment recall procedure etc.). This can be a card file, one card for each piece of measuring equipment. The cards are then filed in next calibration date order, so at the beginning of each month the equipment that requires calibration is identified and located.

o   Detail the individual calibration procedures for each type of measuring equipment. For weighing scales this could be having some calibrated weights placed on the scales and checking the readings correspond with the calibrated weights.

o   Ensure that the inspection and test equipment has the necessary accuracy and precision. For the weighing scales example the accuracy of the calibrated weights could be 10% of the accuracy of the scales.

o   Define the procedures that describe the activities necessary if the results of calibration highlight equipment error. If the weighing scales were found to be in error when calibrated and used for weighing drugs, then it may be necessary to take corrective action, possibly to recall the drugs.

48

Quality Assurance Management

o   Establish calibration history records showing the previous calibration results. **Table 14** shows a typical calibration history sheet.

Table 14 A typical Calibration History Sheet

CALIBRATION HISTORY RECORD SHEET					
Equipment Type:			Model No.:		
Serial No.:			Size:		
Calibration Frequency:			Procedure No.:		
DATE OF LAST CALI-BRATION	DATE OF NEXT CALI-BRATION	DATE OUT/IN	LOCATION	RESULT OF CALIBRA-TION	REMARKS

o   Determine the necessary environmental conditions suitable for accurate calibration.

o   Detail appropriate handling, preservation and storage procedures.

o   Ensure that equipment is sealed to avoid any possibility of adjustments that could invalidate the calibration setting. For the weighing scales - any adjustment screws would need to be sealed.

Calibration and Automatic Test Equipment (ATE)

ATE equipment is computer controlled test equipment. Frequently used for the testing of assemblies and sub-assemblies. Typically these types of machines have either an 'in circuit' or a 'functional' test capability (or a combination of both).

'In circuit' testing confirms that a circuit board has been manufactured correctly (i.e. finds short circuits, open circuits and components that are outside tolerance limits). The in circuit tester usually interfaces with the unit under test (UUT) via a bed of nails fixture that has one pin for every electrical node. This allows measuring of characteristics between any electrical connections (e.g. across each component).

49

Figure 13 shows a typical ATE set up. 'Functional' testing interfaces to the UUT either via a few pins in a bed of nails fixture (e.g. maybe one pin per 100 connections) or by way of flying leads. This means of testing could be used for a printed circuit board or a whole assembly. A 'good' functional test will find any manufacturing defects plus any parameters that are not within design specifications.

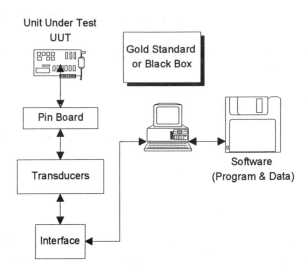

Figure 13 Typical Automatic Test Equipment

Functional testing is quick to highlight a failure whereas in circuit testing is quicker to pin point where the failure lies, (i.e. identifies the fault location down to component level). A typical use for ATE is in medium to high volume production or for high level technology, such as the space industry.

The use of automatic testing ensures that all the assemblies are tested to within predefined tolerances. The testing becomes objective as opposed to subjective. The QA personnel would need to ensure that the preselected tolerances are correct. Once proven this method of testing provides a very high degree of repeatability plus the availability of automatically logged test results for use in SQC and real time fault analysis (RTFA).

Calibration of the equipment i.e. transducers and connection between the equipment under test and the computer: The transducer and connection between the computer and the pin board can be tested, although not completely, by the use of a "Gold Standard" or "Black Box." This "Gold Standard" could be a specially selected unit that is a known standard or quality. This "Gold Standard" would be regularly retested by the ATE to confirm that the hardware is working satisfactorily.

Validation and verification of the test software program and data: The software for ATE could consist of:

- the program to drive the ATE
- the sequencer which runs the sequence and determines which test to perform

o   and the test data (both target value and tolerance)

The program and sequencer will need to be validated and verified. The test data will need to be checked.

Inspection and Test Status

It is important to identify work in such a manner to show whether the work is awaiting inspection or test. Once the work has been inspected it is necessary to indicate whether the work is acceptable or not.

Control of Non-Conforming Product

Where items or products have been found not to comply with the necessary quality requirements procedures need to be established and implemented that identify, and if appropriate segregate, the non-conforming material or product until such time as a decision can be made as to the action necessary. I.e. concession, rework, scrap, regrade etc.

Evaluation of Suspect Material: If suspect material is found an approach that can be adopted in determining possible action is detailed in **Figure 14**:

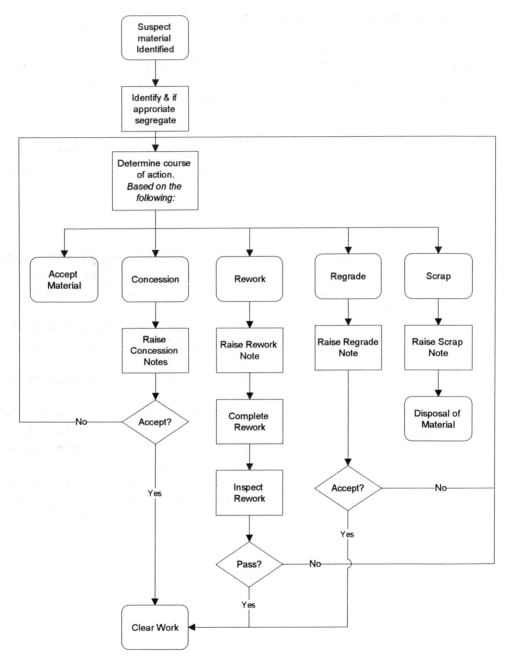

Figure 14 Flow diagram for Non-Conforming Material

Note 1: Suspect material does not necessarily mean faulty.

Note 2: The forms employed could be a combined non-conformance form which could also encompass Audit reports, customer complaints etc.

*Note 3: **Figure 14** only covers the action taken to resolve the immediate problem (non-conforming material) and does not include the action taken to prevent recurrence - see section Corrective & Preventive Action.*

In the case of safety critical products e.g. food manufacturing, electrical goods etc. it may be appropriate to establish procedures in the event of a product recall being necessary. Not only is this good preplanning (hopefully unnecessary) but also because it can possibly lead to a reduction in the insurance premium.

A guide to such a product recall procedure could be:

- o   Circulate a note to key members of the company, including the Managing Director, indicating the situation and proposing the following action.
- o   Establish the seriousness of the problem, where possible the likely effect on health and safety, fit and function, aesthetics etc.
- o   Establish the extent of the problem, how many items are effected and how the items effected are to be identified (date of manufacture, serial number etc.)
- o   Determine the most appropriate corrective action; recall, rectification, check etc.
- o   Determine the most appropriate method for notifying customers or users of the suspect items and the action they should take (e.g. return item to factory for replacement). Hazard or advisory notice to all customers either by letter or in the form of a press release.
- o   Determine the most appropriate method of monitoring the effectiveness of the corrective action. Also the success with which the customers effected have been contacted and items effected have been located.

Corrective & Preventive Action

It is essential that any non-conformance such as a faulty product is quickly detected and quarantined thus stopping any faulty or dangerous items or products reaching the customer. The preference is that faulty work is not produced in the first place. For this reason it may be appropriate to establish, document and maintain procedures that investigate any causes of non-conformance to determine appropriate action to prevent the same non-conformance problem happening again. *Avoiding making the same mistake twice.* Particular attention needs to be paid to any non-conformance of a dangerous nature. **Table 15** indicates some areas that may require corrective action.

Table 15 Corrective Action List

Some areas that may require corrective action could include:
I. Goods Inwards Rejects - Supplier reject notes See procedure for Vendor Rating
II. Bug Reporting - Bug Report notes the Project Controller will review the reports as appropriate.
III. Test Rejects and Concessions - test and inspection sheets, Concession forms. The Project Controller will review these as and when they arise to ensure that corrective action is carried out and that the problem can be solved to avoid recurrence.
IV. Customer Complaints - Customer Complaints form See Section 12 the procedure for customer complaints.
V. Audit Reports - Audit Report form. Audits will identify that corrective action was effective. See Internal Audit Section 16.
VI. Installation Reports - The Service Manager will review these on a monthly basis. The Quality Assurance Manager will review the reports where necessary.
VII. Calibration - The Quality Manager reviews the results and calibration periods when found to be outside specification.
VIII. Service Reports - The Service Manager reviews the Service Reports and issues a report to the Management Review Meeting.

Control of Non-Conforming Product is to do with detection - Corrective Action is to do with remedial acts. **Figure 15** shows how the various systems: change control, non-conforming material, corrective action and improvement team groups may need to interact with each other.

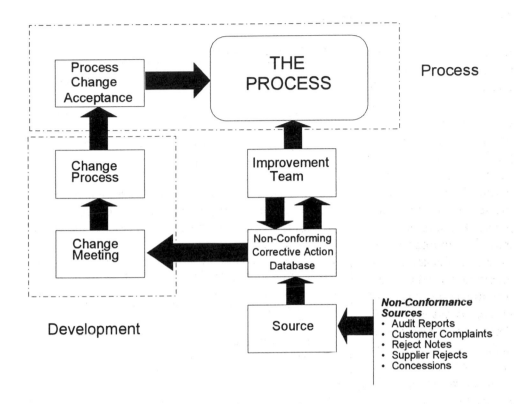

Figure 15 Corrective Action Control

Information regarding the Quality Problem data requires collation, possibly by using a database. This database can be analysed to separate the signal from the noise (the key issues from the trivial issues). This information can then be acted on possibly by introducing a change to either a procedure or design. While what changes to make might be clear, making the changes can be quite sophisticated and involve careful management of change through the change control procedure. The effect on work in progress, stores, stock, equipment in the field etc., will need to be considered. Alternatively the solution or change may not be so clear and require the involvement of the quality improvement team to investigate the problem and to determine an appropriate course of action.

A general approach to corrective and preventive action can be:

- o   Monitoring to determine whether corrective action is required.
- o   Analysis of results to determine what corrective action to take.

- o   Programme, plan and initiate corrective action.
- o   Monitor the effectiveness of the corrective action.

It is the responsibility of each Manager or section head to ensure that reports are made regarding Quality problems so that any adverse trends and/or the major contributory factors causing rework can be identified and acted on.

The corrective action taken in the key areas above will be reviewed at the Management Review Meeting to ensure that it has been effective in solving the immediate problem and will avoid recurrence at a later date:

Where corrective action was necessary in specific departments, confirmation that the corrective action was completed and was effective will be obtained during the regular Quality Audits.

Preventive Action: Corrective action refers to the steps taken to avoid the same mistake being made twice and monitoring trends to take timely action. Preventive action refers to the steps taken to predict or identify possible causes of failure that have not yet occurred. On the face of it this is an impossible task, however, there are numerous techniques available which can help identify possible causes of failure. See section Failure Mode and Effects Analysis and Quality Planning.

Handling, Storage, Packaging, Preservation and Delivery

The handling, storage, packaging, preservation and delivery of the item, if not properly controlled, can affect the quality of the product.

Handling - Procedures need to be established describing the correct and safe methods of handling the product that prevent any damage or deterioration. E.g. static precautions for electronic devices.

Storage - Control of the stores area is important to ensure that no damage or deterioration of the product pending its use or delivery can or has taken place. These controls may need to extend to first in and first out procedures, stock control, issue and receipt etc.

Packaging - Controls of the packaging and preservation and marking of the product may be necessary to avoid any problems in transportation which could adversely affect the quality of the product. This may be particularly important with sterilisation processes.

Preservation - There is a need to identify where the product is at risk from the environment and take steps to ensure that the product is maintained in a satisfactory condition. Controls such as shelf life, date coding and reviews of condition of stock can be employed.

Delivery - Controls still need to be maintained after the product has left the factory, to ensure that adequate protection is maintained.

Quality Records

It is necessary to provide recorded evidence of compliance with the QAMS. Such records may include; design decisions regarding quality, design reviews, any tests or demonstrations that were performed in design, goods inwards, in process or final inspection records. There is a need to establish where and what records will be kept, their contents, the responsibilities for maintaining the records and for how long they will be maintained.

Below is a typical list of some of the records required by ISO9001 (the numbers refer to the ISO9001 paragraph number).

4.1	Management Review Meeting minutes
4.3	Record of contract review and any changes to the order
4.4	Design inputs (requirements)
	Design verification records, i.e.
	calculations
	design reviews
4.5	Index/register of controlled documentation
	Document approval & changes
4.6	Sub-contracts list/performance/approved
	Purchase orders
4.8	Serial No's, Part No's, Material used, Batch No. Drawing No's.
4.9	Records of special processes, e.g. temp charts
4.10	Delivery notes (record of receipt inspection)
	Inspection reports
	Final inspection and test
4.11	Register of measuring equipment
	Calibration history
	Software validation
	Validation certificates
	Calibration certificates
4.12	Release to production records
	Records of progress

Signatories

Condition label, i.e. passed/awaiting inspection quarantine

4.13   Records of non-conformity

Concessions etc.

4.14   Corrective/Preventive action

Record of meeting

Customer complaints

4.15   Stock records

Identification

Storage conditions

Shelf life

Delivery Notes

4.16   Index/register of records

4.17   Audit Reports, Time Tables

4.18   Training schedules

Personnel

Skills history

Staff appraisals

4.19   Register of equipment requiring service

Service history

Guarantees/warranties

Customer records

4.20   Graphical/charts

Trends

Statistical Process Control

Process Capability Study

Internal Audit

With any QAMS it is essential that regular checks are made to ensure that the procedures are effectively implemented. For this reason arrangements need to be made to conduct regular audits. These arrangements need to include the frequency and procedures describing the conduct of such audits. (See section Quality Audit).

Training

It is important that personnel performing tasks that could affect quality are properly trained. Details need to be maintained of who requires training, what tasks require training, the training that should be given, the responsibility for performing the training and what training records need to be maintained.

The answer to who requires training must be everyone in the organisation but they will need training in different things.

Everyone requires induction training and training in their own specific responsibilities within the QA documented system. Everyone should be trained with regard to basic quality assurance awareness. Why quality, what is quality, what is the company's position with regard to quality, what is the company's approach to addressing the needs of their customers? What are the needs of their customers? This can often be included within the induction training.

The Auditors will also require training, whether they are performing external (supplier) or internal auditing.

Servicing

If products are not properly serviced this can have a detrimental effect on the quality performance of the product. For this reason procedures need to be established which describe the proper maintenance and servicing arrangements for the product or service.

For service organisations this may include call escalation procedures.

Statistical Techniques

It may be appropriate or necessary to establish statistical techniques which ensure that the processes are of acceptable capability, initially and consistently throughout the process cycle. (See section Statistical Quality Control).
The previous section followed the approach described by ISO9001. There are, however, omissions from ISO9001, some of these omissions can be found in ISO9004. Detailed below are some additional points which may also be considered for inclusion within a Quality Assurance Management System.

After Sales Servicing

Procedures may need to be established which describe the correct installation and commissioning of any equipment to ensure that it will perform adequately for quality. The installation and commissioning instructions may include specific inspection and tests that may need to be performed. Records on the satisfactory conclusion of the inspection and test may also be required.

Sales & Marketing

Quality Assurance of Sales could include such issues as the setting and monitoring of sales targets for each of the salespersons. Conducting appraisals on their performance, to determine areas of weakness (ability to identify a customer need, presentation and listening skills etc.). Determining an appropriate Sales Strategy for the products - advertising, mail drops etc.

As an early warning of any quality problems in the field, procedures or systems may need to be established for reporting where product failures or shortcomings become apparent. This is particularly important with newly introduced products, where there may not be a sufficiently accurate database describing any possible quality failures or shortcomings.

Another area that may be worthy of consideration is the Marketing department's role and responsibilities with regard to:

Customer Needs How is the marketing brief established and communicated with other departments to gain agreement to the organisation's ability to fulfil the customer requirements? - possibly in terms of price, quantity, quality and delivery. The use of Quality Function Deployment (QFD) may be appropriate (see section Quality Function Deployment). QFD can also be usefully employed in conducting bench marking or competition analysis to compare the advantages and shortcomings of the organisation's product or service over its competitor's. There is a need to create an image of a quality organisation for the customer (quality sells). Third party certification may partly help in creating the impression of a quality organisation with the customer.

Customer Satisfaction There are a number of ways of determining the level of customer satisfaction; marketing or customer satisfaction surveys (see section - Customer Satisfaction), customer complaints analysis etc. The customer complaints may require the creation of a customer complaint log and customer complaint escalation procedure. Where customer problems cannot be immediately dealt with the problem is escalated throughout the organisation.

Marketing Trends The implication of market trends, new technology and legislation. One of the key quality issues can be the accuracy and reliability of any marketing predictions - can the market information be relied on to make future investment plans?

Marketing Literature How is the accuracy of the information approved?

Product Safety and Liability

All safety aspects of the product or service need to be identified. The overall objective is to enhance the products safety and minimise any product liability problems. Steps should be taken which limit the risk of product liability and minimise the number of cases.

These steps may include: identification of the role and safety standards that need to be applied to the design of the product or service; carrying out evaluation and prototype testing, confirming the safety of the products (see Failure Mode and Effects Analysis); maintenance of records of the results of the evaluation and testing; carrying out analysis work on the instructions or warnings that need to be given to the user together with the design of the maintenance and labelling or promotional material to ensure that no misunderstandings occur; the development of means of traceability to facilitate any product recall or the creation of outline hazard or advisory notices should any adverse health or safety features be discovered after the product has been introduced into the market place.

Motivation

All of the above facets of a Quality Assurance Management System tend to concentrate on the system and structure aspects of quality with little regard for motivation for quality, the culture and attitudes. The sections on Quality Philosophy and Total Quality Management address the issues of quality motivation.

Economics

One of the key objectives of any Quality Assurance Management System is to have a positive effect on the Cost of Quality for an organisation. The section Cost of Quality describes the need to examine the cost and provides an approach to reducing quality costs.

ISO9000 for Service Industries

One of the principle criticisms of ISO9000 as a Quality Assurance Management System (QAMS) is that it is readily applicable to manufacturing industries but when applied to service (banks, hospitals, maintenance, financial, scientific etc.) industries then the standard is not suitable - it is not applicable. This is a fair criticism as the background to ISO9000 is very much based in the manufacturing industries. The interpretation provided in the previous section is intended to be a fairly general guide to applying a QAMS. In an attempt to answer this criticism of non-applicability to the service industry, and to help interpretation, the next section has been compiled. The section describes a strategy and approach to applying and interpreting a QAMS (ISO9000) to; first a service industry and then the software industry. The description includes the basic Quality Control elements of the Quality Assurance system that would expect to be found on how ISO9000 can be applied to these industries. The service industry can encompass; Banks, Financial Institutions, Hospitals, Communication, Health, Maintenance, Utilities (Cleaning, waste etc.), Trading, Financial, Professional, Administration, Technical (Consultancy, Test Labs etc.) Scientific (Research, development etc.), Food (Processing and Catering). There are too many service industries to cover in this book, so two particular types have been selected, namely, a Service and Repair Organisation and a Bank. The Service and Repair organisation has been used to describe an overall approach to controlling quality of service. A Bank has been used as an example on how to interpret ISO9001 for the Service Industry.

Quality of Service

Quality Objectives

1. Identification, evaluation and definition of customer requirements. This could be established by conducting Market Research or by the customer providing a specification.

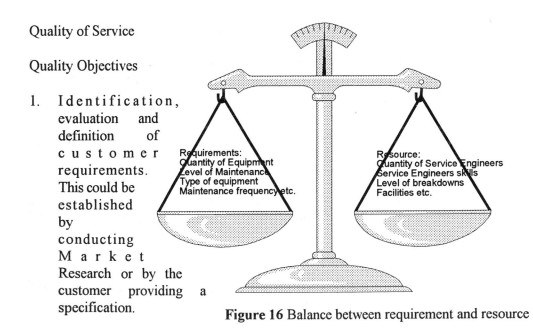

Requirements:
Quantity of Equipment
Level of Maintenance
Type of equipment
Maintenance frequency etc.

Resource:
Quantity of Service Engineers
Service Engineers skills
Level of breakdowns
Facilities etc.

Figure 16 Balance between requirement and resource

For example in the case of a servicing organisation (say maintaining equipment and buildings in a hospital), the list could include: Determining the number of types of equipment that can be serviced; the quantity or number of pieces of equipment to be serviced; the type of equipment that can be supported; job description of the service work content - time allowed; the maintenance periods/frequency/priority (based on past experience); the current level of break downs. *Note this is only the maintenance or service element and does not include any repair aspects.*

2. Organisation of adequate resources that will be able to provide the service to the required specification. Thus, avoiding the provision of inadequate or non-conforming services.

    For the servicing organisation this could include: The number of Service Engineers and their skills; the facilities in terms of equipment, technology, infrastructure, documentation etc.

    Figure 16 shows the balance that needs to be drawn between the requirements for maintenance support and the facilities that are available. It is very easy to have "eyes bigger than your stomach" i.e. the maintenance support requirement desired far outstrips the available labour resource.

3. Establishment of the system to control the relevant key factors which can significantly affect quality performance.

    For our service example these controls could include:

    o   *Control of work acceptance;* Ensuring complete and correct information regarding the work to be performed is obtained (scope, time, cost etc.) and that these service requirements can and will be fulfilled (availability of people, material, equipment etc.)

    o   *Control of Service delivery;* Ensuring that the Service Engineers understands that they are responsible for the quality of work provided.

        Each Service Engineer is responsible for completing the service or repair and conducting any final inspection and test. This inspection and test could include the following:

        a) check that safety test has been performed
        b) check that all previous stages have been performed and signed off and records maintained of tests performed

c) check that the work request is signed off

The secondary overcheck on the Service Engineer's work could be provided by the formalising of the supervisors audits. (It may be considered that good Supervisors do audits as a matter of course - the requirement is that good

Table 16 Supervisor's Audit Check List - Service Engineers

Is the work request available?
Is the work identified?
Are the correct tools and materials being used?
Are the correct procedures/work instruction available and being used?
Is the correct test equipment available and being used?
Has the Service Engineer been adequately trained?
Is the Service Engineer aware of the critical features?
Is the area clean and tidy?
Are all the checks adequately detailed and have they been performed?
Is the customer satisfied?
Are Service logs being completed (If required)?
Have safe working procedures and practices been observed?

Supervisors now formalise their audits). The formalisation could include checking that the Service Engineer has completed the work satisfactorily. The table details a typical Supervisor's Audit Check List:

4. Establish effective measurement and analysis of service quality provided in relation to satisfying customer needs and expectations.

For the Service example such measurement could include average response and down time, number of breakdowns, numbers of service "failures". This information can be collated to establish the overall cost of quality.

It may also be worth considering the use of a customer satisfaction survey (See Customer Satisfaction).

5. Evaluation on enhancement of the quality and range of services.

6. Creation of a positive attitude of each person in the organisation towards satisfying both the customer and organisation, possibly by the introduction of a Total Quality Management programme.

Quality Assurance Management

A guide to ISO9001 for financial institutions e.g. Banks

1. Requirement (4.1) Management Responsibility (No real change from the standard approach)

Quality Policy: The organisation needs to clearly define its commitment to quality. This commitment should be from the highest level of the organisation right through to the lowest.

Organisation: Effective management for quality with all the responsibilities clearly defined in writing. Management with authority - responsibility and ability to resolve problems - and an understanding of where the quality manager fits within the organisation. There must be an "owner" of the QAMS designated the Management Representative.

Management Review: If quality systems are not reviewed they tend to stagnate and not develop, a quality assurance system that provides never ending improvements in quality assurance.

2. Requirement (4.2) Quality System (No real change from the standard approach)

It really states that there is a programme and documentation for quality.

3. Requirement (4.3) Contract Review (No real change from the standard approach)

4. Requirement (4.4) Design Control

Bank and financial institutions design, develop and provide new products. These new products are often not fundamentally new but variations on a previous theme such as new investment and pension schemes that are offered to their customers. These products must be fully validated and verified. They must be not only internally controlled but also externally controlled, by various financial, regulatory and governmental monitoring bodies.

5. Requirement (4.5) Document Control

Some key documents that are issued require agreement or approval that the content of the documents are accurate. Occasionally these documents may get changed and there is a need for a system that controls the change of this documentation and its impact on any reference information or documentation.

6.   Requirement (4.6) Purchasing (No real change from the standard approach)

This is quite a lengthy requirement which means that we should buy products and also services from the right companies. These are companies who have shown good control of their quality, be that a product or a service. We need to monitor their facilities and to satisfy ourselves that they are up to our standards, it may be that we need to go to the extent of assessing the sub-contractors or supplier's ability to meet our requirements. This could include requirements for security, specifically with regard to cheque and credit card suppliers and for controls on banking systems suppliers in terms of the reliability, robustness, maintainability etc. of the computer equipment and software supplied.

We also place orders on these sub-contractors and it is necessary to ensure that the order describes precisely what our requirements are.

7.   Requirement (4.7) Customer Supplied Product

In financial terms this must mean looking after the financial resources provided by the customer or client, ensuring the best return on investment and that financial resources are safe and secure.

8.   Requirement (4.8) Product Identification & Traceability

When appropriate it is important that there are procedures which identify documents - files accounts - locations - source - etc.

9.   Requirement (4.9) Process Control

There are numerous processes taking place within financial institutions; some can be very complex. Almost all of these processes will require clear written instruction on the activities and controls needed to be applied. Such controls may include: defining each activity, the sequence, work instruction for each activity, what records will be maintained etc. It may be that special checks, instructions or training is required.

Consideration could also be given to the inclusion of hard and soft standards. Hard Standards would be very specific, for example:

- o   cleanliness of the office
- o   percentage of debt write off
- o   average response time to a telephone call
- o   average response time to a client
- o   average length of queues

These are very specific standards that must be achieved.

Soft Standards would be non-measurable (not quantifiable) requirements but still nevertheless requirements, for example:

- a warm personal style
- efficient service
- managing the problem, e.g. reasons for the delays
- a realisation that the customer may be upset and want to be told or reassured that you will do something about their problem
- a general air of professionalism

10 Requirement (4.10) Inspection & Testing

Receiving Inspection & Testing

This is checking the quality of the services or materiel supplied, checking that all the resources are available for the operator to fulfil the service that is being provided, e.g. Computer systems and the need to verify and validate any purchased software to ensure it actually fulfils its intended purpose.

In-process Inspection and Testing

There would be a need to validate and verify; data entry (e.g. entering numbers into a computer), also that the procedures as described in the quality manual are being observed. Such verification may be completed by the supervisor or possibly by the application of techniques or methods that validate data entry.

Final Inspection & Testing

There would need to be inspection of any documentation prior to issue, including papers despatched to a customer. Also it would be important to keep records of any inspection or tests carried out.

11. Requirement (4.11) Calibration

Any measuring equipment that is used such as balances would need to be calibrated to ensure its accuracy and consistency.

12. Requirement (4.12) Inspection & Test Status

If documentation is produced, the inspection status of this documentation would need to be identified, i.e. that the documentation has been or is awaiting checking.

13. Requirement (4.13) Control of Non-Conforming Materiel

Even in the best Quality Assurance Management System things can go wrong - on these occasions the suspect materiel needs to be identified for example:

- o   identification of any wrong data that is entered
- o   identification of any damaged materiel
- o   identification of any bad debts

It is unproductive to identify solely the non-conforming materiel or quality problems if no steps are taken to prevent the recurrence, i.e. corrective action - see the next requirement.

14. Requirement (4.14) Corrective & Preventive Action

This involves identifying the factors or performance indicators that give a measure of the organisation's quality achievement. Having identified the organisation's or department's performance indicators, these factors require monitoring and the establishment of a corrective action plan.

Examples of performance indicators could include:
- o   customer complaints
- o   number of bad debts etc.

15. Requirement (4.15) Handling, Storage, Package, Preservation & Delivery

This requirement could relate to:

- o   handling of money or financial resources
- o   the storage of financial resources, e.g. the distribution of statements
- o   the security of financial resources
- o   the location of financial resources; type, owner etc.
- o   electronic data backup and storage
- o   loading of Automatic Cash Dispensers
- o   delivery of statements
- o   transportation of securities

- o electronic transmittal records
- o security of delivery, e.g. cash & cheques

16. Requirement (4.16) Quality Records

Quality records need to be maintained to demonstrate that the system is working effectively, comprehensive enough to trigger corrective action in any of the departments.

17. Requirement (4.17) Internal Quality Audits. (No real change from the standard approach)

All of the systems and procedure requirements explained so far would count for nothing if they were just installed and left at that. The systems must be audited from time to time, are they still compatible - pertinent - do they allow for changes - are we as good as we think we are?

18. Requirement (4.18) Training (No real change from the standard approach)

To perform the tasks satisfactorily and completely the correct techniques and methods must be shown. It is essential to provide the opportunity to acquire the necessary skills to accomplish the task. Where appropriate this training should be regularly provided and records maintained identifying the training needs together with confirmation that training has been given.

19. Requirement (4.19) Service

Not directly applicable; covered mainly by Process Control

20. Requirement (4.20) Statistical Techniques

Statistical methods can help in most aspects of data collection application, these can be used to appreciate more clearly the customer's needs and forecasting or measuring to assist in making better judgements or decisions.

Software Quality Assurance

Introduction

Like most things software development is a process. This process comprises of a sequence of events culminating in the production of a piece of software. The manner in which this software is developed and controlled can have a large bearing on its suitability and reliability.

Although there are numerous examples of good software, there are also examples of software which does not achieve its intended function.

An example of bad software may be an Air Traffic Control System (ATCS) where software has been written to control the position and direction of aircraft. The software has been written, tested and appears to work satisfactorily. Ninety-eight aircraft are being controlled and every thing is OK, ninety-nine aircraft are now on the system and everything is still OK. The one hundredth aircraft appears on the system and suddenly all the ATCS computer screens go blank. Why? - because the software can only cope with up to ninety-nine aircraft the ATCS computer has crashed.

The need to control software development is becoming more and more important, especially when considering not only the previous example but also other examples of where software is used. E.g. Controlling aircraft such as in the fly by wire commercial aircraft now being developed, where aircraft control can be performed by the computer. Finite element analysis or simulation where civil, marine and many other structures are analysed for design purposes. This is to enable design decisions to be made regarding the sizes and strength requirements of the supporting structure. Mistakes in the programme could result in a catastrophic failure.

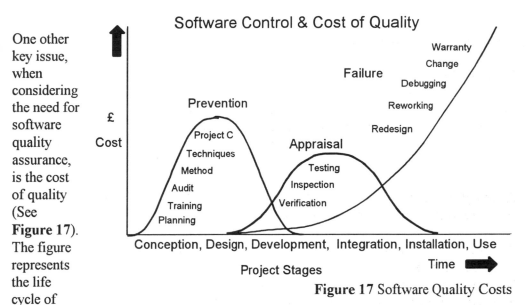

One other key issue, when considering the need for software quality assurance, is the cost of quality (See **Figure 17**). The figure represents the life cycle of software

Figure 17 Software Quality Costs

development; conception, design, development, integration, installation and use. The vertical axis shows the cost expenditure associated with each stage, broken down into the typical cost of quality elements (prevention, appraisal and failure) (see Cost of Quality section). The prevention cost should be spent at the front end of a project and may consist of: project planning, methodology etc. The appraisal cost will be spent in the middle section of the project on: testing, approval, verification and validation. The final cost of quality expenditure is the failure cost which can grow exponentially. This failure cost can encompass any redesign where the original chosen methodology or system design was not appropriate, the cost of debugging because of failures when testing the system software and customer complaints or correction of any faults during the warranty period. One way to address the issue of warranty failures, is by offering to correct, at no cost, any bugs or system failings discovered during the first (say) three months. Any further software bugs discovered after this first three-month period at half cost and after that at the user's cost. In this way the software developer is not forever responsible for the maintenance of the software system.

Guidelines for Software Quality Assurance

When determining an approach to software QA there are a number of issues to consider:

- ○   The acceptable level of risk. Risk is a concept which is very difficult to define. It can include the financial, programme, performance, safety and quality risks.
- ○   The level of Quality Control required. ISO9000-3 provides guidance for software QA but does not define the level to be employed. Three possible levels which could be used are:

Level 1 -	Associated with safety critical or high integrity systems.
Level 2 -	Software to be supplied to the customer which could result in financial or reputation loss to the supplying organisation.
Level 3 -	Software with minimal risk to the software developer, possibly small programmes which may not be used on a long term basis.

Figure 18 represents a detailed software sequence overlaid with the controls which may be expected for the situation described in level 2. Although, even within this level 2, software development can be extremely varied. It can range from development of a database using an application database package, to process control software using a computer processor's own machine code language, or number crunching on a high speed computer simulating or, for example, to ground water flow.

Each of these applications will have their own special needs, problems and approaches to software validation and verification. Consequently, the diagram can only be a general description of software development and control.

Quality Assurance Management

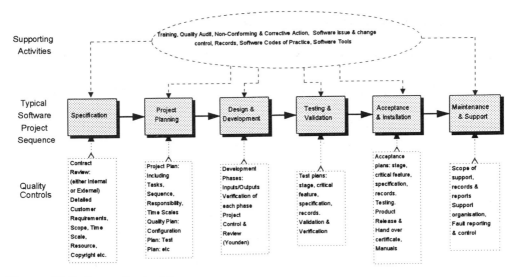

Figure 18 Software Project Sequence

Figure 18 is broken down vertically into three sections:

a.   The central section shows the *Software Project Sequence*.
b.   The bottom section shows the *Quality Controls* that can be applied to each stage.
c.   The top section shows the software development *Supporting Activities*.

Each of these sections will now be explained.

Software Project Sequence and Quality Controls

Although these stages are described as a series of tasks or events it is more likely that many of these tasks will occur in parallel

Specification: Specification development is possibly the most important element and yet it is often afforded the least amount of time and effort. Studies have shown that up to 60% of quality problems stem from not understanding the client's requirements. To avoid such problems the following action could be taken; an agreed format, content and shape of a standard specification could be completed (with examples). An agreed method of approving and accepting this specification could be provided (agreement and acceptance both internally and externally with the client). See Contract Review. The specifications that may need to be produced initially are the software, hardware (including hardware configuration) and support specifications. The support specification may include training, maintenance and assistance requirements. These initial specifications may be adequate for quotation stages but once the order or the authority to proceed with the project is given, then detailed additional specifications may be required. These additional specifications may include the functional specification and test specification.

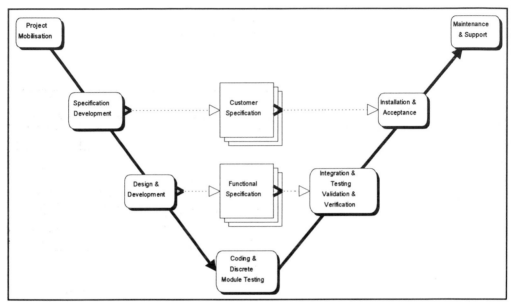

Figure 19 Software Specifications

Figure 19 shows how the specifications can be used in the latter stages of the project. The Customer Specification can be modified without a great deal of work into the Final Installation & Commissioning Test Specification and Plan. By the addition of some acceptance criteria and a column for test results the specification can become the Test Record sheet. This record sheet could be the instruction for the Software Test Engineer and completed during the Final Test Stages. This sheet would show the tests performed, the test data used, the outcome of the test and the name of the tester.

Similarly the Functional Specification produced at the Design & Development Stage can be modified into the Software Integration & Test Specification. Using this approach means that it is much less likely to overlook any key functional or user requirements. It also avoids *reinventing the wheel* in the sense of having to rewrite the test schedule from scratch - simple modification or reinterpretation of existing documentation can produce the required test plans and instructions.

Project Planning: Quality assurance and project management can include (but is not restricted to) the following activities: Quality Planning (See section Quality Planning), Project Control, (which could be based, in part, on the draft British Standards for Software development and BS7000 Managing Product Design). The project plan needs to include:

Identification of the project owner or leader
Project phases and team organisation
Project reporting and analysis
Project, design and development reviews
Specific coding and design practice to be employed
Task assignment or responsibilities

The development methodology of the software needs to be determined (the way in which the software is designed). There are many approaches to establishing the design methodology, from simple flow diagrams to more complex approaches as described in:

Yourdon & Hatley methodologies and requirements analysis
Jackson and Constantine structure charts
Integration of methodologies into the documentation structure

Software Testing and Validation (Test Plans):

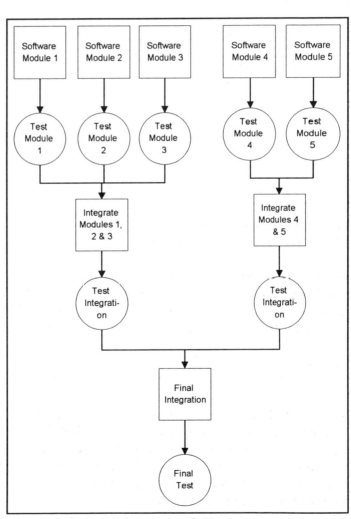

Figure 20 Software Integration & Test

As previously mentioned, the approach to verifying and validating software is very dependant on the type of software being produced. Often the approach to software creation is by development of software modules which are later integrated. See **Figure 20**. The approach to software testing in this case can be to test the individual modules to ensure satisfactory performance against a predetermined test plan. Then integrate each module, retesting after each module integration (Records of the success or otherwise of the testing at each stage need to be maintained). This approach (testing each module) is fine if the software development is to be completed in module elements. The problem is that not all software is developed and produced in this way, so alternative testing methods may need to be found. (E.g. flat code, database software etc.).

Some of the activities associated with integration and test can include:
o   Test plan development and implementation
o   Test scheduling and recording (records of individual tests - showing pass or fail and the action taken in the case of failure; rewrite, concession etc.)
o   Contents of Test Plans and estimating their coverage
o   Installation, commissioning and acceptance plans
o   Integration methods
o   Bug reporting; setting up of the bug report data base, including bugs open (still outstanding) and bugs closed (actioned, corrected and cleared)

One method that can be employed to check specific pieces of software code is detailed in the section on Document Inspection. This method or approach is not only applicable to software code but also to any documentation (specifications, reports etc.) that requires inspection, verification and validation. *See Document Inspection at the end of Software Quality Assurance Section.*

Maintenance & Support: This can include the technical support for both hardware and software - provision of advice and assistance. This can be as comprehensive as the compilation and provision of training plans and courses. Hardware maintenance, providing a preventive maintenance and repair service. This may entail the creation of an equipment and customer database and a maintenance plan. Software maintenance, resolution of bugs and software inadequacies (e.g. within the customer specification but still causes customer complaints or concerns). Again this may entail the creation of a customer software database; listing customer, software supplied and its issue status.

The technical support and the hardware and software maintenance probably requires the creation of a call logging and escalation system. This is similar to the bug reporting system where customer calls or queries are logged on to the call logging database. The call is actioned and eventually becomes either a call open (still outstanding) or a call closed (actioned, corrected and cleared). In the case of a call remaining open for a predetermined time (say two days) the call is escalated up the management hierarchy, possibly until it reaches the Managing Director. Some of the activities associated with maintenance and support can include:

o   Support organisation
o   Types of maintenance activities to be provided
o   Training plan and course content
o   Recording method and reports
o   Software updates release procedures

Support Activities:

Documentation: There can be a considerable amount of documentation produced in the course of a software project e.g. user manuals, maintenance manuals, specifications, test plans etc. BS5515 provides some guidance on documentation for computer-based systems.

This documentation and software may require some of the following to be completed:

o   Documentation and software issue and configuration control
o   Documentation structure in relation to project type
o   Documentation contents, use and format
o   Documentation standards

Configuration control: These previously mentioned documents and software are very often subject to change (see section Change Control)

These change activities will probably require the following systems to be established:

o   Configuration management
o   Configuration activities; plan identification and traceability, change control

Software metrics and estimating: During planning, development, installation and use of software some method of establishing project performance indicators may be appropriate. These can include:

o   Assessing project objectives, critical aspects and timescales
o   Preparing proposals and consideration of contractual conditions
o   Evaluating development performance and utilising the results
o   Number of bugs, Field failures and customer complaints

Reliability Measurement: Software is not necessarily as reliable or robust as expected and tests need to be determined to examine these issues - reliability models.

Auditing Software: See section Auditing.   As with most processes and activities confirmation that the procedures are being followed and records are maintained is necessary. Consequently the following tasks will need to be established and completed - Audit plan, conduct the audit and audit corrective action.

Document Inspection

Introduction

This inspection technique was developed by Michael Fagan of IBM to ensure that all types of project documentation were clear, accurate, and consistent with any agreed standards. (E.g. documentation format standards.) This inspection technique is equally viable when applied to both software and documentation and can encompass specifications, documents, reports, source code etc. It is a logical, structured, formalised quality control procedure which, when used early in the project development cycle, has shown real benefits. Specifically, faster system development and better system quality.

The rules are strict and the initial reaction can be to see the approach as a bureaucratic imposition. However, the technique has shown that benefits are proportional to the extent that the rules are followed.

The Benefits

Performing this inspection should provide:

- Earlier delivery
- Reduced development costs
- Shorter development time
- Lower maintenance costs
- Fewer non-conformities
- Improvement in testing time

The reasons for these benefits are that:

Many software bugs will occur in software before the code is written. Subjective examination of documentation is not as effective as using formal inspection methods. Statistics have shown that inspection is more effective in identifying non-conformances than testing.

Approach to Inspection Sessions

Codes of Practice for
Inspection Sessions

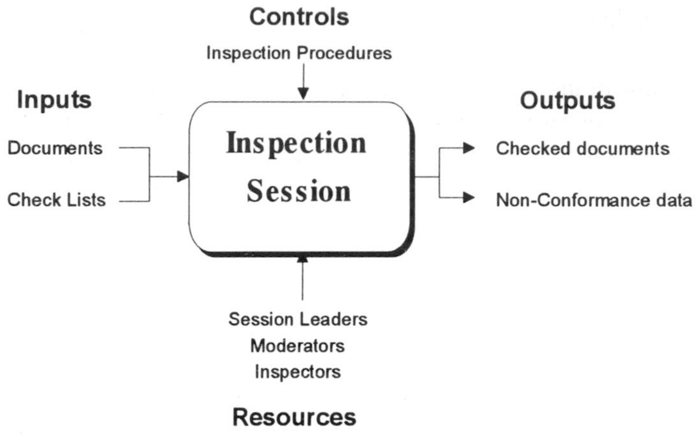

a. Inspection is
   performed in
   process not just at
   the end.
b. Various types of
   non-conformances
   in documents are
   inspected (i.e. not
   only logical or
   functional).
c. Inspection
   meetings are of
   limited duration
   (e.g. two hours).
d. The inspection sessions have a leader.
e. Inspectors are assigned specific roles.
f. Material is inspected at a rate that is found most effective.
g. Statistics are kept on the process to aid fine tuning.

Controls

Inspection Procedures

Inputs

Documents

Check Lists

**Inspection
Session**

Outputs

Checked documents

Non-Conformance data

Session Leaders
Moderators
Inspectors

Resources

Figure 21 Session overview

Roles:

Project Leader	- Owner of the total project
Session Leader	- Coordinator of the inspection session
Inspector	- Session participator
Author[4]	- Owner of the document

---

[4] The Project Leader's, Session Leader's and Inspector's responsibility is only to assist the author. The author has and retains (post the inspection session) ownership of the document or software. Responsibility for the quality of the document or software remains firmly with the author.

Typically, an inspection session will require 2-5 inspectors including the leader. The project leader will usually assign the inspectors and session leader.

Planning of inspection sessions is essential if the Inspection Session is to be successful. The Session Leader needs to divide the work carried out into manageable sections and identify the person responsible for each section inspection. This could be up to thirty pages for a document such as a specification or about three thousand lines of code.

The document author (owner) should:

- o   Print a copy of their work for each inspector. (If inspecting software, then the source code files need to be printed with line numbers).
- o   Ensure that all inspectors have access to the appropriate higher level specifications or objective and purpose of the document.
- o   The inspector needs to have access to the standard or code of practice (if there is one) for document formats.
- o   If source code is being inspected, produce a sorted function listing for each inspector.

All documents and source files being inspected should be uniquely identified and issue numbered under the document/software change control system before commencing the inspection process. (If there isn't a change control system then one will need to be created before starting!)

Prior to starting inspection the document owner or Session Leader should explain or present an overview of the project and the purpose or objective of the documentation.

Figure   22 Inspection Sequence

The inspectors should then work independently familiarising themselves with the documentation and identifying any possible non-conformances in the documentation (approximately two to three hours)[5]. These non-conformances will be presented by each inspector at the inspection meeting. Each inspector may have different roles e.g. checking legal aspects, financial implication etc.

The inspection meeting is attended by all the inspectors but it is not necessary that the document author is there (otherwise there is a danger of becoming defensive).

The role of the inspectors is to identify simply non-conformances in the document not to look for solutions or improvements. During the session the Leader should record the non-conformances found on a standard form. The summaries of these forms can then be fed into a database after the session.

Each non-conformance is graded with two classifications:

Severity Classification - Major/Significant/Minor[6]
and
Quality Classification - Omitted/Wrong/Superfluous/Unintelligible[7]

Once the inspection has finished, the Leader should provide a copy of the report to the original author and file another copy in the non-conforming record database.

After the session the Leader needs to ensure that corrective action on the non-conformances is taken. The non-conformance forms/reports can be used for this purpose.

---

[5]   It is possible to allow longer but the effectiveness of the sessions drops dramatically.

[6]   Class A   Major Discrepancy   One that would effect Health & Safety
       Class B   Significant Discrepancy One that would result in financial loss
       Class C   Minor Discrepancy   A problem that warrants attention

[7]   Omitted   Missing or not available
       Wrong   Incorrect material or information
       Superfluous   Additional material which is unnecessary
       Unintelligible Incomprehensible, incoherent or meaningless

Inspection Non-Conformance Report Log

This Inspection Non-Conformance Log would be completed by the inspectors detailing the document control information and identifying any non-conformances found.

Inspection Non-Conformance Report Log									
Document Number:					Document Number, Issue Number & Date:				
Document Author/Owner:					Session Leader:				
Inspector:					Date:				
#	Location of Non-Conformance	Severity Classification			Quality Classification				Non-Conformance Description	Corrective Action	OK
		A	B	C	O	W	S	U			

Corrective Action

Next to each non-conformance description in the inspection report, there is space for the author to suggest the corrective action to be taken. Once this corrective action has been successfully completed, the tick box can be signed. Note, any corrective action needs to take due account of any document change control necessary. If the author decides that the non-conformance is invalid and no work is necessary then a comment is made in the corrective action column.

Once all valid corrective actions have been fixed then the author should advise the Session Leader. If all corrective actions have been completed then the Summary Sheet will require updating.

Inspection Check Lists

Inspectors should be given check lists to help in identification of errors and to increase the effectiveness of the inspections. The lists can be created from several sources; previous common faults (experience), specialists[8] document format standards, etc. The general check list below, is as its name implies a check list which can be employed for various types of documents such as the quality manual or procedures. Some of the following check lists are more specialised.

General Procedural Document Check List	
#	Question
1.	Does the document follow the approved standard for documents?
2.	Have the documents followed the necessary document control requirements? (Author, Number, Issue Level etc.)
3.	Is the document accurate? Cross references correct e.g., other documents, equipment or form numbers Does the document reflect current working practices? Does the document have any omissions?
4.	Is the document adequate to complete the task?
5.	Has the document adequate depth or detail? Would it be possible to complete the task directly from the document or would further assistance be necessary? I.e. training.
6.	Is the document clear and understandable?
7.	Are there any omissions that could adversely affect quality?
8.	Does the document include the monitoring and control activities necessary to ensure the process is carried out satisfactorily?
9.	Does the document include the control settings?
10.	Does the document state the approvals necessary before the process runs and once the process is running?
11.	Are the workmanship criteria clearly stated?

---

[8] Used when looking for particular requirements, e.g. legal or specific stages in a project; specification, integration, test etc.

This Test Plan check list is for us when checking test or inspection instructions. This type of check list could be employed where test or inspection failure could result in major financial of safety losses.

Test Plan Check List	
#	Question
1.	Does the Test Plan follow the approved standard for Test Plans?
2.	Is the Test Plan issue controlled?
3.	Is there a test covering each individual customer and functional requirement?
4.	Does the Test Plan encompass the User and Maintenance documentation needs?
5.	Does each test specify the test method?
6.	Does the Test Plan specify specific test responsibilities?
7.	Does each test make reference to accept and reject criteria?
8.	Does the Test Plan show the steps to take in case of rejection?
9.	Does the Test Plan specify what records are to be held?
10.	Does the Test Plan specify responsibilities for retaining test results and the retention duration?

This is a check list for Purchase Orders and Purchase Specifications. It may be that this check list would only be used for Purchase Orders of significant size, although even getting the smallest Purchase Order wrong can have catastrophic effect. The responsibilities for employing this check list could be divided into the three aspects: Document control, general and technical.

INSPECTION CHECK LIST FOR THE REVIEW OF PURCHASE ORDERS & SPECIFICATIONS	
#	Question
1	Purchase Order - Document Control Is the Purchase Order approval available and correct person and level? Does the Purchase Order follow the style guide for Purchase Orders? Is the relationship with other documents specified? Is the Purchase Order distribution detailed and correct? Has the Purchase Order classification level been established?
2	General Is the order correctly identified? Does the order contain a description and appropriate technical (drawing specification etc.) information? Does the order contain any Inspection and Test criteria (including certification) or Quality Standards to be applied? Does the order contain delivery instructions? I.e. Is the addresses specified (Payment, Invoice & delivery)? Are the contact points specified? Has the Purchase Order been spell and grammar checked? Is the Purchase Order in sufficient depth or detail? I.e. Is the order pitched at the correct level of understanding for the intended recipient? Does the Purchase Order use too much jargon? Are abbreviations, specialist terms, titles etc. defined? E.g. Is a glossary required? Are units consistent and correct? Is the Purchase Order presentation quality satisfactory? (Including drawings, diagrams etc.) Have responsibilities been identified i.e. specific sections attributed to individual personnel? Have the original Purchase Requirements been clearly stated and been fully addressed? Are references to other documents sufficiently comprehensive and adequate?

#	Question
\multicolumn{2}{c}{**INSPECTION CHECK LIST FOR THE REVIEW OF PURCHASE ORDERS & SPECIFICATIONS**}	
3	Technical Are all Legal issues adequately addressed? Is the scope of requirements specified? Does the Purchase Order specify a period for validity? Are the Terms & Conditions appropriate, adequate and current? Is it clear that prices are specified for duration of the contract? Is the date of issue of the contract clear? Does the contract specify who has the right to change the contract? Has the original source material been specified? Are the risk areas identified?

Note 1: *Use of this inspection check list in no way removes the responsibility of the quality of any Purchase Order from the author. Quality of the Purchase Order (as always) remains firmly with the author of the Purchase Order.*

Note 2: *The Inspection Check List is broken down into three sections. The first section covers Purchase Order Change Control. The second section covers general questions that could be applied to most types of Purchase Order. Section three is more of a technical nature and is intended to be more sensitive to the needs of Purchasing.*

This is a check list for technical (mainly) research reports. It may be appropriate to split the responsibilities for employing this check list into the three aspects: document control, general and technical. The document control elements to ensure the specific organisations document approval and issue procedures are observed. The general questions; which can be used by a non-technical person to ensure the report is up to standard. The technical questions; for use by an inspector with a more technical experience or background.

INSPECTION CHECK LIST FOR THE REVIEW OF RESEARCH TECHNICAL REPORTS	
#	Question
1	Document Control Is the Document approval available and correct person and level? Does the document follow the style guide for technical reports? Is the relationship with other documents specified? Is the document distribution detailed and correct? Has the document classification level been established?
2	General Has the document been spell checked? Has the document been grammar checked? Is the report in sufficient depth or detail? I.e. Is the report pitched at the correct level of understanding for the intended audience? Does the report use too much jargon? Does the report over estimate the level of intellect of the reader? Are abbreviations, specialist terms, titles etc. defined? E.g. Is a glossary required? Are units consistent and correct? Is the report presentation quality satisfactory? (Including diagrams) Have responsibilities been identified i.e. specific sections attributed to individual personnel? Have the original customers' requirements been clearly stated and been fully addressed? Have the report objectives been clearly stated and fully addressed? Have any future work areas been specified? Are references to other documents sufficiently comprehensive and adequate? Is there an adequate method of obtaining and recording customer reaction or feedback regarding the report? Have the Intellectual Property rights been established?

#	Question
	INSPECTION CHECK LIST FOR THE REVIEW OF RESEARCH TECHNICAL REPORTS
3	**Technical** Has the original source material (data, customer specifications, tasking brief etc.) been specified? Have the approach, methodology and any calculations been verified (correctness) and validated (confirmed)? Has any measuring equipment been specified? (Number, calibration status etc.) Have any assumptions made been specified? Are the risk areas in the report identified? (I.e. Novel ideas may need to be stated and risks quantified) Is the report up to date and in line with current scientific thinking? Are the results believable? Are the limits over which the results apply specified? Are the data sources defined, complete and validated? Are the conclusions and recommendations clear and specific? Is there sufficient objective evidence to support the conclusions and recommendations? Is there too much information? Does (should) the report address failures as well as successes? Is the report focused on the customer needs? Do the conclusions and recommendations address and respond to each customer requirement? Have there been any external changes that may invalidate the report or data?

Note 1: Use of this inspection check list in no way removes the responsibility of the quality of any documentation from the author. Quality of the documentation (as always) remains firmly with the author of the document.

Note 2: The Inspection Check List is broken down into three sections. The first section covers Document Change Control. The second section covers general questions that could be applied to most types of report. Section three is more of a technical nature and is intended to be more sensitive to the needs of research.

Inspection Report Summary

The Inspection report is a summary of the inspection activities and results. The report shows the quality statistics for a particular set of documents, (such as all the manuals, software or specifications associated with a project).

The top part of the form details all the documents examined (including issue control information). The bottom half features the overall quality performance indicators of the documentation examined. This form could be completed once all the inspection activities have been completed.

Inspection Report Summary Sheet			
Project Name:		Project Number:	
Document Names:	Document Numbers, Issue Number & Date	Document Owners:	Inspectors
Session Leader:		Date:	
Non-Conformance Type	Total	Percentage of total	Estimated Rework Time
Severity Classification			
Major			
Significant			
Minor			
Total			
Quality Classification			
Omitted			
Wrong			
Superfluous			
Unintelligible			
Total			

Problems with Document Inspection

Document Inspection may be seen as an expensive exercise in that if the job had been completed correctly in the first place it would not be necessary.
This is true but not everyone's perfect and some authors are better than others, this technique gives the opportunity to help the weak authors.

Authors may not do such a good job if they know the errors will be picked up by the inspectors.

The responsibility for the quality of the documentation will always be the authors. This does not change before or after inspection.

This approach may be seen as common sense - and just an extension of the existing reviews and approval.
Yes this is quite true, all the technique does is to formalise this procedure.

Exercise - Document Inspection

1.   Create a check list for one the following situations:

        a.   An Applied Research report
        b.   A piece of Software Code (written in C)
        c.   A functional specification

2.   Complete the Inspection Process for the documentation provided (including completion of the report and summary sheet).

Implementation of a Quality Assurance Management System

Overall programme

Stage 1	Stage 2	Stage 3	Stage 4	Stage 5
Procedure writing Training for the key personnel in the QAMS and Quality Auditing Team Briefing for all employees - their roles and responsibilities)	First Audit *(Training)* Supervisors provide training for their subordinates on the content of QAMS & Quality Manual	Second Audit *(Coaching)* Reinforcement of the roles and responsibilities as described in the QAMS & Quality Manual	Third Audit *(Instruct)* Confirmation of application of the QAMS	Final Assessment
	Review I Workshop 1 & Audit 1 Feedback	Review II Workshop 2 & Audit 2 Feedback	Review III Workshop 3 & Audit 3 Feedback	

Detailed programme of work

a.   Initial assessment of the organisation to determine the current situation. This initial assessment is to determine the initial project requirements, prepare terms of reference and complete a detailed project plan. It is not necessary that to have a QAMS in operation to conduct the first preliminary assessment as this assessment is intended to be informal. The objective being to gather information, rather than a formal audit against a Quality Standard.

b.   This initial assessment requires turning into the Terms of Reference for the Project, including a report of the findings of the preliminary audit.

The project plan can be plan based on the following stages:

c.   Present the report and findings to agree the need for a QAMS and to gain approval and agreement to the approach from senior management. *Do not embark on any Quality Assurance Programme without the full, committed and written support of the Management. If senior management are not prepared to "buy into" the scheme then the programme will almost certainly fail.*

d.   Present the reason for the QAMS programme, report and findings to all personnel to gain their agreement and approval of the approach. Again commitment to the programme and eventual accreditation is essential.
The allocation of work and ownership of certain procedures needs to be determined.

e.   Compile Volume 1 Quality Manual which will be the policy document used for marketing and customer confidence purposes. (See section The Quality Manual)

f.   Together with support from relevant departments compile Volume 2 Quality Manual which will be the actual working Quality Manual. (Commercially confidential to the organisation). This Quality Manual will describe the company's Quality Assurance Management System and should/must meet the requirements of the appropriate quality standard (ISO9001?).

g.   If necessary, with support from relevant departments, compile any Departmental specific procedures and forms. These will contain specific procedures which are particular to some of the processes performed within the organisation.

h.   Determine the Quality Assurance training needs of the organisation's personnel and provide the necessary updates to ensure that they understand the requirements of the QAMS and also their responsibilities and roles within the Quality Assurance System.

It may not be immediately apparent but the above stages a to h are the easy part. The most difficult stage is yet to take place - namely getting personnel to work to the new procedures. It is all very well in isolation or in a small team formulating the quality system procedures that are intended to be observed, but it is a very different story when these procedures are used in practice.

i.   Distribute the Quality Manuals. (See Document Control)

j.   Repeat the presentation on the reasons for the new QAMS and gain agreement to the new procedures. It may now be clear why early Management Commitment is so essential.

k.   Audit (see the section Audit) the company against the compiled Quality Manuals and prepare a report indicating where the organisation does not meet the requirements of the particular Quality Manual and therefore whether they would meet the requirements of the QAMS.

l.   Discuss the report with Management and determine any necessary corrective action. This audit may need to be repeated a number of times before the QAMS is fully operational and to gain confidence in the operation of the QAMS (4 months records of the QAMS in operation). The first audit could be in the form of *Training* for the supervision and subordinates on the content of QAMS & Quality Manual and their roles and responsibilities. The next audit could be in the form of *Coaching*, reinforcing the roles and responsibilities as described in the QAMS & Quality Manual. The final audit could be in the form of *Instruction*, confirming the application of the Quality Assurance Management System.

The Quality Manual (The Documented Quality Assurance Management System)

The Quality Manual is a collection of all the policies, organisational structure, responsibilities, procedures, processes and resources for implementing quality. The quality system should only be as comprehensive as needed to meet the quality objectives.

The Quality Manual can have several purposes:

Analysis: The discipline of documenting the organisation's procedures, objectives, responsibilities and structure requires detailed analysis of the organisation activities. The result of this analysis can identify and resolve inconsistencies and anomalies in the existing systems.

Stability: The Quality Manual should describe the authorised and agreed approach to achieving quality. Consequently the manual can be the reference document for all employees.

Training: The Quality Manual can assist in introducing new employees to the organisation's procedures. Providing a clear statement regarding the tasks required, how these tasks should be performed and who is responsible for the task's successful completion.

Audit: The Quality Manual provides the basis for examining the organisation's actual practice against some concept of good practice.

Assurance: The existence of a Quality Manual provides both the customer and the management with confidence in the organisation's services and products.

Demonstration: Shows compliance with a recognised Quality Assurance System standard e.g. ISO9000.

Structure of the Quality Manual

The shape of the Quality Manual could be broken down into three levels, Volumes 1, 2 & 3. See **Figure 24**. The object of these sections could be:

Volume 1: Introduction to the organisation and its structure, description of the product or services offered, general policy and management commitment to a Quality Assurance Management System. Basically, this is the marketing document that can be given to customers and employees to indicate the organisation's commitment to Quality.

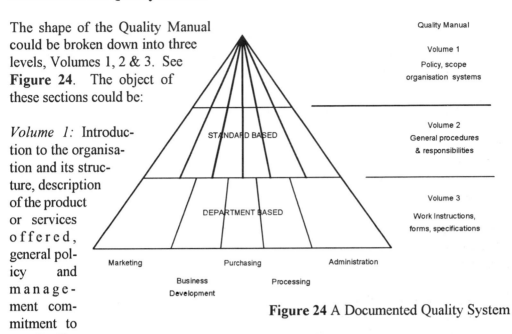

Figure 24 A Documented Quality System

Volume 2: Describes the general procedures and responsibilities for operating the Quality Assurance System.

Volume 3: Contains the detailed procedures which may relate to task specific activities such as, work instructions, test specifications, forms, calibration instruction etc.

Generally the contents of the Quality Manual can either follow the order of the most appropriate Quality Assurance Management Standard (QAMS) or alternatively be in the sequence best suited to the organisation. Organising the Quality Manual in the sequence of the requirements of the standard (ISO9001) makes it easier for auditing purposes but may make the manual more difficult to follow for those people not familiar with the QAMS clause titles. It should be noted that the structure of the QA Manual documentation described above is just one example and there are many other ways to structure such documentation.

The Quality Manual

The Quality Manual should contain the following:

Quality Policy: A general statement of intent. The policy should include the management's commitment to quality and that the QAMS is based on or meets a defined quality standard. Finally the policy statement should indicate that the procedures included in the quality manual are mandatory for all employees. All of these elements need to be confirmed and authorised by the signature of the Head of the organisation. If the Head of the organisation cannot sign such a document then this clearly indicates that the organisation is not sure that a documented QAMS is the right approach for the organisation. This is a positive not a negative position, as the introduction of a QAMS when unsure is almost guaranteed to fail. If by not signing it has exposed this uncertainty then the QAMS programme can be delayed or abandoned until full commitment by the Organisation Head and management can be obtained, thus avoiding any unnecessary and potentially damaging work.

Approval: Approval and authorisation (possibly by the Quality Manager) of the issue of the quality manual.

Amendment record: A record of the issue status of the quality manual indicating for example issue date, section number, page number, approval etc. See Interpretation of ISO9001 - Document Control.

Distribution: Distribution list of the manual showing holders of controlled copies of the quality manual.

Contents: Contents list of the quality manual. The sections of the quality manual could be based either on the organisation's process cycle or in the order of the chosen quality standard.

Definitions and terms: Explanation or description of some more commonly used terms or abbreviations.

Organisation: An organisation chart, showing the relationship of the quality department with other departments. A brief description of the organisation's background and business could also be included.

Procedures: The procedures and activities affecting quality should be described or made reference to if the procedures are maintained in a separate document (the company operating procedures). It may also be appropriate to provide a look up table showing where each of the quality standards requirements are encompassed. The general format of each procedure could be:

Introduction to the procedure describing its objective, aim or purposes, the scope and topics covered and the applicability of the procedure.

Responsibilities for performing the procedures.

Reference documents that may be required such as forms or work instructions. The input documents (documents required to successfully complete the procedure) and output documents (documents produced as a result of completing the procedure).

Procedure or methods that describe what tasks are to be performed and how to perform the tasks.

The aspects covered can be:

> The inputs to the process e.g. raw material, documents, information etc.

> The output from the process i.e. what the process turns the input into e.g. material.

> The controls e.g. instructions, drawings, audit, monitoring method, inspection, validation, verification etc.

> The resources e.g. people, skills, knowledge, facilities, equipment (measuring and process), consumables, money etc.

Issue control data to describe the title, title number, issue number, author, approver, circulation etc.

One of the most difficult aspects in preparing work instructions is deciding the level of detail. In principle there is a need to strike the correct balance between instruction and training.

As a general rule, for unskilled workers, it may be necessary to break down the tasks or steps. The content of the instruction should be sufficiently detailed for the person to satisfactorily complete the task. The instruction should include the process or task inputs, the process resources, the process controls and the process output.

Skilled people may only require general training on what is to be achieved. The work instruction then may only describe the task objectives and not on how these objectives are to be achieved. For example, a Researcher may only be requested to examine a particular phenomena, not on how to undertake the research. However, a Laboratory Technician may require instruction on how to use a piece of equipment to provide experimental results. See **Figure 25**.

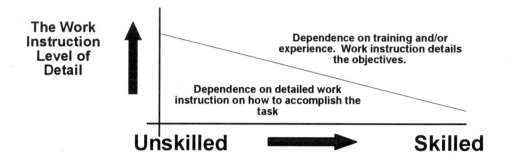

Figure 25 Procedure Detail

Exercise:

Gaining benefit from ISO9000 after Approval

Introduction: Gaining ISO9000 approval for an organisation will probably be a major project involving almost all departments (some more than others). The project often starts with the best of intentions - not just to gain approval but to improve the overall performance of the organisation. Unfortunately, as the deadline for certification gets nearer then the emphasis can often change to doing just enough to gain approval. This is because the implication of failure for the organisation and individuals within that organisation has become more important than improving the effectiveness and efficiency of the organisation. Not surprisingly jobs and reputation can be on the line and failure could be very embarrassing. Failure to gain approval could be disastrous for the organisation concerned.

Of course just doing the things that are necessary to gain approval should improve the performance of the organisation. However, all too often these things are done solely to satisfy the assessor. The ISO9000 project often takes one to two years to complete and the conclusion - hopefully gaining approval, can be something of an anti-climax. People look round and ask "what changed, what has been achieved?" This is asked not because there has been no change but because these changes have been gradual. It is not always apparent that the improvements have been made as personnel have become used to working to the new (possibly improved) system.

There is a danger for managers to see gaining ISO9000 approval as an end in itself. The programme of introducing and implementing ISO9000 has necessitated a considerable amount of change and motivation. Having gained approval then the need to change and motivate has reduced. If managers see this approval as an end in itself then a great opportunity is lost. One consequence of conducting the ISO9000 programme is that people have become used to change and implementing change. Now is the time to start a new quality initiative, rather than just conducting the audit programme or surveillance programme to ensure continued registration. This is a great opportunity to make further improvements in the performance of the various systems and processes running through the organisation. Some particular examples of this could be in the Design and Development Department. Rather than just blindly following the procedures for contract and design review (without gaining real benefit) the procedures could be used to minimise design problems and avoid costly mistakes. Another example, but this time for the Marketing Department. The Marketing Department having gathered data regarding customer complaints, take no real action on understanding the customer's fundamental problems with the product or service.

There is also a danger for Quality Managers to see gaining approval as an end to their role in Quality improvement. Following approval, maintenance of the audit system and programme fully occupies the Quality Manager's time. This leaves no resource or time to consider new initiatives or improvements to the Quality Management System (QMS).

One key complaint in operating an ISO9000 system is that it becomes a bureaucratic imposition of producing forms and documentation. Will anyone actually read the Quality Manual anyway? Possibly, all the Quality Manual achieved was to document the current ways of completing tasks and processes. Cementing (in writing) all the bad habits and working practices that have been followed religiously over the life of the process.

Questions that now need to be asked are:

o   Has the QMS become a bureaucratic imposition?

o   Do the procedures reflect on how tasks *are* completed or *should be* completed? Does the procedure integrate the process or do people work as individuals?

o   Have people within the organisation noticed an improvement in the organisation as a whole?

o   Is there a sense of ownership of the QMS - or is the QMS owned by the quality department? Examples of this can be: The inability of obtaining any corrective action for the audit discrepancies. The non-updating of superseded procedures. The mad panic when the surveillance visit comes around.

o   Have the customers noticed an improvement in performance of the organisation's product or service?

o   Finally, the bottom line, has ISO9000 saved money?

To help identify the issues raised by these questions, the following section has been written. The section is intended to be used to improve and build on the existing system, grasping the opportunity that registration has brought and reinforcing positively the controls of ISO9000. This is because the basic concept and the reasons for implementing ISO9000 still hold good. It is the practical implementation of ISO9000 that needs continually improvement.

Quality Assurance Management

Identification of the improvement area. As in most things, if the reasons and objectives for a task are clearly and properly explained, then people are more motivated and will likely take on responsibility for that task. It is now necessary to evaluate the degree with which ISO9000 and the QMS have been applied and the benefits (if any) that approval has brought.

The following check list is intended to be used to help evaluate managers' perceptions about the performance of the quality assurance management system. The statements need to be rated according to whether they are true or false - with reference to the current status of the organisation. If the question is completely false then score one, if completely true score ten. However, the statement may be partly true e.g. that the quality assurance system has made some contribution to the performance of the organisation. Here a score of five may be appropriate. To help interpret the questions guidance notes, shown in italics, are provided.

The general intention is not only to obtain a score but to promote discussion and stimulate action.

1. Application of the quality assurance system can make a positive contribution to the overall performance of the organisation?

	False									True
Scale	1	2	3	4	5	6	7	8	9	10
Mark										

ISO9000? - This question is about whether we truly believe ISO9000 approval can make a positive contribution to overall performance of the organisation. If managers can't truly buy into this, then there is a need to go back to basics and review the need for this style of quality management system.

2. There are clear and positive measures and data available that demonstrate the quality assurance management system is improving the overall performance of the business?

	False									True
Scale	1	2	3	4	5	6	7	8	9	10
Mark										

Quality Performance - Here the question is about the management information systems regarding quality assurance management systems. Is it effective enough? Is it giving sufficient feedback to determine that the quality assurance management system is working as effectively and efficiently as it possibly can?

3.   We know clearly where the quality assurance management system has been best applied to positive effect?

	False									True
Scale	1	2	3	4	5	6	7	8	9	10
Mark										

Quality Manual - This question is attempting to review and identify those areas within the organisation that have improved because of ISO9000, the areas that haven't benefited and the areas that could be improved with proper application of ISO9000.

List the areas where the quality assurance management system is weakest and needs to be stronger.

List the areas where the quality assurance management system is strongest and the organisation has gained the most benefit.

4.   Quality Auditing is an invaluable management tool?

	False									True
Scale	1	2	3	4	5	6	7	8	9	10
Mark										

Auditing can be seen as the method of retaining approval rather than a management tool. Auditing may provide management with important information regarding the compliance of the process and personnel to accepted working practices. Managers may not take notice of the results of audit and not take appropriate or prompt corrective action. This may be due to the managers' workload, the standard of the audit being poor or the results of the audits being trivial.

Quality Assurance Management

5. The quality assurance management system fully reflects the way in which the organisation works?

	False									True
Scale	1	2	3	4	5	6	7	8	9	10
Mark										

Ownership - All employees have a role and responsibility for quality. Their contribution and compliance with the quality assurance management system is essential if the system is to succeed. The quality manual may not be used - gathering dust on a shelf. This could be because personnel understand the contents and have no need to refer to the manual. It may be that the manual is difficult to read and understand. Could (or even should) the quality manual be put to greater use? There may be a need to change the quality manual to reflect current working practices.

6. The standard (ISO9000) has made a positive contribution towards customer satisfaction and the standard of our product and service?

	False									True
Scale	1	2	3	4	5	6	7	8	9	10
Mark										

Has the product or service measurably improved since the implementation of ISO9000? Has the number of customer complaints reduced?

7. The standard is active in helping to improve the performance of our processes?

	False									True
Scale	1	2	3	4	5	6	7	8	9	10
Mark										

Process Improvement - There are numerous processes running through an organisation e.g. buying, training, development etc. Proper use of the quality manual may help to improve the task or activity and, consequently, the process performance. It may be that there are better ways of achieving the objective of improving process performance.

Note, a process is different from a procedure. A process is a sequence of parallel or serial activities that have an input and output. A procedure is the instruction that describes the way in which an activity is to be performed.

8.   Maintaining a quality assurance management system is a cost-effective exercise?

	False									True
Scale	1	2	3	4	5	6	7	8	9	10
Mark										

Improving the profitability of an organisation can be achieved by improving the efficiency of the processes and reducing costs and waste.

The QMS should work on both levels:
o   *Improving process efficiency by describing the most efficient and effective way of completing various tasks.*
o   *Reducing waste and costs by the analysis of failures and waste and taking preventive action.*

Calculation of your ISO9000 score

Add up the score from each question and evaluate the organisation's score against the following assessment criteria.

0 - 40   ISO9000 doesn't seem to be working within your organisation and real benefits are obviously not being obtained. It may be appropriate to conduct a complete evaluation of the organisation's strategy towards ISO9000.

40 - 60   Obtaining benefits from the ISO9000 Quality Assurance Management System but possibly greater benefit could be derived. An analysis of the answers to the questions should reveal and possibly identify some areas that could benefit from review and evaluation.

60 - 80   Tangible benefits are being derived from the application of ISO9000. The effort could be towards maintaining and enhancing the gains and advantages already derived.

System Review and Evaluation

"I kept six honest serving men they taught me all I know. Their names are: what, where, when, why, how and who and the seventh is show me"

Rudyard Kipling

These questions can be successfully used in a number of circumstances (problem solving) but they can be particularly helpful when auditing. The questions could form the basis of audit questions: What procedures are required for this task? Where are the procedures kept? When are the procedures used? Why are the procedures necessary? Who and how are the procedures used? Possibly the most important question would be - can you show me the procedures?

Quality Audit

Definition; Quality Audit, A systematic and independent examination to determine whether the quality activities and related results comply with the planned arrangements and whether these arrangements are effectively implemented and are suitable to achieve objectives. (BS 4778, ISO8402)

An Audit is: The study of actual practice against some concept of good practice, carried out by someone independent of, or having no direct responsibility, for the conduct of the activity undergoing audit. The audit would be carried out by someone trained or experienced in auditing techniques and skills. Scheduling of the audit should be done in advance rather than in response to a crisis and conducted with the prior knowledge and participation of those whose area or work is being audited.

Different levels of Audit

Figure 26 shows diagrammatically the different levels of audit from the accreditation body National Accreditation Council of Certification Bodies (NACCB) accrediting the certification bodies. The certification body e.g. BSI independently assessing other organisations to approve these organisations under a registration scheme such as ISO9001. Customers auditing suppliers to determine the suitability and effectiveness of their QAMS. To finally the organisation's own internal audits to ensure continued implementation of the documented QAMS.

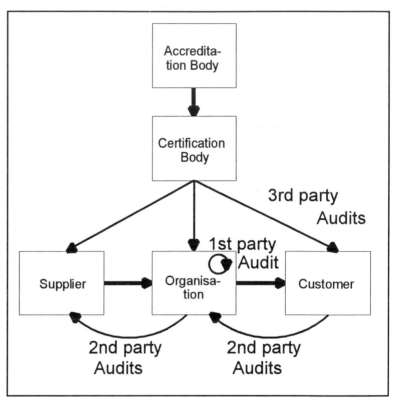

Figure 26 Levels of Audit

External Certification (3rd party); An external certification audit generally consists of a two-tier assessment.

a)   Adequacy audit - assessment of the quality system documentation against the 'Goal'. E.g. ISO9001.
b)   Compliance audit - assessment of the implemented quality system against the system documentation or the 'Goal'. I.e. Assessment of the system in practice.

External Audit (2nd party); An external audit is an assessment of a supplier or sub-contractor's quality system by the customer. The basis for this type of audit may be a recognised standard such as ISO9001 or the customer's own standard. The audit may be performed by auditors from within the customer's own company or they may call on a professional auditor to provide this service.

Internal Audit (1st party); An internal audit is carried out by a company on its own systems, procedures and activities. The audits are generally conducted by company staff, however, on occasion there may be professional auditors engaged to act on behalf of the company. The key difference between an external or third party audit is that the third or second party audits are against a standard (ISO9000) whereas an internal audit is against the organisation's own procedures and systems. The results of these audits are recorded in a similar way to an external audit and used as a basis for the company to develop and improve its operation.

Some of the following sections describe in more detail any differences in approach between internal and external audits.

Accreditation of Certification Bodies

The United Kingdom Accreditation Service operates accreditation schemes for Certification Bodies. Namely the National Accreditation of Certification Bodies (NACB) for the accreditation of Certification Bodies and the National Measurement Accreditation Service (NAMAS) for accreditation of Calibration Laboratories or Test Houses. In the case of the NACB used EN 45000 series to accredit Certification Bodies who certify organisations using the BS EN ISO9000 series of standards. In the case of NAMAS - they use the EN45001 (M10) as the basis for their accreditation.

Diagrammatically the hierarchy of these Bodies would be as shown in the diagram **Figure 27.**

The National Accreditation of Certification Bodies (NACB)

The NACB operates a system of accreditation of Certification Bodies such as BSI, Lloyds, Bureau Veritas Quality International, United Register of Systems etc. who certify organisations using the BS EN ISO9000 series.

The purpose of NACB is to assess the independence and technical competence of UK certification bodies to the requirements of EN45011/2/3.

EN45011 is the standard for certification bodies when issuing certificates of product conformity.

EN45012 is the standard for the certification bodies own Quality Management System usually based on ISO9001. Ie the Certifi-

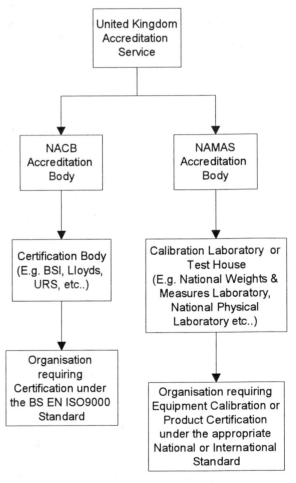

Figure 27 Accreditation Bodies

cation Bodies Quality Manual, Quality Manager, Internal Audit procedure etc.

EN45013 is used to assess the competence of the certification bodies own personnel (assessors).

Together these standards cover the structure, operation and management of the certification body.

NATIONAL
ACCREDITATION OF
CERTIFICATION
BODIES

Cerification
Body Number

Figure 28

Once the certification body is accredited, it is granted the right to use the Tick and Crown symbol. It is this symbol which denotes the authority of the certification body in any particular industrial sector, as not all certification bodies are accredited in all industrial sectors. For example, some certification bodies are not accredited by the NACB in the medical or software sectors. In this situation, certification bodies may still assess and certificate companies working in the medical and software industrial sectors. However, the certificates issued cannot carry the Tick and Crown.

The accreditation process is very similar to the ISO9000 certification process with application, preassessment, adequacy audit, full assessment and if successful accreditation.

Once a certification body is accredited by the NACB then any organisations certificated by that body can appear in the DTI QA register of approved companies. Together with the certification bodies own guide eg. BSI Buyers Guide.

The National Measurement Accreditation Service (NAMAS)

The purpose of NAMAS the National Accreditation Service is for the assessment, accreditation and the monitoring of testing and calibration laboratories. The value of this accreditation is based on the need to ensure that products are produced to specification and that products are safe. Note; product certification not management system certification. NAMAS accredited laboratories can provide this necessary assurance of the competence of calibration and testing houses. It is this competence which will avoid the need for multiple assessment of calibration and testing laboratories. NAMAS certificates of calibration and test reports have now been recognised by organisations such as British Telecom, Ministry of Defence, Rolls Royce etc. NAMAS are also involved with gaining agreement on the recognition of other National Schemes and as a consequence International acceptance of the competence of the accredited laboratory.

Following the stringent examination to the requirements usually of the standards M10 and M11[9], laboratories would then be authorised to use the formal certification and reports to record the results of any measurements and tests taken. These standards are very similar to ISO9001 but with reference to calibration.

The method of certification also very similar to the approach that would be adopted by the NACB or any other accreditation body. There is an application. The laboratory documentation is examined. There is a pre-assessment and then a full assessment of the laboratory.

Non-compliances to M10 and M11 and would then be raised (if any were found). Corrective action would be taken and on satisfactory completion of these corrective actions NAMAS would offer the laboratory accreditation. The NAMAS certificate would then be issued and the surveillance visits would then commence on a regular basis. Once certificated the accredited laboratory services would be publicised through the NAMAS directory of accredited laboratories.

These accredited laboratories can include commercial calibration laboratories and test houses as well as laboratories forming part of larger organisations such as a manufacturing company, University, or some Government organisation.

Only laboratories accredited by NAMAS may use the NAMAS logo in conjunction with their accreditation number. This is an important distinction and one which is carefully guarded by NAMAS to the extent that forging of these NAMAS certificates has resulted in custodial sentences for the misuse of these certificates.

---

[9]   M10 & M11 are similar to BS7500 series, EN45001 & EN45002 and ISO Guides 25 & 54. These documents cover the accreditation standard, the measurement & calibration system and the regulations

A typical example of one of these NAMAS certificated reports is shown in **Table 17.**

Table 17 Typical Calibration Certificate

CERTIFICATE OF CALIBRATION

Issued by the Quality Management & Training Laboratory
Date of Issue: 13 July 1995   **Serial No: 1234**

NAMAS

Quality Management & Training Laboratory
P O Box No 172
Guildford Surrey GU4 7GS

Tel: 01252 344454
Page 1 of 1 pages

CALIBRATION NO:
Approved Signatories
Mr F Tickle BA Ceng MIQA
Signed *F Tickle*
Mr G Vorley MSc MIQA
Signed *J Vorley*

CUSTOMER: Vakes Ltd Benley Park Guildford
DESCRIPTION: 1 off Micrometer to measure 0 to 25mm ± 0.01mm
SERIAL NO: 12345
DATE OF CALIBRATION: 13 July 1995

REPORT

BASIS OF TEST: A specified tolerance of ±1%
DIMENSIONAL: The gauge was measured for pressure at seven positions across the range
of the equipment using the Butenburgh testing rig. Serial No 123456.

The results were taken at 20°c +/- 2°c

MEASURING POSITIONS		RESULTS (mm)
1	0 mm	0
2	5	5.001
3	10	9.995
4	15	15.008
5	20	19.996

Uncertainty of measurement ± .5%
All measurement values were within the tolerance specified above

Signature *F Tickle*

The uncertainties are for a confidence probability of not less than 95%.

Different types of Audit

Management Reviews or Management Audits; Management audits are a review of the company's operation. The particular areas for review being allocation of responsibilities, efficient deployment of resources - both personnel and plant, effective communication, possible streamlining and simplification of the paperwork systems and operational procedures. These audits are generally done at Board of Director level.

Adequacy Audit (Desk study); This audit involves comparing the organisation's documented Quality Assurance System (QAS) against an appropriate Quality Assurance Management Standard (ISO9001). For each paragraph of the Quality Standard (ISO9001) there needs to be some reference in the documented QAS which addresses and fulfils the requirements of the standard. This adequacy audit can be against the standard (ISO9000) or alternatively the check list below may be employed.

a. Is the procedure clear and complete?
b. Can the procedure be worked to or followed?
c. Is the procedure up to date (version level) and current (in line with current working practices)?
d. Does the procedure correctly reference other documents?
e. Is the input information (etc.) to complete the task specified?
f. Are the outputs from the task specified?
g. Are the resources to complete the task defined?
h. Are any checks, approvals or monitoring of the procedure or tasks defined?

This list is not exhaustive and the answers to these question need not be yes!

Systems Audits (Vertical Audits); System audits are a review of all company procedures relating to quality. Increasingly, the quality of work depends on the quality of written procedures and the degree to which operators are aware of, understand and adhere to such procedures. The aim of a systems audit is to examine the effectiveness of the specified system procedures.

Project Audits (Horizontal Audits); Communication is a common problem in many organisations. One method of examining the effectiveness of communication is by conducting a project audit across departments. This is a very searching technique and can uncover some strange anomalies. A project audit is conducted by following a project through departments, reviewing all the documentation, materials, etc. applicable to the chosen product or project. Project audits aim to establish the extent to which the projects comply with the contractual or specified customer requirements.

Procedural Audit; Audits against a specific procedure or work instruction. Procedural Audits usually start with an adequacy audit of the procedure or work instruction. Adequacy audits were described previously.

Once the procedure has been reviewed for adequacy, the audit aspects of the procedure can be identified. This can be achieved by reading the procedure and underlining all elements of the procedure that need to be audited. Below is an extract from an Enquiry/Quotation Review procedure with the elements that can audited underlined.

On receipt of a customer enquiry or specification: when the enquiry is special (e.g. away from the standard price list) the Salesperson concerned <u>completes an enquiry form/check list detailing the customers requirements</u>. (See appendix). On completion of the enquiry form the form is <u>signed by the reviewer and where appropriate submitted to the Manager for approval</u>. If the enquiry is acceptable to the organisation and the customers requirements are understood, <u>a quotation is raised</u> on the basis of the information contained within the enquiry form.

This is possibly the most powerful method of auditing and is more extensively employed when procedures are in more common use. It ensures compliance with procedures (which is the most important) rather than the standard ISO9000.

Product Audit; These audits are very different to the above audits as they generally involve performing actual measurements or tests on a product to determine if the product (in all respects) meets the specified requirements or International or National product standard (e.g. the product standard for an electrical plug). This audit can necessitate the stripping down of the product into its individual parts and checking each part against a drawing. The audit may also include some reliability or durability tests.

ISO 10011 Auditing Quality Systems

This international standard has been developed to provide guidelines for personnel carrying out internal or external audits. The standard is in three parts:

ISO 10011-1 Guidelines for Auditing Quality Systems Part 1: Auditing
ISO 10011-2 Guidelines for Auditing Quality Systems Part 2: Qualification Criteria for Quality Systems Auditors
ISO 10011-3 Guidelines for Auditing Quality Systems Part 3: Management of Audit Programmes.

ISO 10011-1 Guidelines for Auditing Quality Systems Part 1: Auditing. This section establishes basic audit principles, criteria and practices. It also provides guidelines for establishing and planning the audit and the methodology for performing audits and how audits should be documented. The standard contains certain definitions:

Quality System: The organisational structure, responsibilities, procedures, processes and resources for implementing quality management.
Auditor (quality): A person who has the qualification to perform quality audits.
Lead Auditor: An auditor designated to manage a quality audit.
Client: A person or organisation requesting the audit.
Auditee: An organisation to be audited.
Observation: A statement of fact determined as part of the audit process and substantiated by objective evidence.
Objective evidence: Qualitative or quantitative information, records or statements of fact pertaining to the quality of an item or service or existence and implementation of a quality system element, which is based on observation, measurement or test and which can be verified.
Nonconformity: The nonfulfillment of specified requirements.

The objectives of an audit are defined as, to determine conformity with the recognised and agreed standard. The audit needs also to determine effectiveness of the Quality Management System in controlling quality and to provide the opportunity for quality improvement. The audit can also confirm compliance with a specified regulatory requirement, with a view to permitting entry in a recognised listing in a register.

The roles and responsibilities of auditors, audit teams and lead auditors are explained in the standard. They include the qualification for the auditor and their authorisation to carry out the audit. The need for the auditor to be independent, objective and at all times ethical in their approach to auditing.

The client and the auditee also has certain responsibilities with regard to ensuring that all relevant employees are informed of the intended audit. That briefed and appropriate guides are appointed. The client and auditee needs to establish that there are adequate resources provided and that access and cooperate will not be a problem. Lastly and possibly most importantly that for any nonconformances appropriate corrective actions determined are initiated.

The Audit organisation responsibilities are identified as determining scope and frequency of audits. Together with preparing the audit plan and executing audit following pattern described in these guides to auditing.

ISO 10011-2 Guidelines for Auditing Quality Systems Part 2: This section of the standard details the qualification criteria for quality systems auditors and to provide guidance in the selection of auditors. Whilst there are no specific educational standards, a secondary school education would be expected, together with being able to demonstrate oral and written fluency in the officially recognised language. The auditors would need to be adequately trained and knowledgable in understanding the standards against which quality systems audits may be performed. The training could include assessment techniques of examining, questioning, evaluating and reporting the audit findings. Additional skills required for managing an audit could include planning, organising, communicating and directing the audit and audit team members. Examination of the competence to be an auditor should be demonstrated through written or oral tests and other suitable means. The auditor should have a minimum of four years full-time appropriate practical workplace experience and at least two years in quality assurance with at least four audits totalling not less than 20 days. The personal attributes of an auditor should include open mindedness and mature. The auditor will need to possess sound judgement, analytical skills and have the ability to perceive situations in a realistic way. To understand complex operations from a broad perspective and to understand the role of individual units within the overall organisation.

To meet the criteria for the selection as a Lead Auditor the auditor will need to have completed at least three complete audits as qualified auditor and have demonstrated competence and ability.

ISO 10011-3 Guidelines for Auditing Quality Systems Part 3: Management of Audit Programmes. This part of the standard gives guidelines for managing quality systems audit programmes. The guidelines include, identification of the department within organisation which has the responsibility to plan and carry out the series of programmed quality audits. Ensuring that this department is independent of implementation of quality system. The department needs also to set up a method of monitoring and maintaining auditors performance, to ensure that the audits are achieving the consistency required. This could be achieved by:

o   holding auditor training workshops
o   making auditor performance comparisons
o   reviewing of audit reports
o   holding performance appraisals
o   rotating the auditors between teams.

Logistical and operational factors and facilities needed to perform audits needs to have been considered. The commitment of resources, the establishment of auditing and corrective action procedures, etc.

The need for and benefits of Internal Quality Audits

a)   Once a job is understood by an individual there is generally no further need to refer to documented procedures etc. and the supervisor tends not to monitor the process.
b)   A Supervisor has many jobs and his monitoring/auditing of operating practices may not be as frequent as they ought to be.
c)   A deviation created in an emergency may become common practice.
d)   What the management believe in good faith is happening, frequently differs from what is actually happening.
e)   The policy and goals of the company can be audited to ensure that they are being met, allowing for changes in targets etc.
f)   Audits improve communication and understanding at all levels.
g)   Auditors tend to be less severe as they themselves are subject to audit.
h)   Audits enable individuals to 'air' existing problems that are evident within their area but the solution is outside their control.
i)   Auditing can be a powerful tool for training people in the requirements of the procedures and standards.

What does Auditing Involve? There are four basis questions to be answered before conducting an audit; those being:

What?   Before starting an audit it is important to determine what is to be audited, i.e. the area and the scope of the audit. This can be decided on a departmental basis, e.g. Purchasing, Sales, Manufacturing etc. or on a functional basis such as document control or training which may involve several departments.

When?   Audits should be scheduled in advance and the relevant areas and personnel notified beforehand. The timing of the audit should ensure that it does not infringe upon normal company activities such as the regular Monday morning production progress meetings towards the end of the working day as this could cause problems such as availability of personnel. The frequency of the audits may be based upon a 'Pareto' type analysis where functions or departments may be identified as being the source of quality failures. The frequency depends on the stability of the procedures and confidence established by track record. The generally accepted frequency is that any function or department is audited at least once per annum. An Audit Programme or Audit Time Table needs to be created. The following table below shows the typical content of such an audit time table. Included on the audit time table are the scheduled dates for the internal and supplier audits and the Management Review. As each of the audits are completed half the box can be shaded, when all the corrective actions have been concluded then the full box can be shaded.

Table 18 Audit Time Table

Audit Time Table												
Area/Item Months	J	F	M	A	M	J	J	A	S	O	N	D
Internal Audits												
Contracts	*					*						
Purchasing		*					*					
Processing			*					*				
Dispatch				*					*			
Management Reviews					*					*		
External Audits												
Supplier A	*											
Supplier B						*						
Supplier C											*	
Approved by:					Date							

Who?   Audits should be conducted by personnel independent of the function being audited. These personnel should also be experienced and/or have had training in auditing techniques. Many larger companies employ full-time auditors to carry out audits and continuously monitor follow-ups. It frequently falls upon the Quality Manager to perform the auditing function but more commonly now, companies are using the 'mutual auditing' method where departmental managers audit each other's departments. Professional auditors are also sometimes employed to conduct audits on behalf of the company.

How?   An auditing procedure should be available which details the method to be adopted when carrying out an audit. E.g. Method for notifying the department concerned, conducting of an opening meeting, how to record the results etc.

The diagram **Figure 30** shows a Typical Audit Sequence from, *determining the need to perform an audit*, through to, *the follow up action*, having completed the audit. Below, each of the stages/boxes in the flow diagram are explained.

The need to conduct an audit may be determined from the audit time table, alternatively Purchasing may wish to use a new supplier whose products will have a significant effect on quality.

The Audit will then require planning - the next section headed "Audit Organisation and Planning", describes some of the actions necessary in planning a successful audit. The section also includes the possible format for communication advising the auditee of the forthcoming audit.

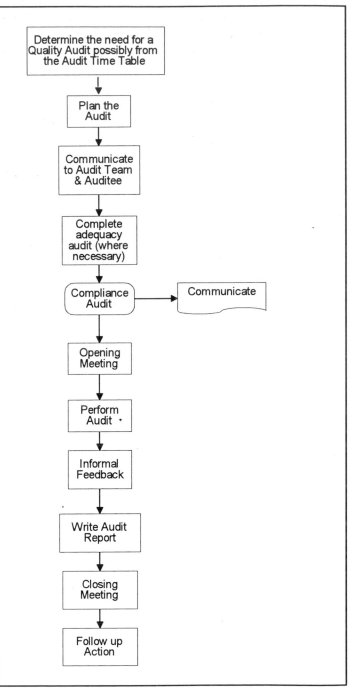

Figure 30 Flow Diagram of a Typical Audit Sequence

Before commencing the compliance audit an adequacy audit of the quality documentation may be necessary. An adequacy audit can be appropriate either in the case of a new supplier or if the quality document has been significantly changed. Adequacy audits are also useful for; the creation of the audit check lists, determining the shape of the audit and in completing an audit schedule (See **Table 22**).

To complete a compliance audit an opening meeting will be required. It is advisable to conduct an informal opening meeting with the department head not only in the case of an external audit but also in the case of internal audits.

The section Gathering the Information, describes the various means by which audit information can be gained.

Once the audit has been completed, an audit report needs to be completed and a closing meeting held at which the corrective action can be agreed and subsequently confirmed. Each of these stages will now be explained in more detail.

Once the information has been gathered, it is important that it is agreed with the supervisor or manager of the area being audited. This ensures that the information is correct and that when the report is issued there is no opportunity for argument or disagreement.

Audit Organisation and Planning

Audits can be undertaken by teams of two or more[10]. One of the team is appointed to be the team leader whose job it is to:

- o Decide how much work is involved; department or organisation size, structure, documentation etc.
- o Determine the team size and composition. **Table 19** may be helpful as a guide.

Table 19 Audit Resource

Quality Standard	ISO9001			ISO9002		
Organisation size	1500-600	400-100	60-15	1500-600	400-100	60-15
Number of man days	8-5	6-4	4-3	6-4	4-3	3-2

- o Preparation of a draft audit schedule (See **Table 22**).
- o Allocate tasks to team members
- o Ensure that team members are fully prepared for the audit. Including an audit time table of the areas to be visited and on which day
- o Advise the auditee of the date and duration of the intended audit
  If this was an internal audit then it would be necessary to detail:
  > Date & time of the audit, are department's personnel aware that the department is being audited, ensure that the department head or nominated representative will be available, that the auditor's role will be to determine: has the department a Quality Assurance System? is the department working to the Quality Assurance system? is the QAMS effective in preventing poor quality?
- o Run the audit
- o Present a report of the auditors' findings

---

[10]   Audits can be performed by more than one individual

The Role of the Auditor

The auditor's role is to collect information and report on the findings. It is not for the auditor to accuse, criticise or apportion blame. The auditor must observe, question, listen and record the observations in an objective manner. This report should mirror what has been seen, heard and learnt about the activities and operation of the function being audited. The auditor should be appropriately dressed for the area/function that is to be audited.

Opening Meeting

An opening meeting, *in the case of an external audit,* can be a formal meeting between the auditor and the auditee. During this meeting it is necessary to complete the introductions (audit team, guides etc.), advise the auditee of the conduct of the audit and to determine the local requirements of the company.

To advise the auditee that the audit is confidential. Confirm with the auditee the scope of the audit (e.g. ISO9001). Describe the audit areas, time table, the audit and reporting method and the audit sequence (conduct the audit, write report, closing meeting). The status of the quality documentation (quality manual) needs to be determined (it may have changed since the adequacy audit). It may be necessary to confirm the lunch arrangements and that employees are aware of the audit. Determine if there are any no go areas, special clothing or health requirements etc.

The duration of this opening meeting needs to be as short as possible (more time spent in the opening meeting means less time auditing) - 10 minutes if possible.

An opening meeting, *in the case of an internal audit,* can be less formal but will still need to cover the key elements described previously. The emphasis may be geared more towards putting the auditee at ease, reassuring the auditee that the audit is intended to be positive and that there will be an informal feedback to the departmental head before the written audit report is completed.

Gathering the Information

There are a number of methods that can be employed when comparing practice against written procedures. The most common is by the use of check lists. Check lists are a series of questions designed to test compliance with the key procedural requirements. The check lists require careful compilation and consideration to ensure that attention is being paid to important activities. Examples of ready made check lists can be found in Appendix A of Parts 4, 5 and 6 of BS5750 1979 (prior to the issue of the latest ISO9000 series). Check lists should be used as a basis for questioning and not be found to inhibit questioning which may provide valuable insights into system weaknesses. They should be used as a guide and aide-memoire rather than a questionnaire.

A second source of questions for the check list can be the quality manual or the local procedures. The question compilation process involves scrutinising the quality manual for particular activities that should be completed or possibly records that need to be maintained. The audit can then involve simply stepping through each question in turn to determine conformance to the agreed procedures.

The concept of auditing is to gather information and there are several ways to do this:

Observation; Observing people at work can often be used as a means of comparing practice against written procedures and work instructions. Handling, storage and protection can be observed and compared against acceptable standards.

Interview; Questioning people about the activities they are conducting reveals information about problems they have encountered and what actions they have taken to solve them. It is frequently found that the most naive of questions can lead to the most basic non-compliance with procedures etc.

Examination; The examination of documentation, drawings, registers, records, batches of work etc. can reveal where there may be areas for concern. For example drawings may be found to be at an incorrect issue, incorrect products being used or test and inspection stamps are not recorded.

Sampling. A method which can be employed to ensure a full examination is by the use of sampling. Sampling is very useful to confirm procedures are being reliably and consistently observed. Taking one example or sample is not statistically reliable. It is better that a number of observations or samples are taken, as this will provide a greater degree of confidence that procedures are being followed. An example of this could be in the Purchasing Department. The first thing to determine is what to sample? In Purchasing this probably would be Purchase Orders. To determine the sample size to take sampling tables like BS6001 can be used, alternatively taking a sample of 10% may be satisfactory. Just taking a sample ten items (Purchase Orders) may be all that is required. What is each of the samples examined for? Well in the case of Purchase Orders the following Table shows the results of such an Audit Sample. The second column shows what the Purchase Orders were checked against. The third column the results. Note; although only five orders were not approved this would imply that some 50% of all the Purchase Orders have not been signed.

Table 20 Audit Sample Check List

		AUDIT SAMPLE CHECK LIST											
#	Question	Purchase Order Number										Result Number NOK	%
		1	2	3	4	5	6	7	8	9	10		
1	Has all the Purchasing Order been completed correctly?												
1a	Precise identification of what is being ordered (title, specification, drawings etc.)?	✔	✔	✔	✔	✔	✔	✔	✗	✗	✗	3/10	30%
1b	Delivery Date Correct?	✔	✗	✗	✔	✔	✔	✔	✔	✔	✔	2/10	20%
1c	Inspection & Test instructions included?	✔	✔	✔	✔	✔	✗	✔	✗	✔	✔	2/10	20%
1d	Terms & Conditions included?	✔	✔	✔	✔	✔	✔	✔	✔	✔	✔	0/10	0
2	Has the Purchasing Order been approved?	✗	✗	✗	✔	✔	✔	✗	✔	✗	✔	5/10	50%
3	Is the Purchase Orders filled in correctly (in sequence)?	✔	✔	✔	✔	✔	✔	✗	✔	✔	✔	1/10	10%
4	Is a requisition available?	✔	✔	✔	✔	✔	✔	✔	✔	✔	✔	0/10	0
5	Is the supplier on the Approved List of Suppliers?	✔	✔	✔	✔	✔	✗	✔	✗	✔	✔	2/10	20%

Other samples that can be taken could be contracts, drawings, stores items, inspection results etc.

Sequence of the Gathering Information

Having, for the department or section under investigation, compiled the Audit Schedule and established a set of questions derived from the Quality Manual and the audit standard (ISO9001?), there is a danger of the assessor immediately starting to audit without first understanding the role, tasks and duties of the department being audited. Assessors who only audit by following the book or set questions are in danger of overlooking key issues which may only be discovered by understanding the department or process. It may be better to follow the sequence shown in **Figure 31**.

The first stage is to understand the process, section or department main roles, tasks and responsibilities. The process may be quite simple, such as an assembly process but the process could equally be

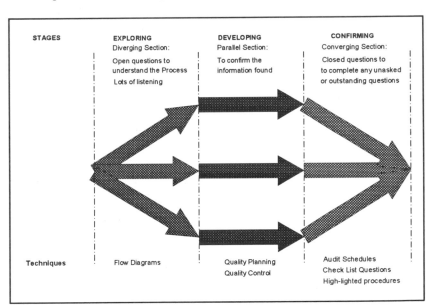

Figure 31 Audit Question Sequence

quite complicated such as modelling the way radioactive materials decay, using a very high speed computer. The approach to quality controlling these two processes would be quite different and the expected and operational methods of verification and validation of these processes needs to be understood. It is not possible to audit in a vacuum and the assessor needs to understand the process to determine whether the controls are complete and satisfactory applied. So the first stage is to *understand the process*. The techniques that can be employed to understand the process can be to draw a flow diagram of the sequence of typical departmental tasks or to simply list out the tasks of a department.

The next stage is to follow through any specific issues uncovered by understanding the process. It may be that the:

o   Assembly operation is not foolproof, which would not have been uncovered without discussion with the operator.

o   Computer model has not been validated or verified. Methods of validation and verification could include a review by other appropriate engineers or by the creation of an alternative model or method.

It is important to remember to follow any issues, which may be seen to be discrepancies, through to a logical conclusion. This is to ensure that the issues of concern really are discrepancies not just a misunderstanding. So the middle stage is *follow through*. The techniques that may be appropriate to use are quality planning or to establish the expected quality control methods that would normally be applied to such tasks and activities.

The final stage is *confirmation*. This is to clear up all of the outstanding questions, i.e. questions not yet asked from the check list of questions and audit schedule. During this stage it may be more beneficial to asked specific closed or yes/no type questions. These closed questions are where the auditee is only expected to confirm with evidence the existence for records etc. See Questioning Skills page 130.

The techniques that may now be employed are the use of the audit schedule (See **Table 22**). Where the audit schedule table (which was completed before starting the audit) can be employed. This audit schedule identified the paragraphs of the ISO9000 standard that the department being audited needs to comply with. The list of questions compiled before the audit can be asked.

Procedural Audit - the quality manual or procedure can be examined prior to the audit and key activities (such as record keeping) can be identified or highlighted. This is so that these key activities can be confirmed as satisfactorily taking place. During this confirmation stage it may be more beneficial to ask specific closed or yes/no type questions. An example could be where the auditee is only expected to confirm (with evidence) the existence of records - can you show me the records of contract review? See Questioning Skills page 130.

Informal Feedback

It is essential that the auditor completes an informal feedback to the department head confirming the audit findings. That is not to say that all the findings will result in discrepancies but to confirm the findings are accurate and factual. This helps put the auditee at ease - there should be no nasty surprises in the audit report, thus avoiding arguments at the closing meeting about the accuracy of the report.

Social Skills required of an Auditor

From the above it is apparent that auditing requires special skills and attributes. These are achieved by careful selection and training.

Desirable attributes of an auditor include: Ability to communicate, Unbiased, Patient, Articulate, Diplomatic, Inquiring mind, Interested, Industrious, Professional, Open minded, Analytical, Listener, Thorough, Polite.

Negative attitudes which undermine effectiveness of audit can include: Critical, Nit-picking, Argumentative, Opinionated, Gullible, Egocentric, Cynical, Shallow, Condescending, Emotional.

Questioning Skills

Leading questions; If you make a point of studying a television interviewer, you will notice that they ask "leading" questions. In other words, questions which lead the person to respond with an explanation, description, recollection or further "tit-bits" of information rather than a yes/no response. Interviewers are trained in this technique and it is easy for them to manipulate people's answers to say what they want the audience to hear. An auditor should, however, avoid putting words into people's mouths.

Informative and interested questions; If a person detects a lack of interest then they will not be very forthcoming, therefore, ask questions out of genuine curiosity or from information already gained.

Open questions; Questions where it is not possible to answer yes or no - used when trying to understand the process. "What are main tasks you perform?"

Closed questions; Questions that only allow a specific or yes/no answer - useful when the auditee is procrastinating or avoiding the point. "Do you have inspection and test records for this item?"

Naive questions; It is often surprising how a simple question can bring forth the most significant information. Questions which nobody asks for being thought ignorant or the answer is generally taken for granted can open up new avenues of information.

Why? Why? Why? Very often the first response given to a question does not give the necessary information. It may merely be the answer they think you want to hear, or it may be an assumption or guess because the person does not know the answer, they may even have been briefed on the answers to give. It is often worthwhile repeating the question until you are satisfied with the answer. It is, however, important to be careful not to alienate or belittle the person. If they do not appear to know the answer make it easy for them to say so rather than have them inventing answers to avoid looking foolish.

Association of ideas; Use the information gained to guide you to further questions but not to the extent that you are misled or follow a "red herring." Adopt a theme to act as a thread in a line of questioning.

Taking notes; Excessive note-taking means that you will miss what the speaker is saying, on the other hand, not taking notes at all will certainly mean that important key facts will be forgotten or remembered incorrectly. When taking notes it is useful that what is written can be seen by the auditee and also confirmed with the section head before leaving the section. This is not that the findings or notes necessarily indicate a discrepancy but rather to confirm that the notes are correct.

Check your understanding; There are approximately 600,000 words in the English language, the average person uses 2,000 of them and 500 of the more commonly used words have an average of 28 meanings. If in doubt ask the question in a different way and perhaps a little later in your discussion.

Table 21 Typical Audit Form

Internal Audit Report			Report No.		
Organisation:			Date:		
Standard: ISO9001	Requirement:		Discrepancy Category		
			A	B	C
Assessor:	Section Head:		Dept:		
Discrepancy:					
Action Recommended					
Action taken:					
Discrepancy A Significant non-compliance with the standard B Significant number of minor non-compliancies with the standard C Minor problem area that warrants attention.					
Signature:			Date:		

Reporting the Findings

The findings of the audit are frequently presented in the form of a series of audit report discrepancy forms and a summary sheet produced stating the main findings of the audit. The report can only contain the non-compliancies but sometimes it is worth including the compliancies. The compliancies can be used to ensure that subsequent audits do not unnecessarily repeat any audit trails previously followed. The final written report is normally issued to the company's management for their consideration. An approach to compilation of an audit report can be:

o   Examine the audit notes and identify any possible discrepancies
o   Phrase, reword or clarify as necessary each discrepancy statement

o   Determine the appropriate Quality Standard (ISO9001) paragraph number and discrepancy category - A, B or C. See **Table 21**.

Closing meeting

A closing meeting is often held between the supervisor, departmental manager and auditor. During the meeting the audit findings are presented and discussed. The aim of the meeting is to agree the findings and determine the action proposed to correct the discrepancies. It is important to remember that it is not the auditors' brief to determine what that action should be, but they can be asked to advise on recommended action. The implications of any proposed corrective action should be evaluated at this stage as it is a well known fact that a solution to one problem often leads to the emergence of another problem elsewhere.

A typical format and sequence of a closing meeting could be:

o   Introduction;
        Remind meeting of the reason and scope of the audit. Thank the auditees for any help and assistance (don't mention any problems). Auditing only tends to identify the bad points, it is often worth noting the good aspects as well.
o   Request that questions are withheld until after the report has been presented (other than possibly questions regarding clarification of the audit report).
o   Present the audit report:
        Remind the meeting that the audit findings were either witnessed by the guide or reported to the section head at the time of audit. Hand over a written copy of the audit report. If there are a number of discrepancies it may be appropriate to only identify certain key issues - (e.g. no final inspection and test inspections) rather than totally de-motivate with a huge list of discrepancies.
        Present each report in turn detailing the appropriate quality standard (ISO9000) paragraph name, the category A, B or C and the discrepancy. The discrepancy report needs to as clear as possible, with where ever possible examples; quality manual reference, part or procedure numbers, location etc. The report needs to be sufficiently clear so that suitable corrective action will be taken, if the report is not clear then wrong or no action may be taken.
o   Summarise the findings (See **Table 22**).

o Request and
record the
corrective
action to be
taken (what,
when, how,
who).
o Make a note
of the atten-
dees and
close the
meeting.
o Distribute
copies of
the audit
report.

Table 22 Typical Audit Schedule

Audit Schedule		Report Number				
Department/Company:		Date:				
Requirement		Check	A	B	C	D
Management Responsibility						
Quality System						
Contract Review						
Design Control						
Document Control						
Purchasing						
Customer Supplied Material						
Product Identification						
Process Control						
Inspection and Testing						
Calibration						
Inspection & Test Status						
Control of Non-Conforming						
Corrective Action						
Handling, Storage, Packaging, Preservation and Delivery						
Quality Records						
Internal Quality Audits						
Training						
Service						
Statistical Techniques						
Summary: **"D"** means no evidence of non-compliance						
Signed (Auditor):		Date:				

Action after the Audit

Implementation of corrective action; Having agreed the corrective action to be taken it is important to ensure that everyone affected by the change is properly informed. Any modifications to procedures or manuals should be carried out and issued to the relevant parties in the shortest possible timescale.

Follow up; Now that the agreed corrective action has been agreed and implemented, is that it? The trouble with human nature is that if we are not monitored we tend to fall into bad habits. This can be true for new procedures and amendments to existing procedures, they can fall into disuse as a result of neglect. To remove the chances of this happening it is necessary to carry out what are called 'follow up' audits. These are normally conducted after an agreed time and are intended to verify that those new procedures are being adhered to and that they are effective with regard to removing the non-compliance. These audits are only intended to check on those areas where non-compliance was found and are not to check on areas that were not covered in the original audit.

PART B

"To lose one parent, Mr. Worthing, may be regarded as a misfortune; to lose both looks like carelessness."

Lady Bracknell from The Importance of being Earnest by Oscar Wilde

The idea is - making one mistake is forgivable, repeating the same mistake may be seen as carelessness. However, making the same mistake for the third time may be seen as incompetence? What would be even better, is to prevent the mistake being made in the first place!

Quality Philosophy: There are a number of influential figures in the field of Quality Assurance. Although this list is not exhaustive possibly the best known are:

Philip C. Crosby - Zero Defects
W. Edwards Deming - 14 Points
A. V. Feigenbaum - Total Quality Control
K. Ishikawa - Quality Circles
Joseph M. Juran - Breakthrough and Control
Genichi Taguchi - Taguchi Technique (Analysis of Variance) and Loss Function

Although they all share a common ambition - 'the attainment of quality', they each have their own very individual style or approach to achieving the ambition. However, there are some issues which do tend to occur in all of their approaches.

o   Management Commitment is essential for success.
o   Cost of Quality - Identification of the critical quality problems or issues.
o   Understanding of the processes and characteristics that require control - indicating what to change and how to measure performance.
o   Prevention rather than detection.
o   The application of statistics.

It may be unfair to associate each person with a specific concept or idea (possibly in the case of Ishikawa particularly so) as each of these influential individuals has worked extensively in the quality assurance field and to describe all their work would take too long. The concept or idea most commonly associated with each of these individuals is, however, described.

Philip C. Crosby - Zero Defects

Philip Crosby was the Director of Quality for the Pershing Missile Project and there he launched a programme to achieve Zero Defects in the Missiles. He was also Vice President for Quality at ITT Corps where he established a Quality College to teach ITT employees "how to do things right". The concept is that "quality is free" - sounds silly but it's true. It costs money to do things wrong. It costs money to make mistakes. This is because when things are done incorrectly they have to be repeated - costing money. When things are made wrongly, they have to be repaired or scrapped and remade - it costs money. To do tasks in the most efficient and effective manner (the quality way) saves money - quality is free. Do things right or in the most efficient manner and you get quality for free. In other words there is not necessarily a conflict between achieving the required output or completing the process or service as quickly as possible, in the most effective manner, with no mistakes. In fact by improving the performance of the process i.e. no waste, you get quality for free.

There are very mixed (almost polarised) views regarding Philip C. Crosby. Some regard his approach as over the top and too much a salesman (ICL), others claim major savings (Motorola). He is without doubt American in style and for this reason is not everyones cup of tea. However, some of his material is excellent and well worthy of consideration.

Philip C. Crosby talks of Four absolutes of Quality

Definition -	Definition of quality being Conformance to Requirements
System -	The system of quality needs to be Prevention or preventive
Measurement -	Price of Non-Conformance. The cost of quality needs to be measured in terms of failure.
Performance Standard -	
	There is only one standard namely Zero Defects, anything else misses the point

The concepts embodied in this performance standard - Zero Defects (ZD) are; ZD as a performance standard achieving no rejects, doing it right first time, prevention rather than detection. The approach that Crosby associates with implementing Zero Defects is:

Step 1 *Management Commitment:* Objective; To clearly define the management position with regard to Quality. The objective in action; The policy statement i.e. Fitness for Purpose at the right price. (This is so that all personnel will understand the management position with regard to quality.)

Step 2   *Quality Improvement Team:* Objective; To establish the improvement team's role in operating the quality improvement programme. The objective in action; To schedule the improvement programme. This involves team members representing their department on the team and representing the team in their departments, together with facilitating the team's proposals within their department.

Step 3   *Quality Measurement:* Objective; To establish the quality measurement areas which will allow evaluation and correction. The objective in action; To determine what needs to be measured, how will the data be obtained, how to display the data, including targets and identify the problem in terms of priority, seriousness, cause and responsibility.

Step 4   *Cost of Quality:* Objective; To quantify the cost of quality. The objective in action; requires the identification, quantifying and totalling all the factors that go to constitute the total cost of quality. To assess the figures against targets.

Step 5   *Quality Awareness:* Objective; To make all employees aware of the teams activities. The objectives in action; This involves two activities; holding regular meetings between Management and employees to discuss non-conformance problems and to provide information regarding the quality programme i.e. posters, articles, etc.

Step 6   *Corrective Action:* Objective; To establish a structured organised and permanent approach to resolving problems. The objective in action; Correct the identified problems and prevent recurrence.

Step 7   *Zero Defects Planning:* Objective; To complete the preparation for launching the Zero Defects programme. The objective in action; Determining the most suitable method of launching the ZD programme. Defining what is to be achieved and the method of recognition in praising improved performance. Establishing the time scale and participants. Identifying the
Error » Cause » Removal Programme
and explaining the error, cause removal concept to supervision. This can include obtaining the supervisor's visible commitment to the Zero Defects programme by requesting the supervisor to voluntarily sign a pledge. The pledge confirms the supervisor's commitment to doing the job right first time and making all efforts to improving quality performance.

Step 8   *Supervisor Training:* Objective; To determine the training that the Supervisors require to accomplish quality improvements. The objective in action; Training in the measuring system, cost of quality, corrective action system, purpose of quality awareness and the Zero Defects programme.

Step 9   *Zero Defect Day:* Objective; To let employees realise that a transformation has happened. The objective in action; A series for presentations and speeches celebrating the introduction for the Zero Defects programme. Possibly an opportunity for the employees to sign the ZD pledge.

Step 10   *Goal Setting:* Objective; To turn the pledges into action by setting goals. The objective in action; Team discussion to allow personnel to establish their own goals and to publish each team's targets and goals.

Step 11   *Error ▸ Cause ▸ Removal* (E.C.R.) Objective; To provide a method for employees to communicate any problems which the employees have in achieving the right first time goal. The objective in action; A form known as an E.C.R. Form can be completed by each by employee when such a problem is encountered.

Step 12   *Recognition:* Objective; To recognise all those employees who have participated in the programme and achieved goals. The objective in action; Using praise and competition as a means of encouraging achievement. Once the goals have been achieved then showing gratitude and recognition for those employees who have achieved goals

Step 13   *Quality Council:* Objective; To promote discussion and communication between specialist quality people. The objective in action; Regular meetings between Quality specialists and employees to exchange ideas, information and approaches.

Step 14   *Do it over again:* Objective; To maintain the momentum of the improvement programme. The objective in action; Once the goals are achieved the programme could run out of steam and the quality improvement plan stop. To avoid such circumstances it may be necessary to rebuild the improvement teams and review the targets and goals.

W. Edwards Deming - 14 points

In 1947 Deming went to Japan to help with the 1951 Japanese census, two years later he returned to give a series of lectures. As a mark of the esteem with which Deming is held in Japan there is a 'Deming Prize' awarded annually by the Japanese Union of Science and Engineering (JUSE).

He identifies the need of transformation in the style of management, requiring a new structure and direction. Deming's 14 points are the new direction suggested. See **Table 23**.

Table 23 Deming's 14 Points

#	Point	Interpretation
1	Create constancy of purpose. Innovate and establish a long term plan	To improve the competitive position of the company - Putting resources into research and education. Constantly improving the product and service provided.
2	Adopt a new philosophy	The normally accepted levels of rejects can no longer be accepted. New improved quality performance targets need to be achieved. Rejects and mistakes cost money. The obstacles to reducing rejects and costs need to be removed by the adoption of the 14 points.
3	Cease dependence on inspection.	Prevention rather than detection, it saves time and money. It is not possible to inspect quality into a product - quality comes from improving the process. Mass inspection generally is an unreliable technique. This is because people get bored or tired looking for the same thing (eg. 100% inspection for paint faults) and as a consequence are likely to overlook or miss some of the faults. The *"counting the e's test[11]"* is a good demonstration of the fallacy of 100% inspection.

---

[11] Ask a group of five people to count the e's in a paragraph, taking only one minute. Examination of the five counts will show that at least one of the counts will be different. Does this mean that the person who obtained the different count was a bad inspector or were they the only one to get the count right? In either event, someone has not completed the inspection or check correctly. Incidentally, the reason for the difference is normally due to missing the e's in the prepositions.

141

Quality Philosophy

#	Point	Interpretation
4	End the practice of award-ing business on the basis of price tag.	Price by itself has no meaning without a measure of the quality of the product or service being purchased. The initial costs compared to the life time costs of products can give a very different picture when maintenance, down time and poor performance are taken into account. Single sourcing provides; reduced lot variation, better understanding of requirements and reduced stocks.
5	Improve constantly and for-ever the system of produc-tion and service process.	Never-ending improvements in quality performance in every stage of the process. The next project must be completed quicker than the last with fewer mistakes and problems. The design must be better than the last.
6	Institute on the job training	Training for Management so that they understand the company and the interrelationships and problems. Training for operators and personnel so that they understand what to do and how to do it!
7	Institute Leadership	Modern methods of leadership and supervision must be employed, moving from numbers or output dominated thought, to improvement in quality being the key issue - helping supervision do a better job.
8	Drive out fear	One of Deming's key and most important objectives; drive out fear so everyone can work effectively for the company (security). Fear of change, improvement, new ideas etc., Fear that having made a suggestion for improvement that it may not work and then they will look foolish. Fear of the sack if improvements are made. Peer pressure suggesting that no one in the group makes improvements that could endanger their jobs. Making an improvement is like signing your own death warrant, because the natural progression of an improvement will be that the organisation will not need so many people.
9	Break down the barriers between departments	Departments (Quality, Production, Engineering etc.) must work as a team to identify, predict and avoid problems. The quality department seeing the production department as the enemy. One approach may be to promote the concept of the team approach. The organisation working as a team win and losing together. Feeding off each other to develop ideas.
10	Eliminate slogans, posters and numerical goals	Urging employees to achieve numerical targets or zero defects will only provide temporary improvements.
11	Eliminate work standards or quotas	Remove numerical quotas such as work measurement and replace with leadership and systems and method.
12	Remove the barriers to pride of workmanship	Remove barriers such as merit rating or daily quotas, give the work force the chance to work with pride.
13	Institute a programme of education and self improve-ment	Organisations need people that are improving with education giving wider career opportunities
14	Action plan to accomplish the transformation	Create an organisation and structure that will push the above 13 points constantly.

These 14 points are the aims or objectives and do not describe the approach, method or tools. The action plan for change and to accomplish the organisation transformation includes seven stages.

Stage   Description

1.   Management needs to agree the meaning of the above 14 points and to struggle over the deadly diseases and obstacles that inflict their business, (lack of purpose, short term profit, merit rating, job changing or hopping, management by use of visible figures alone).

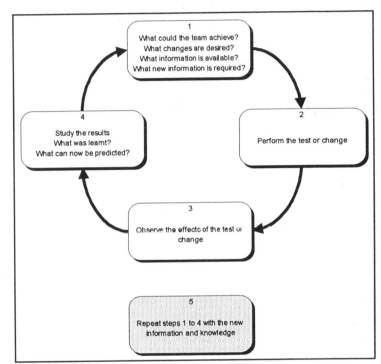

Figure 32 Shewhart Cycle

2.   Management take pride in their new philosophy and responsibilities.

3.   Management present to the whole organisation the need for change

4.   Every activity is part of a process which contributes to quality, understand who the customer and suppliers are.

5.   Guide the organisation towards continual improvement of quality, the Shewhart cycle could be used to assist in this stage. (See Shewhart Cycle diagram **Figure 32**).

6.   Use of the team approach to contribute ideas, plans and data.

7.   Organise for quality (with the active participation of a statistician).

A. V. Feigenbaum - Total Quality Control

Possibly the most important figure with regard to Quality Assurance and very much overlooked. Feigenbaum's book Total Quality Control was originally written in 1951 but organisations are only now employing some of the concepts and principles embodied in his book. Total Quality Control may be considered the forerunner to BS5750, although not to be confused with Total Quality Management (TQM). In this respect the title of the book is now a little misleading as BS5750 or ISO9000 is generally not considered to be the same as TQM. This is explained in the section on TQM. What Feigenbaum's book provided was more of a model for a Quality Assurance Management System (possibly a forerunner to BS5750) rather than TQM which may be considered more of a motivational concept. It is important to remember that although the words Total Quality Control are used what is really being described is a Quality Assurance Management System.

Originally Quality Assurance was mainly considered to be controlling the quality of manufacture, Feigenbaum had the foresight to see that this was only part of the story - Quality was Total and needed to involve all functions associated with the process of fulfilling the customer requirements; from initial specification and design control through to the manufacturing stages (see Introduction to Quality Assurance - Traditional Quality Control). More recently this concept has been extended vertically, into service industries and horizontally, by encompassing all departments within an organisation - with the introduction of the concept "internal customers," (see Departmental Purpose Analysis).

Feigenbaum's Approach

One of the key elements of Feigenbaum's Total Quality Control message is the need for a coordinated and documented approach to controlling quality across the complete organisation. These documented procedures are the guide for the action of

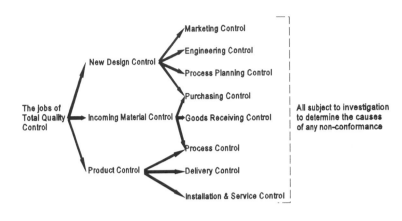

Figure 33 Feigenbaum's Total Quality Control Triangle (Adapted from A. V. Feigenbaum's Total Quality Control)

personnel throughout all of the process stages of delivering a product or service. The Total Quality Control approach to each of these process stages is shown in the diagram **Figure 33** and explained below.

New Design Control includes the techniques and documented procedures used to ensure that the customer's requirements are fully understood and interpreted into a practical and viable manufacturing specification, with due consideration for all performance, safety and reliability related requirements. (See sections Contract Review, Design Control and Document Control).

Purchasing Control includes all the techniques associated with ensuring that the quality of supplies consistently meet the specified requirements in terms of price, delivery, service and quality. (See section Purchasing Control)

Product Control includes all the documented methods associated with ensuring that the product conforms to specified requirements. The control of the process - the section on Process Control gives some guidance as to appropriate shape and content of the procedures that can be used to regulate the process. In certain situations these controls could embrace some of the statistical techniques described in the section Statistical Quality Control. This control will need to include subsequent stages such as packaging, installation and servicing. (See sections Handling, Storage, Packaging and Delivery and Servicing).

Quality Philosophy

It is worth noting that none of the references regarding A. V. Feigenbaum work is to any other section than the section Quality Assurance Management Systems (QAMS). This would tend to reinforce the view that Feigenbaum is discussing QAMS rather than Total Quality Management.

Juran - Breakthrough and Control

Juran worked for the Bell Telephone Co. and after the Second World War he became an independent teacher. He was the author of the Quality Control Handbook first published in 1951. Juran is well known and respected world wide in the field of Quality Assurance.

Juran's approach can be broken down into two sections; breakthrough and control. Breakthrough and control the system at the new standard level of performance is the objective. To achieve this objective a determined and coordinated effort is required to make improvements so that the old standard level of performance becomes obsolete and the new improved level of performance is the norm. The difference between the old level of performance and the new level is known as the "chronic disease" which must be diagnosed and cured.

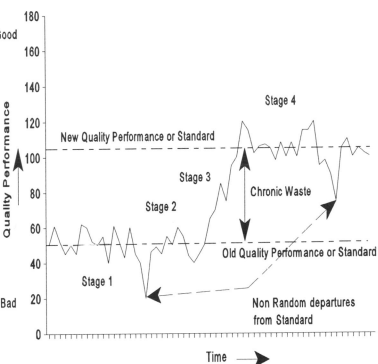

Figure 34 Breakthrough & Control (Adapted from Juran's Quality Planning & Analysis

The diagram **Figure 34** shows the approach to Managerial Breakthrough. The diagram takes the form of a quality control chart (see section on Statistical Quality Control) showing the old standard and old levels of quality performance with, on occasions, departures from the old standard (or non-random events) giving rise to sporadic problem solving (fire fighting). What is needed is a *breakthrough* to new levels of quality performance, (the old standards are not good enough). Having achieved the breakthrough in performance then it is necessary to *control* at the new quality performance level. Juran's approach to achieving Managerial Breakthrough is outlined below. These stages should be read in conjunction with **Figure 34** and **Figure 35**.

Stage I.   Breakthrough in Attitude
Provide a favourable climate for embarking on the introduction of company-wide quality planning. A challenging opportunity to make improvements, selling the idea to management and the workforce.

Stage II.   Pareto:
Identifying the priorities by concentrating on the vital few and ignoring the trivial many. See section Pareto Analysis.

Stage III.   Organisation
Coordinating the project work, studying and analysing the problem by:
i.   Breakthrough in knowledge (steering and diagnostic)
ii.   Breakthrough in culture (overcoming resistance to change)
iii.   Breakthrough in performance (to the new standard level in performance)

Stage IV.   Control at the new standard level of performance.

Stage V. Repeat the above stages.

Having achieved the breakthrough to the new quality standard, the process needs to be repeated continuing the cycle of improvements to new even greater heights in quality performance. See **Figure 35**.

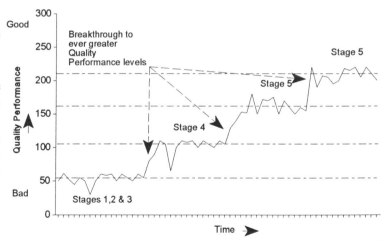

Figure 35

148

K. Ishikawa - Quality Circles

K. Ishikawa was involved with the Japan Union of Scientists and Engineers (JUSE) and helped write JUSE's book on Quality Circles.

Motivation for quality: In the 50's and 60's the Japanese were going through a reconstruction of their industry in an attempt to remove the image the Western World had of them as being producers of poor quality products. They set up teams, groups, sections and departments with defined objectives to be achieved. These teams then met voluntarily, in their own time initially, to discuss how to overcome and solve problems affecting them as a group. These meetings became known as Quality Circles.

Quality circle definition: Quality circles are defined as follows:

A.   A small group of employees
B.   who do similar work
C.   voluntarily meeting regularly
D.   on company time
E.   with their supervisor as their leader
F.   learning to identify and analyse work related problems
G.   recommending solutions to their management and, where possible, implementing their own solutions.

Introducing and implementing quality circles - **The FACILITATOR**

The facilitator must be carefully selected, for he becomes the focal point and will largely determine the future success of the programme. The facilitator requires a

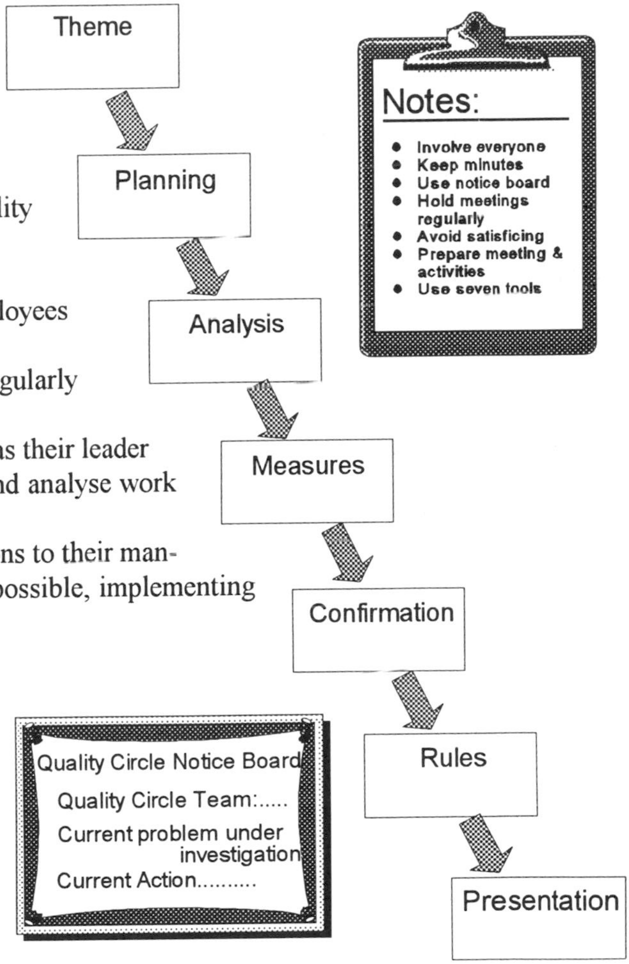

Theme → **Planning** → **Analysis** → **Measures** → **Confirmation** → **Rules** → **Presentation**

Notes:
- Involve everyone
- Keep minutes
- Use notice board
- Hold meetings regularly
- Avoid satisficing
- Prepare meeting & activities
- Use seven tools

Quality Circle Notice Board
Quality Circle Team:.....
Current problem under investigation
Current Action.........

Figure 36 Typical Quality Circle Sequence

149

personality that will allow him to get on well with people at all levels within an organisation. Once a facilitator has been appointed, he should be capable of training the Circle leaders, coordinating the activities of all the Circle groups and assist in inter Circle investigations acting as say the 'go-between' to ensure lines of communication are maintained. The facilitator is generally responsible for obtaining any specialist advice from other departments or section required by the Circle. Although the term facilitator is used in the UK, the role is usually performed by a Supervisor in Japan.

Training for the Quality Circle members: Training of the group leaders is essential to the success of the Circle. The 'quality' of his leadership will determine the level of subsequent achievement. The training should expose the group leader to the basic Quality Circle problem solving techniques to the extent that he is able to pass this training onto the other members of his Circle. To start a Circle the level of knowledge need only be a good understanding of the basic techniques. During the course of running the Circle it may be found that further training is required to update members on the latest problem solving techniques, for example statistics, process capability, etc. In Japan now foremen are often capable of using degree level statistical techniques for problem solving activities.

Training of the group leaders in other skills is also important as they need to retain their position as leaders. Training should cover such topics as control of meetings, encouraging development of the other members of the Circle and most importantly to develop the members as a team and not as a group of individuals.

There are seven tools of quality control that need to be taught to all circle members

1.   Pareto analysis - see section Pareto Analysis
2.   Cause and effect diagrams
3.   Stratification (see Sampling)
4.   Check sheets
5.   Histograms
6.   Scatter diagrams
7.   Shewhart's control charts and graphs (see Statistical Quality Control)

For more information on the seven tools or techniques, see the corresponding section.

Starting a Quality Circle: There are 7 stages of activity involving members of the Quality Circle, although these stages sometimes merge and are repeated. **Figure 36** shows a typical sequence:

Selection of the theme or problem
Planning the approach to the problem
Analysis of the problem
Determination of the measures to take to avoid the problem occurring
Confirming that the measures were successful
Determination of the rules that need to be applied to avoid recurrence and finally
Presentation of the Quality Circle activities.

a.   *Theme* or *Select the problem:* Once the Circle members are chosen the first stage is to select the problem. Problems may be identified by anyone within the company and may be the result of customer complaint data, management information, quality control feedback, production engineering or design. Circles often identify problems themselves of which Management are sometimes unaware, problems such as handling, damage and short comings on route cards or specification sheets etc. The problem may be identified by the use of Pareto Analysis.

      It is vitally important that the Circles should be free to choose their own problems for solution.

Table 24 Typical Quality Circle Minutes Form

Minutes of Quality Circle			Circle Leader:	Facilitator:
Department:	Group:	Date:	Time:	
Attendance %	Absent:	Quality Circle Steps		
1 Theme ☐	2 Planning ☐	3 Analysis ☐	4 Measures ☐	5 Confirmat'n ☐
6 Standard'n ☐	7 Presentat'n ☐	8 Study QCC ☐	9 Others ☐	
Proceedings				
Overall decision or conclusion for next stage (who, what, when, how, why, where)				
Comments by Facilitator or Supervisor				
Next meeting date/time				

b.   *Planning:* The Quality Circles meeting is an important part of the Quality Circle activities. A well organised and prepared Quality Circles meeting will help in the smooth operation of the Quality Circle. To help in the coordination of the Quality Circle activities it is useful to plan the meeting and to take notes regarding the agreed actions and responsibilities. **Table 24** shows one way of recording the actions agreed by the Quality Circle's Team. The 15 to 45 minute meeting can be held in working hours. As well as the minutes it may also be appropriate to use a notice board to communicate and detail the Quality Circle; members, theme, activities, action, responsibilities, progress etc.

State and re-state the problem It is often easy to jump to conclusions about what the cause or solution to a problem may be, i.e. Satisficing - using the first solution that comes to mind. It is important to make sure that the chosen problem is a problem and not a symptom of a problem. Curing or solving a symptom will not solve the problem and a lot of time and effort could be wasted resulting in loss of enthusiasm or disillusionment for the Quality Circle. Cause and effect diagrams may help in understanding the problem.

c. *Analysis - Collection of facts*: The collection of all the facts is a key part of the problem solving process. An inaccuracy in information or data could cause the group to 'head in the wrong direction'. Information and facts to be collected includes all data relating to the identified problem and possible related problems elsewhere. Information should also be gained, via the use of histograms, scatter diagrams, check sheets, stratification and Statistical Quality Control Charts, so that any limitations are known in, for example, the cost to be incurred, timescales, space available, etc.

Organised Brain Storming - writing down all ideas: Almost all Quality Circles around the world make use of the cause and effect diagram. This is also known as the Ishikawa diagram or fish bone diagram. After the problem has been selected then the Circle may produce one of these diagrams.

Build on each other's ideas: Having identified the main causes and sub-causes the members can start to build upon each other's ideas. One idea may lead to a new line of thought or it may spark off another and so on. It is important never to ridicule any member's ideas.

d. *Measures - Choose a course of action:* Once the main causes and sub-causes have been found it is generally possible to identify which of the causes, if removed, would solve the problem. A course of action to be taken can then be planned and prepared. The course of action determined could include details regarding the steps or measures to be taken to eliminate the causes of the problem.

e. *Confirmation:* After the measures have been determined and implemented the success of the adopted approach needs to be established. Again, check sheets and Statistical Quality Control Charts can be employed to confirm the resolution of the problem.

f. *Rules:* Having confirmed the success of the suggested solution then rules or control methods need to be established that will avoid the problem ever happening again. These rules may be a new set of procedures or regulations but these procedures need to include the monitoring activities that ensure the new procedures are consistently and reliably observed.

g.   ***Presentation:*** This is possibly the most important stage where the Quality Circle Team has the opportunity to demonstrate their achievements to management and colleagues. It is also an opportunity for management and colleagues to show approval and recognition of a job well done and to praise the achievements of the Quality Circle Team. This recognition does not have to be in the form of monetary reward - in fact this may be counter productive.

It may be worth noting that, for various reasons, it is not always possible for the Circle to actually implement the chosen solution. These may be that significant costs may be incurred or additional staff will be required, the solution lies within another area of the company, etc. Quality Circles can often realise the solution by gaining support from Management. This could be achieved through well planned presentations of the problem and recommended solutions to Managers.

Gauges of success: The success of the Quality Circle can be gauged in a number of ways, for example:

Quality -   Which can be measured by defects/man hour, scrap/unit manufacture, customer return data etc.

Cost -   Which can be measured by failure cost, cost of manufacture, cost of quality etc.

Attitude -   Which can be measured by improvements in labour turnover, absenteeism, reduction in accidents, stoppages etc.

Companies have found the following benefits:

- o   Savings of time lost due to conflicting job instructions
- o   Savings of time in locating precision tools
- o   Elimination of oil leaks contaminating materials
- o   Savings of money on tin-plate finish problems
- o   Savings of money by changing processes
- o   Savings of money by changing handling and packaging methods
- o   Productivity is boosted
- o   Lower product defects
- o   Enhanced job involvement and work running more effectively
- o   Workforce more conscious of problem spotting and solving

o   Improvements in communications and manager-worker relationships company-wide etc.

Failure of Quality Circles: While a lot of companies have experimented and subsequently failed with Quality Circles it is invariably found that they did not follow the recognised 'rules', e.g.,

The group was mixed, i.e., different disciplines
The group was not allowed to choose their own problem
The group had to meet in their own time
Not all the information had been collected or was inaccurate etc.

Also see Deming's points on "Drive Out Fear"

Genichi Taguchi - Loss Function & Taguchi Techniques (Experimental Design and Analysis of Variance)

Dr. Genichi Taguchi was born in 1924 and in the 1970's developed the concept of the Quality Loss Function and had books published on Design of Experiments.

The Taguchi methodology is based on:

o   Ensuring that quality is built into the product right from the design stage - with a bad or faulty design the best that manufacturing can do is make the design perfectly wrong
o   Product optimisation prior to commencing manufacturing
o   Avoiding inspecting the quality into the product. I.e. Make the product right first time rather than using inspection to sort the good from the bad.

The methodology can also be used to identify and resolve manufacturing quality problems which cannot be solved by the normal routine problem solving methods.

Loss Function

When a designer determines a tolerance or specification, is the tolerance determined by sophisticated means of analysing the optimum value by carefully evaluation, tests, trials and calculations on the proposed design solution? Or, alternatively, does the designer make an estimate or judgement based upon the designer's experience and skill? The truth is more probably the latter (an estimate) rather than the former (tests and trials). The reason being the time, expense and effort involved in completing the various trials, tests and calculations to determine the tolerance. Sometimes, because of lack of trust between the designer and the pro-

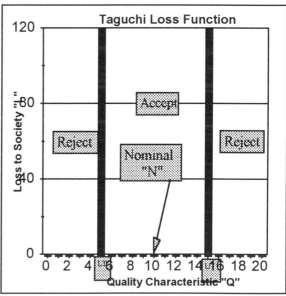

Figure 37 Traditional Tolerancing

ducer, the designer may specify too tight a tolerance believing that the producer will produce outside tolerance anyway.

What do manufacturing do with these tolerances and how are the tolerances used? Well, the tolerances will be used to determine; whether a process should run or not, if the process output is acceptable. As a consequence of this possibly arbitrary judgement by the designer a considerable amount of money will be spent getting the process to run to tolerance and if rejects are produced that are judged to be outside tolerance these items may be scrapped off. (See Statistical Tolerancing). To the producer the tolerance is often seen as black and white. **Figure 37** shows this situation. Anything to the left of the LT (Lower Tolerance) line is a reject no matter how slightly to the left it is. Anything to the right of the UT (Upper Tolerance) line is also a reject even though this may be only by an infinitesimally small amount.

Are tolerances black and white? Well, Taguchi thinks not. What must be aimed for is minimum variation (rather than some arbitrary tolerance) because minimum variation reduces losses to both the customer/society and the producer and improves quality.

Taking wire production as an example. The process capability of wire drawing is very good (see section Statistical Process Control). I.e. Wire can be drawn or produced easily within the manufacturing tolerance. One of the largest costs to a wire producer is the material (copper wire) used. If the copper wire diameter is minimised (within the tolerance) then there are large material savings for the producer. However, the consequence of minimising the diameter wire for the customer or society will be electrical power loss. Minimisation of variation to an agreed nominal value will benefit both parties.

Often Quality Managers see their role as only ensuring the output meets the tolerance or specification, mistakenly thinking this alone will achieve customer satisfaction. The tolerance is only one persons (designers) view on achieving the customer requirements and it may not be correct. The Quality Manager blindly following the tolerance misses the point that it is the reduction in variation that will satisfy the customer.

Figure 38 shows how this minimisation of variation can affect the loss to society. Following the curved line, as the quality characteristic moves further away from the nominal or target value, the greater becomes the loss.

The normal way of interpreting the tolerance is that any item inside the tolerance is acceptable. Any items below the lower tolerance and above the upper tolerance are rejected - black and white. In other words, if the Quality Charac-

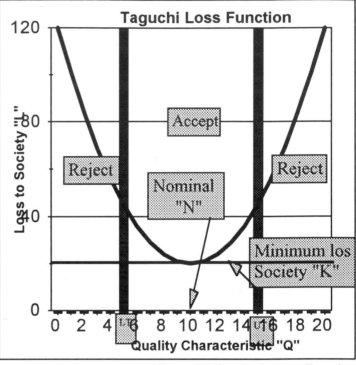

Figure 38 Quadratic Loss Function

teristic is just slightly to the left of the Lower Tolerance or slightly to the right of the Upper Tolerance the items are rejected. However, if the Quality Characteristic is just slightly to the right of the Lower Tolerance or slightly to the left of the Upper Tolerance the items are accepted. Logically this is nonsense. How can a very small variation in the Quality Characteristic make an item acceptable or rejectable.

A best approach would be, if the variation in the quality characteristic around the nominal or target value was minimised this would minimise the losses to both society and the company and improve the quality performance.

$$Loss\ to\ Society\ L\ =\ C*(Q-N)^2+K \qquad\qquad (1)$$

Where

N	= Nominal	
L	= The loss to society	
C	= The cost coefficient	
Q	= The Quality Characteristic	
K	= A constant equating to the minimum loss to society	
T	= The tolerance	
LT	= The lower tolerance	
UT	= The upper tolerance	

The target must be therefore to minimise variation rather than just working to tolerance.

Experimental Design

Another of Taguchi's well-known writings is in the field of experimental design using orthogonal arrays.

The problem solving techniques described in the section on quality circles only go so far. (Pareto, Cause & Effect Diagrams etc.) These techniques provide a means of logically analysing a problem with a view to tackling the root cause. However, for sophisticated problems where there may be one or more causes and a number of variables, these techniques start to show their limitations. So it may be appropriate to use a more sophisticated problem solving technique like analysis of variance.

Analysis of variance can be used when there is a problem which could have a number of different contributory factors or variables. To study this situation, all of the factors except the factor currently under investigation will be held constant. The one factor is then varied and the effect on the problem monitored. No effect - then the next factor is selected; all of the other factors are held constant and the one factor varied and the effect on the problem monitored. This process is repeated until the factor causing the problem is finally identified.

There are certain difficulties with this approach:

- o   Two or more factors may be combining to cause the problem - so the problem may not be observed.

○ Five variables tested at three points would require 50 tests.
○ This is very time consuming approach.
○ It can be difficult or even impossible to hold the other variables constant while varying only one. Think about golf and trying to keep the swing constant while varying the grip. (I only wish I could keep my golf swing just slightly constant!)

Using Taguchi's matrices the number of tests can be greatly reduced. These matrices can be used to determine the main factors. It is this experimental design that provides considerable information concerning the best combination of levels of factors which will minimise process variation.

TOTAL QUALITY MANAGEMENT

"There is nothing more difficult to carry out, nor more doubtful of success, nor more dangerous to handle, than to initiate a new order of things. For the reformer has enemies in all who profit by the old order, and only lukewarm defenders in all those who would profit by the new order. This lukewarmness arises partly from fear of their adversaries, who have the law in their favour; and partly from the incredulity of mankind, who do not truly believe in anything new until they have had actual experience of it."

Machiavelli in 'The Prince' (1513)

Introduction

There are possibly as many definitions and approaches to Total Quality Management, (TQM) as there are Quality Assurance Consultants. Some may argue that it is ISO9001, 2 or 3. This standard has, however, several omissions as exposed by ISO9004 (see section QAMS), namely: economics of quality, motivation for quality, quality in marketing, product safety and product liability.

So can ISO9004 be TQM? Well possibly but TQM is more of a motivational technique than a Quality Assurance System standard. TQM is aimed at motivating personnel for quality rather than giving guidance for the shape of a Quality Assurance Management System.

So what is TQM? Well TQM is more of an objective or goal rather than a set of requirements, (as with ISO9000) although both ISO9000 and TQM necessitate a structured approach to implementation.

Total Quality Management does not happen by chance. It requires careful organisation, planning and programming. The TQM objective being the never-ending improvement in the quality performance of the whole organisation. Not just in the sense of the performance of its products (reliability, its ability to meet specifications and to satisfy the customer etc.) but the performance of every process and every person within the total organisation.

Total Quality Management achieves the objective of never-ending improvement by embracing:

    o   Company-wide improvement by concerned and motivated personnel, involved and participating in the application of TQM.

o   Concentrated effort in achieving customer satisfaction (both internal and external customer), by showing to all personnel that they can actively help in providing a better quality service.

o   Quality performance measures which will provide personnel with the means of assessing current performance and making a commitment to possible future performance targets or objectives.

Thus, Total Quality Management enables never-ending improvements in every facet of the company's activities; improving productivity, increasing employee participation, reducing costs and providing complete customer satisfaction at lower cost. Consequently Total Quality Management can provide a distinguished company image and dedicated management and work force.

Total Quality Management is about fostering a state of mind for the employee that says; we cannot afford to stand still we must make continuous efforts to make improvements. To make work more interesting and rewarding; not necessarily with monetary rewards but making the quality of the working life more exciting. With economic pressures to be ever more efficient, then the tendency is towards flatter organisational structures, fewer layers of management and less specialisation. The consequence of these new organisational arrangements will be that the normally expected promotional route - up though the management structure will no longer be available. There will be a need to provide another outlet for the creative talent other than by providing promotion. There is a wealth of knowledge and talent available in an organisation. TQM is about providing the environment that allows that talent to develop and grow, harnessing that talent in a positive way and so improving the performance of the individual, team and organisation. When employees come to work, they do not hang up their intellect with their hat and coat on the way into work. TQM is about making positive use of that intellect.

There is a need to embrace change, change to make improvements, making the processes more effective and efficient. Often people have a fear of change and improvement. Fear that they will lose their job. Fear of making or suggesting improvements because they will be seen as helping management or being too clever for their own good. Fear of failure - failure to achieve the promised improvements. See Machiavelli in 'The Prince'

There are three interlinked and overlapping elements that need to be considered and addressed in any Total Quality Management programme namely: Systems, Structure and Culture. Each of these elements cannot be dealt with in isolation, each element needs analysis and a strategy found.

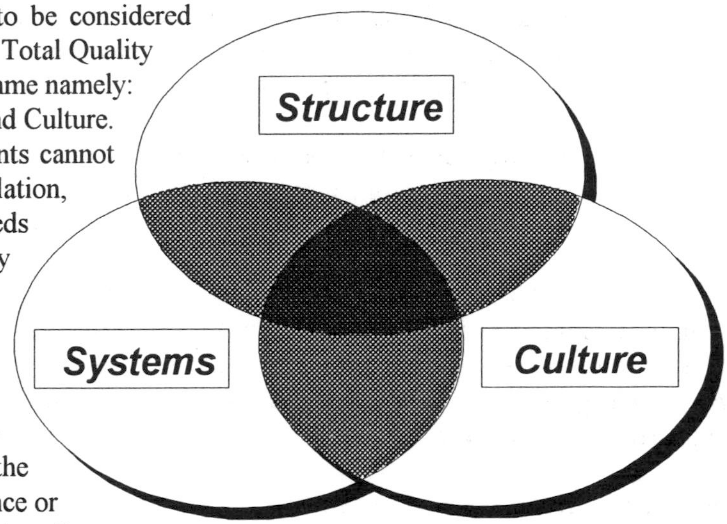

Systems: The way in which the various tasks within the company are organised, the manufacturing sequence or the way documentation flows around an organisation. Systems - the procedures that are followed to accomplish various

Figure 39 Structure, Systems & Culture

tasks. There is often a concern when discussing process improvement - 'that means that we, the employees, need to work harder' - no; this is exactly what is not required, what is needed is for the employee to *Work Smarter not Harder.*

There are two erroneous comments that are often heard concerning Quality Assurance namely:

a.   "If you want the quality, you cannot have the quantity" - This is no longer true (if it ever was in the first place!) Achieving productivity improvements requires actively understanding and improving the process, eliminating waste and inefficiency. In this way the process quantity or output is improved and the quality element improvement is provided free.

b.   "If you want the project finished on time then you must provide more resource" - This is no longer valid. Studies comparing the ability to design and develop motor vehicles has shown that project teams 50% smaller than the norm have halved the motor vehicle's production time. The resultant motor vehicle was also more reliable and cheaper as well. Other studies into curable diseases have shown, that diagnosing and curing diseases is not to do with money spent on the health service or social deprivation (although these can be factors). It is to do with the systems or the way in which the illness is identified and remedied.

It is necessary to closely evaluate all the organisation's systems and processes to ensure they are effective, efficient, adding value etc. (See Cost of Quality)

Structure: The formal relationships within the organisation - communication and reporting. The balance between grouping people with regard to their specialism rather than grouping people with regard to the tasks or process.

For example, the usual approach may be to group all the buyers together and all the engineers together according to their specialism. The TQM approach may be to group people within a process or manufacturing cell which includes multi-disciplined personnel (e.g. combined buyer and engineer).

To some extent ISO9000 describes the way organisations need to be *structured* and influences the *systems* employed. However, ISO9000 may not be the most appropriate route for all organisations - it may hamper free thinking or a creative approach. There may be major advantages in the company assuming the responsibility for finding their own approach to TQM, (ownership of the problem). Consequently, TQM needs to involve all levels in the organisation, providing the catalyst to debate the issues and determine the most appropriate approach, which will affect the culture of the organisation.

The final element is often considered the most important.

Culture: The company policy and objectives; the management style (authoritarian or democratic), the employees attitude (negative against change or positive and receptive to new ideas and approaches), the employees motivation for quality, change and improvement.

An example of the usual response to company policy may be - *"The company's prime objective is to make a profit."* The TQM response may be *"The company's prime objective is to satisfy its customers, everything else happens as a consequence of satisfying the customer."* The Management style may be *"I run a tight ship; there are few improvements that I can make to the tasks I control."* TQM style may be *"Employee involvement is essential if continual process and task improvements are to be made." "The employee must be actively encouraged to make improvements and entrusted with the power to make changes."* Employee attitude could be *"I can have no effect on the quality performance of the company because I work in the administration department, it's the people on the shop floor that influence quality. It is the responsibility of the quality department to control quality."* The TQM approach is *"Quality is every one's business, we all have customers who depend upon us and need to be satisfied, and we all have suppliers who must understand our needs and requirements."*

Since there are many definitions and views on TQM there are consequently numerous approaches to implementation. The more commonly recognised ones are listed below. This list is not exhaustive. The list includes a brief overview of each approach. More information regarding application and implementation each of these approaches can be found by making reference in this book to the sections indicated at the end of each paragraph.

So the structure of this TQM section is as explained - firstly a list and overview of the most commonly recognised approaches. Next, each of these overviews are broadened out giving more detail in terms of: an introduction to the approach, how to motivate or sell the idea - benefits and how to implement or effect each approach. Note: This overview is not in any specific order.

Overview List of Approaches to TQM

    a.   TQM Profiles
        Evaluation of the company against some profile or example of what is considered good practice may identify short falls or gaps in the quality improvement initiative. It may also help point direction or strategy with regard to quality performance improvement and training needs. There are many such profiles, Cosby's Maturity Grid was an early example of such a profile. Today they can be much more sophisticated with profiles such as the European Foundation for Quality Management model which will be discussed later. See section TQM Profile.

    b.   Customer Focus
        This approach has been mainly applied in the service sector (Banks, Hospitals, Hotels etc.) although interest has been shown in the manufacturing sectors. Typically the approach is characterised by slogans such as *"Delighting the Customer", "Voice of the Customer", "Customer Driven Quality"*. It is intended to focus attention on the external customer and improve the quality of service provided. This is achieved mainly by understanding the customer's needs and problems. Having established the customer's needs then comparing and contrasting company performance in meeting these customer needs both within the company and with the company's competitors. The techniques associated with this approach can be found by reference to the following sections of this book. Quality Function Deployment (QFD), Customer Satisfaction Surveys, Hard & Software Standards (or Bench Marking), Product Enhancement.

c. Internal Customers
Whereas Customer Focus deals with the external customer, there are also internal customers of our services. Internal Customers - the persons or departments within the organisation who are the consumers of our product. We need to ensure that our internal customer is completely satisfied with our level of service just as much as if they were an external customer. This approach is often characterised by the phrase *"The Internal Market"*. Approaches such as Departmental Purpose Analysis are used to evaluate departmental role and performance. See section Departmental Purpose Analysis.

d. Economics of Quality
"There's gold in the mine" - suggesting that rather than go out and win new business or obtain more orders, perhaps there's money to be made (saved) by looking inside the organisation. Techniques such as the Prevention, Appraisal and Failure model or the Process Cost model are methods by which the cost of quality for organisations or processes can be established and hopefully reduced. See section Cost of Quality.

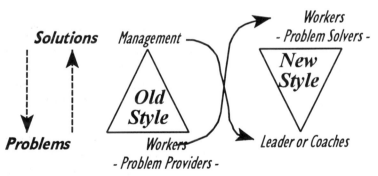

Figure 40 Management Style

e. Problem Solving - Team Approach
Possibly one of the more popular approaches to TQM which embraces the idea of using teams to analyse and solve quality related problems. These team approaches are typified by the use of Quality Circles or Kaizen Teams. The concept is for small gradual change rather than attempting step changes in performance. Step changes in performance are very difficult to manage and achieve. Things are much better achieved by small, gradual and continuous improvement. Quality Circles are teams of people who do similar work, learning to identify, analyse and resolve work related problems. Kaizen Teams or

Improvement Teams are multi-discipline teams whose role is to generate and implement schemes to improve quality and productivity. These techniques (Quality Circles & Kaizen Teams) do require a different style and thinking from management. As **Figure 40** shows, the old management style was for the workers to pass problems up to management and for management to pass the solutions down. This meant that decisions regarding problem solution where made at the furthest point from the source of the problem. Often without full knowledge and participation of those people who would have to implement the management suggested solutions. Quality Circles & Kaizen Teams turns this approach on its head. Now management suggests the problems[12] and has a team of problem solvers working for them. Managers, as leaders or coaches, supporting and understanding the needs of the teams in problem solving. Managers, being part of the solution not the problem. See section Quality Circles.

f. Quality Award Schemes
    British Quality Foundation (BQF)(UK), European Foundation for Quality Management (EFQM) (Europe), Malcolm Baldrige (USA), Deming Award (Japan).

    There are certain similarities of these award schemes and TQM profiles. Where TQM profiles may be self generated, self assessment, the award schemes (e.g. EFQM) listed here are nationally and sometimes internationally accepted profiles or models which organisations can use to self assess themselves. Possibly some organisations may choose to take the scheme further and enter a competition for the award. The primary purpose of these award schemes is as a means of self assessing or bench marking organisations against some concept of good practice. These schemes are considered to be *a concept of good practice* as these models have become generally both nationally and internationally well accepted. Other models of good practice can be ISO9000 but this standard, as explained previously, has certain limitations. It is these limitations which the award schemes have attempted to address.

g. Business Process Analysis
    Organisations are full of processes but unfortunately organisations are not always structured to optimise these processes. Organisations are often structured on the basis of functional (specialised) departments. This can lead to

---

[12]   Although Quality Circle Teams generally chose their own problems or agenda.

process inefficiency, unclear responsibilities and lack of focus. One way to evaluate organisations with a view to optimising key processes is to use the business process analysis techniques. This involves structuring the organisation along process rather than functional lines. Making the process key rather than the departmental functions. This approach has led to dramatic savings in process, lead and running times and costs. Even to the extent that some quality philosophers see this as the next major break through in quality performance levels. See section Business Process Analysis.

Each of the above approaches to TQM has now been enlarged giving additional information and detail.

TQM Approaches

TQM Profiles

The following is a typical approach to the application of TQM. See **Figure 41**.

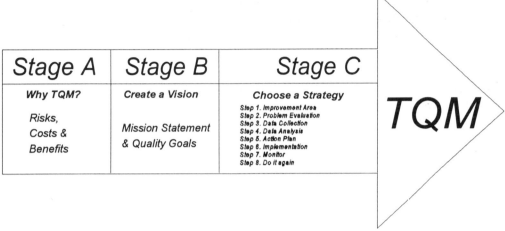

Stage A	Stage B	Stage C	
Why TQM?	**Create a Vision**	**Choose a Strategy**	
Risks, Costs & Benefits	Mission Statement & Quality Goals	Step 1. Improvement Area Step 2. Problem Evaluation Step 3. Data Collection Step 4. Data Analysis Step 5. Action Plan Step 6. Implementation Step 7. Monitor Step 8. Do it again	*TQM*

Figure 41 An Approach to TQM

STAGE A   *Why TQM?*

In this stage it is necessary to explain and introduce Quality Assurance. This includes background material regarding what is: quality assurance, quality control and some of the modern quality assurance philosophies as described by Deming, Feigenbaum, Crosby and Juran. (Much of the above has already been covered in the introduction and previous sections of this book.) This information could be drawn together in a presentation detailing such issues as Cost of Quality, Cost of conformance and non-conformance. Audits that may have identified Quality Losses. The risks, costs and benefits to be gained from a TQM programme.

STAGE B   *The organisations vision for the future.*

During this stage it is necessary to explain the concepts embodied in Total Quality Management and to gain commitment from top management to embark on a TQM programme. If the top management are not able to provide total commitment to the TQM programme then don't start. *If anything less than total management commitment is obtained then the TQM programme will fail.* This requires an understanding of the structure, the systems and the cultural needs of the organisation. To assist in determining these needs the TQM profile can be employed. (See TQM

Profile section). The Senior Management team also needs to be clear regarding what are the organisation's goals and objectives - a clear understanding of the key issues facing the organisation. The organisation's goals can be outlined in a Quality Goals and Mission Statement. In order for the Total Quality Management Teams to have a clear understanding of what is intended to be achieved, a defined and agreed statement is required from Senior Management indicating positively what the Quality Goals are. Establishing these Quality Goals is usually agreed at a meeting of the Management Team. As stated previously, in establishing the Quality Goals the TQM profile can be used to help determine the key areas of concern. Once defined and agreed the statement should be communicated to all employees. Some examples of possible Quality Goals and Mission Statement could be:

Improve on time delivery to 95%	Currently running at 80% on time delivery
Improve response and lead time by 30%	In all areas; Engineering products into production, Purchasing in placement and delivery of orders, administration in processing documentation.
Clean work place policy	In offices as well as work shops
Improve reject performance by 30%	In all areas; Engineering - number of drawing change notes, Purchasing - number of supplier rejects.

The organisation's wide strategic quality goals will require translation into departmental or sectional goals, i.e. how can each department contribute to these total company goals? What are the implications for the individual departments in achieving these goals? It may at this stage be appropriate to employ the technique Departmental Purpose Analysis. (See section Departmental Purpose Analysis).

STAGE C   *Chose a Strategy*

This is one of the key stages in embarking upon a TQM programme. It can involve an improvement team approach, including the appointment of the TQM council and executive committee, necessitating the training and education of a Group Leader and Quality Improvement Groups. It is not possible to be prescriptive about the approach to TQM; it may involve the 'Eight Step approach'; organising the quality improvement teams and implementing TQM. Alternatively the Management may decide that a completely different approach is required and the improvement team style is really not appropriate for their organisation. Mission Statement and Quality Goals may demand or suggest that a different route be taken. Deming in his 14 points does not provide solutions only issues that need to be considered and fully addressed within the TQM programme. Management needs to own the approach for and implementation of TQM and providing a ready-made solution does not enable Management to feel part of the improvement process. So it is with some caution that the following improvement team approach is suggested or adopted. What is important is that Management select an approach that is much more appropriate to their own set of circumstances.

Typical Improvement Team Approach

Step 1   Identification of the improvement areas (within the scope of the Quality Goals)

Step 2   Problem evaluation, understand the background to the chosen area for improvement. (Where are we now?)

Step 3   Data collection, acquisition of information and data appertaining to the improvement area

Step 4   Data analysis, review of the information and data obtained to determine its relationship or effect on the chosen improvement area

Step 5   Development of an action plan which culminates in real improvement in quality performance

Step 6   Implementation of the action plan

Step 7   Monitor the effectiveness of the action plan, including feedback, reviewing and testing of the proposed quality improvements

Step 8   Repeat the exercise again.

Total Quality Management Profile

There is no fixed or absolute approach to TQM, it can be dependent on the needs and requirements of the particular organisation wishing to embark on a TQM programme. The following TQM profile has been developed as a means of assisting with formulating and establishing an agreed approach to TQM implementation.

The purpose of the TQM profile is not to either score or derive a mark, greater importance should be placed on the completion of the profile and determining the appropriate action rather than numerical value of the score obtained.

The profile can be used to:

A. Establish the level of commitment at all levels within the organisation (including top management)
B. Establish the effectiveness of the existing Quality Assurance Management systems and structure
C. Determine the level of awareness, quality education and training needs
D. Ascertain possible areas for application of TQM techniques
E. Ascertain the areas in need of the application of TQM techniques
F. Determine which TQM techniques are appropriate
G. Determine the level of application of TQM
H. Establish of possible improvement areas
I. Provide a catalyst to promote further discussion
J. Provide a guide for establishing the TQM approach
K. Identify areas for further work or improvement
L. Measure real quality performance improvement
M. Assess whether the organisation as it stands is a Total Quality Organisation or how close the organisation is to being a Total Quality Organisation

The method of determining the organisation's TQM profile is by completion of **Table 25** (it is preferred that the TQM team individually complete the questionnaire). The first column describes the category to be judged. The second column is for the score awarded on the basis of:

Question a. *What is the organisation's policy or what does the formally documented Quality Assurance Management System state or declare with regard to each category?* A scale of 1 to 10 is used. A 1 would indicate no statement or approach, a 10 would indicate a clear statement or approach.

172

Question b.   *What do you believe is the case?* A scale of 1 to 10 is used. A 1 would indicate no implementation of the statement or approach, a 10 would indicate the statement or approach is fully implemented

Question c.   *What do you believe should be the case?* Again a scale of 1 to 10 is used. A 1 would indicate that the approach is of no value or significance. A 10 would indicate the approach is of great value and significance.

The third column provides a guide to assist in awarding the appropriate score for each category. *Note, where high scores have been awarded for "what you believe should be the case" this must be supported by documentary evidence.*

The TQM profile is first completed on the basis of each question in turn, i.e. a, b then c.

The completed questionnaires are then collated and analysed for trends and common views.

This analysis can then be employed to:

- Identify any weaknesses in Quality Philosophy
- Assist in agreeing and establishing the strategic plan
- Identify the key cost of quality areas
- Identify any organisational quality education short comings
- Assist with agreeing an approach to attaining employee involvement
- Assist with agreement to process improvement programmes
- Assist in determining key performance indicators

Table 25 Total Quality Management Profile

Category	Question			Guide
	a.	b.	c.	
1. Quality Philosophy a. Management Commitment b. Mission Statement c. Quality Goals d. A & B Communicated				Is there a clear quality philosophy? Has Management given a clear and unequivocal mission statement with regard to quality? Has this statement been turned into Quality Goals and are the statement & Goals clearly understood and implemented at all levels? Do the controls include understanding the needs of internal and external customers?
2. Strategic Plan developed for the implementation of the TQM scheme				Is there a clear documented programme indicating tasks, responsibilities, time scale sequence, ownership etc.?
3. Quality Costs a. Prevention b. Appraisal c. Failure (Internal/ External) d. Process Failure				Are all the categories which go make the total cost of quality known, quantified and an action plan established for the reduction in the cost of quality?
4. Employee Involvement a. Provided with the power (empowerment) b. Operator Quality Control c. Team development and involvement				Are employee teams involved in the decision making process, actively encouraged to make improvements, made aware of the basic tools and techniques for achieving process improvements and have the power to implement the improvements?
5. Process Improvement Programmes a. Implemented b. Coordinated c. Effective				Has the improvement programme been organised?

Quality Assurance Management

Category	Question			Guide
	a.	b.	c.	
6. Performance Indicators a. Internal Customer/ Supplier Relationships established b. Performance Measurement Criteria established c. Performance Measurement criteria understood d. Performance measured and data collected e. Performance targets achieved				Have departmental performance indicators been established? Are departments doing the RIGHT thing? Are departments doing things RIGHT? Can the department do the RIGHT things better?
7. Customer Satisfaction (External Customers)				Are the customer needs clearly understood? What is the level of customer complaints (are they measured)? Have customer satisfaction surveys been carried out and what action has been taken? Has a Quality Function Deployment study been performed?

175

Category	Question			Guide
	a.	b.	c.	
8. Quality Education Brain Storming Cause and Effect Diagram Check Sheets Customer/ Supplier Relationships Decision Analysis Department Purpose Analysis Document Flow Charting Failure Mode and Effects Analysis Hard and Soft Performance Standards Histograms Non-Value Added Activities Pareto Analysis Performance Measurement Problem Solving Process Capability Studies Process Flow Charts Quality Circles Quality Planning Quality Function Deployment Sampling Scatter Diagram Statistical Quality Control Team Building Value Analysis				Are any of the techniques listed opposite applicable, relevant or have value in any future TQM programme? Which of the techniques listed could be most effectively employed in any TQM initiative? How well and widely are the techniques understood and used? Are personnel trained in the use of any of these techniques?

Summary of Findings

Having established the Mission Statement and Quality Goals for the organisation and completed the TQM profile this information requires analysis to determine:

o   Are the Mission Statement and Quality Goals still relevant having completed the TQM profile?

o   Are the questions on the TQM profile relevant? Should some additional questions be asked?

o   How does the company's position (what you will do) compare with actual practice (what you are doing)?

o   How does the company's position compare with what should be happening?

o   Is there a consistent pattern emerging from the profile?

o   What action is now apparent combining the Quality Goals with the TQM profile?

Now summarise all the above in an action plan which may be similar to the Improvement Team Approach (see Stage C) or may reflect the Management Team's view of the correct approach.

Techniques

In order for improvement teams to follow the above TQM approach, it is necessary for the groups to be trained in some of the techniques and methods, which can be applied in achieving Total Quality Organisation. Just some of these improvement techniques are shown in the TQM Technique Selection Table.

Table 26 TQM Technique Selection

Section	Identify Improve- ment Area	Evaluate Improve- ment Area	Col- lect Data	Data An- alysis	Develop Action Plan	Imple- ment Action Plan	Monitor Action Plan	Remarks
Activity Sampling		●	●	●				Statistical technique for monitoring
Brain Storming	●	●			●			Generate ideas
Business Process Analysis	●	●		●	●	●	●	Process Analysis method
Cause and Effect Diagrams		●			●	●		Logical approach to Problem Analysis
Check Sheets			●			●		Method for recording data
Customer Satisfaction	●	●	●					Method of monitoring customer reaction
Department Purpose Analysis Customer/ Supplier Relationships	●	●	●					Method of analysing the purpose of a department or section
Document Inspection	●							An inspection method for checking software & documents
Failure Mode and Effects Analysis	●	●			●			Logical method of identifying possible system failures

Quality Assurance Management

Section	Identify Improvement Area	Evaluate Improvement Area	Collect Data	Data Analysis	Develop Action Plan	Implement Action Plan	Monitor Action Plan	Remarks
Performance Measurement Hard and Soft Standards	●	●				●	●	Method of setting performance targets
Histograms				●				Method of displaying data
Non-Value Added Activities	●							Approach to analysing processes
Pareto Analysis	●			●			●	Method for identifying the important issues
Performance Measurement	●							Method of target setting
Process Capability Study	●	●	●	●			●	Statistical method of process evaluation
Process Flow Charts Document Flow Charting	●	●	●					Process Analysis
Quality Circles	●	●	●	●	●	●	●	Team approach to Quality Improvement
Quality Function Deployment	●	●			●	●		Technique for understanding customer requirements
Quality Planning					●		●	Quality Control
Sampling			●					Statistical technique
Scatter Diagrams				●				Statistical method for investigating relationships
Statistical Quality Control	●	●	●	●			●	Statistical method for process monitoring
Value Analysis	●	●						Cost reduction method

Having gained an understanding of these techniques and where these techniques can be used to their best advantage, it is then possible to commence the implementation programme. This requires the monitoring, review and supervision of the progress of the Quality Improvement Groups culminating in the company wide quality performance improvements and achievement of customer satisfaction.

Activity Sampling

Introduction

Sampling can take many forms and is used in numerous applications

- o   Batch Sampling - Goods Receiving Inspection (see Stratification)
- o   Process Sampling - During the manufacturing charts such as attribute charts can be used to record the information gathered (see Statistical Quality Control)
- o   Activity Sampling - Can be used to take a snapshot of activities at any particular time.

To gather information about how much time is being spent on various activities, a study can be performed that monitors the activities or process on a 100% basis, continually examining the process and noting process changes and activities. This approach will necessarily involve a considerable full time resource and only a limited number of activities can be observed in this way. It is very difficult to monitor the process 100% of the time and while not under observation important process activities may be missed. To provide more objective results sampling can be employed, this technique gives the opportunity to quantify the current situation making the problem less subjective and more objective. The activity can be sampled at predetermined intervals to provide a more reliable and accurate account of the situation.

Activity Sampling can be used to monitor: The proportion of time spent on particular activities, waiting time, equipment utilisation time, labour utilisation time etc.

Activity Sampling Guidelines:

Pre-study Guidelines

A.   Determine the process or activities to be studied - this may involve defining the problem more clearly.

B.   Determine the likely scope of the study; factors to be recorded, frequency, duration, the required accuracy of the study, the recording method. It may be appropriate to conduct a pilot study first.

181

Table 27 A typical check list table for Activity Sampling recording

Factors\Sample Number	1	2	3	4	5	6	7	8	9	10	11	12	13	14	15
Waiting Instructions															
Waiting Work															
Break down															
Running															
Other															
Total															

In the row Sample Number, the date and time of the activity sample can be recorded. In the column Factors various activities are listed that could be observed when the activity sample is taken.

C.   Ensure that all the correct or agreed activity sequence, usage and method is understood.

D.   Communicate the reason for conducting the study to all personnel concerned.

Analysis of Results

E.   Having collated the results it may be necessary to repeat the study on the basis of the information gathered. Alternatively the situation may now be much clearer and the appropriate course of action may now be apparent. A report can be compiled which identifies the key factors, Pareto Analysis may be useful for this.

Brain Storming

Introduction:

The purpose of brain storming is to generate as many ideas as possible that come from many different perspectives. The concept is that teams tend to generate more ideas than individuals. As individuals we may run out of ideas quickly, brain storming in teams is an effective way of obtaining more new ideas. One person's ideas may trigger ideas that others would not have thought of by themselves. It is in this way that the team build on each other's ideas which trigger off individuals imagination. The technique is also useful in team building and cohesion. There are many ways in which brain storming can be carried out. The following guidelines have been created to help ensure a successful brain storm session.

Guidelines:

The team should be sitting in a room away from distraction. Identify the theme or problem that the team wishes to discuss. Sometimes it helps to brain storm something silly before attempting to brain storm the chosen theme e.g. *How many uses for a brick?* This can make the team more relaxed. To get the best out of brain storming there are some simple rules which have been found to work.

Rule 1   Encourage everyone to participate by presenting only one idea per *"turn."* One way is by taking in turns to suggest one idea at a time. If an individual cannot think of anything, say "pass."

Rule 2   There are no silly or bad ideas. So, team members should not put each other down by making them feel stupid. Encourage each other to say whatever comes into their heads.

Rule 3   Criticism or judgement is not allowed.   Team members should not criticise the ideas of others. The idea is to be open minded and constructive.

Rule 4   Discussion of the ideas should not take place until after the brain storming has finished. Accept everything without comment - it could trigger off new ideas.

Rule 5   Exaggeration and enthusiasm are helpful - there is no such thing as a crazy idea. Very often so-called crazy ideas lead to new ways of thinking and imaginative solutions.

Rule 6   Look for possible combinations of ideas, in this way the team may arrive at new ideas.

Rule 7   If you run out of ideas try using the six key words - What, When, Where, Why, Who and How.

Rule 8   Build on other people's ideas where possible.

Rule 9   Record all the ideas.

There are different types of brain storming, some are listed below. It can also help to return to the problem at some later date - Incubation.

Table 28

Brain Storming Approaches	
Advantages	Disadvantages
Free Style: The team calling out ideas to be written down (usually on white board or flip chart, by the team leader).	
• Spontaneous • Can be more creative • Possible to build on each others ideas	• Strong personalities may dominate the session • Can be confusing; listing ideas and too many talking at once
Round Robin: Each team member in turn calling out their idea to be written down.	
• Difficult to dominate the session • Discussion tends to be more focused • Everyone is encouraged to take part	• Difficult to wait one's turn • Loss of spontaneity • Embarrassing if cannot think of any ideas - puts participants under pressure • Reluctance to pass • Not as easy to build on others ideas
Notebook Style: Each team member writes on pad or sheet of paper their own ideas, later to be collated by the team leader.	
• Ensures anonymity if sensitive topics are to be discussed • Can be used with very large groups • Not necessary to speak	• Not possible to build on ideas of others • Some ideas may not be legible, understandable • Difficult to clarify ideas

Exercise: Brain storm
          "Why do improvement teams some times fail?"

185

Cause and Effect Diagrams

Introduction:

These diagrams provide a means of logically analysing a problem with a view to tackling the root cause. Generally the construction of a Cause and Effect Diagram is a team exercise. The diagram is to formalise and to keep a record of the team's logical approach to the problem. This provides a method by which the team's thoughts and deliberations can be documented, and provides a catalyst for discussing the problem.

Cause and Effect Guidelines

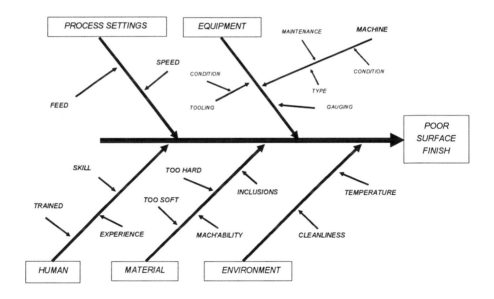

Figure 42 Cause & Effect Diagram

The first stage is to clearly define the problem. This definition may be provided from a Pareto Analysis or from statistical process control data. The diagram **Figure 42** records from a fixed point what the team considers are the main causes of the problem. Such as human, material, machines, environment, sequence, procedure, process system, equipment etc. Having determined the major group causes, the team brain storms the likely sub-causes within the major groups and possibly the further sub-causes.

Having established the team's views on possible suspects or causes of the problem, the team next needs to consider which, in their view, is the most likely culprit. The possible causes can be ranked in order of most likely, most easy to eliminate from the investigations etc.

Having prioritised the most probable culprits an action plan for investigation can be drawn up and implemented. This plan would detail the most likely causes, the method of evaluation and who is responsible for conducting the investigation. This stage would be repeated until the actual guilty party was discovered, again Pareto Analysis may be put to useful effect. (See section Pareto Analysis)

In certain cases the problem may be so complex that more sophisticated statistical methods may need to be employed such as Taguchi Techniques; sometimes known as an analysis of variance.

Customer Satisfaction or Market Driven Quality

It is very important to establish the customers' perception of the quality of product and service provided. This may be in some part determined from customer complaints or warranty returns but it is often stated that the customer rarely complains, they just don't come back. When this statement is balanced with the amount of investment (financial and resource) that is being placed on identifying and gaining new customers (i.e. increasing market share) then perhaps the effort and resource is being placed in the wrong area. If old customers are being lost, possibly at the same or higher rates as gaining new customers, then a new approach is required. It may be worth considering investing money on retaining existing customers.

Delighting the Customer

The idea of delighting the customer can sometimes grate on British ears. It has a ring of jargon and hype surrounding the phrase - *"Delighting the Customer"*. Unfortunately, there doesn't appear to be another appropriate phrase. Even reference to a thesaurus does not provide a better word than *delight*, other than possibly *enthral* but that seems over the top and doesn't convey the correct meaning. So it appears we're stuck with this phrase. Possibly more important is to examine the background to the concept.

In a price sensitive market, where organisations do not wish to embark on a price war, what will distinguish their product or service from its competitors? E.g. mobile phone industry. Advertising may be one (expensive) way, but as already explained, does this only replace customers lost though poor quality? Quality of Service may be seen as a more cost

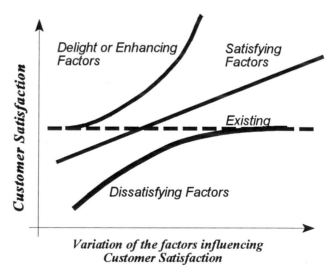

Variation of the factors influencing Customer Satisfaction

Figure 43 Variation of the factors influencing Customer Satisfaction

effective route. Delighting the customer - in this situation it can bring enormous rewards in improving market share. Even if a price increase was contemplated, it may not be possible unless the customer sees that the product or service is in some way superior.

Reference to **Figure 43** shows diagrammatically the factors influencing customer satisfaction: Dissatisfying Factors, Satisfying Factors and Delighting Factors.

Dissatisfying Factors: These are the factors which bring about a negative or adverse reaction from the customer. Things which the customer does not expect to happen, which when they do occur, decreases a customer's satisfaction with the product or service. Dissatisfying factors can make a customer less satisfied but the total absence of dissatisfaction factors does not make a customer more satisfied. This is because these factors are the standards of quality and grade normally expected by the customer - the industry norm. Examples of dissatisfying factors are: first time use failures, delivery problems, unhelpful or uncooperative staff, being kept waiting, lack of support, lack of understanding, customer complaints etc. Addressing these issues will return the organisation to the industry norm but will not take the product or service beyond this point. Issues which influence satisfaction and delight will need to be identified and improved to increase customer satisfaction further from this point.

Satisfying Factors: These are the factors which can provide the customer with greater satisfaction with the product or service provided. These factors are proportional to the level of customer satisfaction. Examples of these factors can be reduction in price, increase in the number of features, enhancements to the product or service, better value for money, reduced lead or response time etc. As the number of factors are identified and provided, then the greater the customer satisfaction. However, satisfying factors cannot compensate for dissatisfying factors. E.g. low price is no use if the service is slow or the product fails on first time use.

Delight Factors: These are the factors which when provided elicit a very positive or surprise reaction from the customer. Such features or enhancements were not expected when purchasing the product or service. These factors invoke a feeling of even better value for money as these features were neither expected nor specified. Examples of these factors are: a bouquet of flowers on the back seat of a newly purchased or serviced car, the receptionist of the hotel knowing and calling you by your name, being able to provide an immediate flat battery service from the Hotel or Car Park.

Improving Customer Satisfaction - Action Planning:

- o   Reduce dissatisfaction
- o   Increase satisfaction
- o   Provide delight features

The first stage is to identify and eliminate or minimise the dissatisfaction factors. No increase in the satisfaction and delight factors is going to improve customer satisfaction without first resolving dissatisfaction. Customer complaints monitoring, analysis and corrective action will help identify key dissatisfaction factors. (See section Quality Assurance Management System - ISO9000). Often organisations will plot graphs to monitor trends and compare performance against the target. Establishing a customer call escalation system or product support system is also a necessary prerequisite to understanding and reacting timely to customer problems.

Improving customer satisfaction may be achieved by clearer understanding of the customer needs and expectations. A customer satisfaction survey is a way of determining the customer needs and expectations and whether the current product and service lives up to these expectations.

Customer Satisfaction Surveys

The customer satisfaction survey that follows is derived from one used by a service and repair organisation and as such may be biased towards a particular industry and in need of conversion for use in other industries.

The questionnaire provided can be used as a guide but it is important to make the questions positive, not negative. If the questions are negative, the questionnaire may emphasise the bad points instead of building on the good.

Negative: What do you dislike about our service?
Positive: What do you like about our service?

As well as the questionnaire consideration needs to be given to the manner in which the information is obtained.

By post - the problem is, will the questionnaire be completed, will the questions be understood? Will a response be obtained from the most valuable customers? However, it will speed up the data gathering exercise.

By the manager having face to face discussion with the customer. Although this could be a less efficient way of gathering the information it may be an important marketing and personal relationship exercise which provides more information than from a questionnaire. These questions may be used as a guide to the customer discussion process.

By the service person, (possibly the service engineer) having face to face discussions with the customer. This may be an opportunity for the service provider and the customer to see the service person's role in a different light, extending the service person's role and the service provided.

How will the information obtained be analysed and most importantly will action be taken to correct any shortcomings? Who should receive the results of the customer satisfaction survey; managers, service providers, the customer and how will the results be communicated?

Customer Satisfaction

Name:	Position:
Organisation:	Date:

#	Question	Response
1. a. b. c. d.	**Service offered:** Are you aware of the range of services offered? *(Lists the services provided)* Are you aware of the procedure of requesting our services? *(Describe the procedure)* What other services would you like to see offered? Would a visit be helpful to describe the services offered?	
2. a. b. c. d. e. f. g. h. i. j. k. l.	**Performance:** What is it about the service provided that satisfies you most? In what way could the service be improved? Have you any complaints regarding the service provided? The response to requests for service should be *(detail response time)* Is this response time adequate? If not, what response time would be adequate? In your view is the response time met? The completion time for the service provided should be *(detail completion time)* Is this completion time adequate? If not, what completion time would be adequate? In your view is the completion time met? Is the service provided carried out as effectively as possible? If not how could the service be more effective & efficient?	
3. a. b. c. d. e. f. g.	**Managing the problem:** During the service - if a permanent solution could not be achieved was an alternative or temporary solution offered? Was concern shown if the service was not achieving the required objectives? Are you advised of the service person's presences? Are you advised of the service being completed? If the service was interrupted are you advised of the reason? Generally, are preventive measures taken to avoid any recurring problems? Are there any discussions regarding preventing the problem recurring?	

#	Question	Response
4.	**Attitude:**	
a.	Are the service providers courteous? In what way were the service providers most helpful?	
b.	Are the service providers interested? In what areas were the service providers most help?	
c.	Are the service providers suitably dressed?	
d.	Were constructive comments made?	
5.	**Customers Questions:**	
a.	Is there any thing you wish to bring to our attention?	
b.	What is the single most important change that you would like to see that could improve our service?	

THANK YOU FOR YOUR HELP IN IMPROVING OUR SERVICE TO YOU

Note: The questions are only meant as a guide to assist discussion regarding establishing the most appropriate questions.

Delight factors could be established by the use of techniques such as Quality Function Deployment, although this technique also helps with customer satisfaction.

All of these factors (dissatisfaction, satisfaction and delight) are extremely dynamic and the consequence of some of these actions needs to be considered. Often delight features, with time, become satisfaction features and eventually the absence of these features could become a dissatisfaction factor.

Exercise - Customer Satisfaction:

1. List three Dissatisfaction, Satisfaction and Delight factors for your industry or department.

2. Convert the Customer Satisfaction Survey table into one suitable for your industry.

Departmental Purpose Analysis

Introduction

Departmental purpose analysis is to clearly understand the relationship between your department, the supply departments and user/customer departments. This analysis can extend all the way down to individuals.

This analysis will ensure:

- o   that the department's objectives coincide with the company's objectives and plans,
- o   the inter-relationship between internal customers and suppliers is clearly understood
- o   and that levels of performance are understood, agreed and achieved.

A good example of this is the secretary/manager relationship. When the manager dictates a letter to the secretary, the secretary becomes the customer. The manager (the supplier), needs to supply all the information and provide all necessary resource for the secretary to successfully accomplish the task.

Subsequently, the secretary completes and returns the letter to the manager. Here the manager becomes the customer. The secretary (the supplier), needs to supply a finished product, which completely satisfies the manager's requirements and needs. The manager's requirements could include: time taken to complete the letter, letter layout, grammar and spelling. (See **Figure 44**).

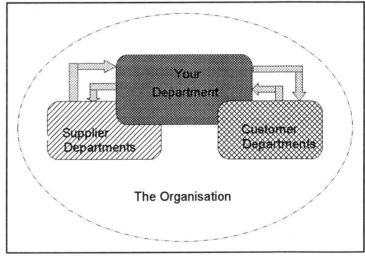

Figure 44 Internal Customers

This supplier/ customer process can be extended to include every-one within the organisation from the person receiving the customer's order though to the person delivering the product or service to a satisfied customer. In this way each person in the

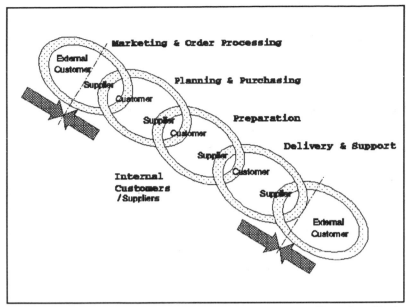

Figure 45 Customer/Supplier Chain

process can be seen as an important link in a chain of events. Any breakdown or quality failure at any stage or link in the sequence will have an immediate and catastrophic effect on the process as a whole and the delivered product or service. The next person in the process is a customer of the previous person's work. As an example of this approach, possibly instead of the inspector inspecting each stage in the process, the next person in the process could be seen as the customer. The supplier or deliverer will need to completely check their own work to ensure customer satisfaction. The customer or receiver will check the incoming work as well as their own outgoing work.

Figure 45 shows such a process in action. Initially from the external customer's requirements to Marketing (and hopefully a customer's order). Having reviewed and accepted the order, the next step in the chain is for Order Processing (an internal supplier) to supply Planning & Purchasing (an internal customer) with sufficient information. This information should be adequate (e.g. complete, accurate, reliable etc.) for Planning & Purchasing to satisfactorily complete their task in the chain. Next Purchasing (the internal supplier) to supply Preparation (the internal customer) with all the materials and facilities Preparation requires. This chain is then continued until delivery and handover to the satisfied external customer.

Departmental Purpose Analysis is an opportunity to evaluate the contribution of all departments to the overall quality performance of the organisation. For example the people in the indirect areas (e.g. Planning and Purchasing, Administration, Training - areas that do not directly add value) may feel that they cannot contribute to the overall quality performance of the organisation. The indirects may feel that this contribution can only come from the people in the direct areas (manufacturing, test - areas that add value). The proportion of the salary bill is often split 60% indirect/40% direct. In monetary terms for a salary bill of £1M this means £600K is spent on indirects £400K on directs - are the directs getting £600K worth of support from the indirects? If not why? If not what are the indirects doing about providing value for money - Departmental Purpose Analysis? Departmental Purpose Analysis gives the opportunity so show how these indirect areas can contribute.

To assist in investigating the customer/supplier relationship the technique **Departmental Purpose Analysis** can be employed. Establishing:

- o Are we doing the RIGHT tasks?
- o Are we doing tasks RIGHT?
- o Can we do the RIGHT tasks better?

Initially, the overall approach is to establish that the department is performing the right tasks - the tasks its customer needs (what are the department's customers needs?)

Secondly to establish that the department is completing the tasks correctly - fulfilling the needs of the customer (what are the characteristics that the customer needs fulfilling?)

Finally to establish if it is possible to do the tasks even better - is it possible to improve the performance of the department (what are the quality performance measures for the department, what are the important factors to achieve customer satisfaction?)

Guidelines for Departmental Purpose Analysis

Definitions:

Internal Customer: People or departments inside the organisation who receive the output (product or services) from the supplier (your) department.
External Customer: People or departments outside the organisation who receive the output (product or services) from the supplier (your) department.
Customer needs: The actual products or services the customer is prepared to pay for. (right tasks)

Customer characteristics: An interpretation of products or services that the customer needs into specific individual attributes of the product or service. (Customer specification)
Quality Performance Level: The performance that the customer requires from the product or service provided.

Note: Although reference is made throughout this section to the department this analysis can equally be performed by an individual.

Table 29 Right Tasks

Are we doing the right tasks?	
List the Suppliers (Inputs).	List the Customers (Outputs).
Detail what is passed to the department (inputs). The information, material, products and services provided.	Detail what is passed on to the customers (the outputs). The information, material, products and services provided.
Detail all the departmental tasks - the purpose of the department.	
Confirmed by Suppliers:	Confirmed by Customer:
Name:	Name:
Date:	Date:
Title:	Title:
Department:	Company:

Are we doing the right tasks?

Using **Table 29**:

a.   Detail the names of all the department's customers and suppliers. It may help to detail all the various tasks performed by the department.

b.   Detail the output from the department. What are the products produced, what is the information or data supplied, what are the services provided?

c.   Establish the purpose of the department. What does the department exist for, what are the aims and objectives of the department?

What are the tasks of the department? What work is performed to bring about the output from the department?

The tasks listed do not need to be detailed specific tasks but an overview of the major activities within the department.

d.   Compare the departmental purpose with the department tasks:

   o   are they compatible?
   o   are there any inconsistencies?
   o   are all the departmental purposes fully addressed?
   o   are there any customer requirements that have been overlooked?
   o   are there any non-value added activities which can be eliminated? (See Non-Value Added Activities)

e.   Identify which of the tasks are of highest priority.

f.   Having established the above information, it is essential that the customer has the opportunity to confirm its accuracy and emphasis and to formally accept the agreed level of service.

To assist in detailing the suppliers and customers from the section Cost of Quality, a diagram (**Figure 46**) can be drawn to show the inputs to the department (process) and the outputs from the department (process).

Quality Assurance Management

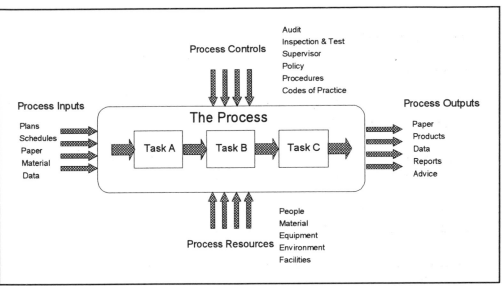

Figure 46 Process input/output diagram

Are we doing the tasks right?

Having established that only the right tasks are being performed then it is necessary to compare the actual practice with the customer specification. The activities, tasks and sequence that follows coincides with what the customer needs. **Table 30** opposite can be used in conjunction with this procedure.

Table 30 Tasks Right

Customer:	
Need	Specification or Characteristic

g.   For each internal
or external customer identified decide what are the customer needs, what does the customer require in terms of a product or service.

199

Once these needs have been listed, how can these needs be characterised, what is the specification that the customer requires? Break down each need into specific characteristics or customer specification.

h.   Examine what is currently supplied to the customer, with what the customer needs. The current priorities with the customer priorities, are they the same? For example, for the Purchasing Department the priority may be the placing of a £1M contract, whereas the Purchasing Department's customer may see the delivery of a £2.00 bolt, which is stopping production, the priority.

i.   Confirm the tasks are being performed correctly and in the proper sequence, (is there an agreed method, is the method documented?) (See Audit)

j.   Review any problems or complaints that the customer has identified which are not being corrected or addressed.

Again the input/output diagram **Figure 46** can be used by adding to the diagram the controls and the resources necessary for the department (process) to successfully complete all the right tasks.

The output from this departmental purpose analysis stage can be to establish some Service Level Agreements (SLA). Establishing these SLA can be a useful vehicle for debate between the internal customer and internal supplier. SLA give the opportunity for the internal customer to express clearly the level of performance expected from the internal supplier, rather than just saying things must improve. They actually place some measurable target or performance figures against which the supplier can be judged, not only for current and future reference but against external performance, i.e. the performance of similar external bodies that do similar work. (Bench Marking). How does the supplier's performance compare with the performance of an outside agency or contractor? How does the supplier's performance compare with departments doing similar in other organisations? Would it be cheaper and would a better service be provided by buying in the service?

Can we do the right tasks better?

Having established that the customer needs are completely understood and that the right tasks are being performed correctly, then improvements need to be made to the task efficiency. Establishing what factors need to be measured, what the current level of quality performance is and what quality performance level the customer demands and deserves.

k. Determine what factors need to be measured, e.g. average time to complete an activity, average cost of each task, average service level provided. In real terms for the Purchasing Department this could be average time to place an order, average time to receive goods, costs per transaction cost/order

Table 31 Tasks Better

Customer:			
Need	Specification or Characteristic	Perfor- mance Level Required	Perform- ance Level Achieved

placed. **Table 31** shows how **Table 30** has been extended to include the Quality Performance Levels required by the customer and the actual Performance Level achieved. (See section Performance Measurement)

l. Having established appropriate performance criteria the current quality performance level needs to be determined next. Taking the Purchasing Department as an example again this could be average time to place an order - six weeks, average time to receive goods - six months, costs per transaction cost/order placed - £50/order. On this basis is the customer getting a satisfactory service from the Purchasing Department? - would it be considered world class, is it possible to do better?

Note: Although this is for the Purchasing Department it could just as equally be applied to the Marketing, Administration or other Departments.

m. These current performance levels can now be compared with what the customer requires or deserves. What performance does our customer require? Can the requirements be met, can the performance be improved still further?

n. Can tasks be combined to make the task more efficient? (See section Process Flow Charts)

Failure Mode and Effects Analysis

Introduction

Failure Mode and Effects Analysis (FMEA) is a logical technique used to identify and eliminate possible causes of failure. The technique requires a sequential, disciplined approach by engineers to assess systems, products or processes in order to establish the modes of failure and the effects of failure on the system, product or process. This is to ensure that all possible failure modes have been fully identified and ranked in order of their importance. The FMEA discipline requires the engineers to document their evaluation with regard to the failure mode, effect and criticality. The analysis work can be applied at any stage; design, manufacture, test, installation or use, but is best performed at the design stage. In a simple system the study may be performed on the total system or product but with more complex systems it may be necessary to break the product down into various sub-systems or sub-assemblies.

The reason for FMEA

With ever increasing demands to ensure that QUALITY is achieved **RIGHT FIRST TIME** then still greater pressures are placed on the Design Engineer. This is to ensure that the Engineer's design performs consistently, reliably and safely throughout the life of the product, thus providing a quality product that completely meets the demands of the customer. Designers are only human, they can make mistakes and have off days just like everyone else. FMEA ensures that any inadequacies in the design are quickly identified, preventing the possibility of releasing sub-standard products. Product testing will of course help identify any design deficiencies. There are however, possible limitations with this approach:

a)   if the product fails the trial then the modified and hopefully improved design will need to be retested - this can lead to inefficient use of resource.

b)   tests and trials can usually only be performed on a limited number of products, consequently all the possible variations in specification and build standard cannot always be evaluated. Using small samples may also not be sufficiently accurate to predict field failure rates, particularly when attempting to identify causes of potentially low field failure rates (½ or 1%). These missed potential failures may result in the need for product recall or the issuing of advisory notices, (particularly in the case

202

of safety critical failures). This can be not only expensive but also damaging for both the company and product's credibility and reputation.

So FMEA provides the potential for:

A.   Reducing the likelihood of service failures
B.   Reducing the chance of campaign changes
C.   Reducing maintenance and warranty costs
D.   Reducing the possibility of safety failures
E.   Reducing the potential of extended life failures
F.   Reducing the likelihood of Product Liability claims

With FMEA the emphasis is on removal of the likely cause of any potential failures, however FMEA can also indicate to the Engineer the features in the design which require sophisticated quality control monitoring, possibly with the use of Statistical Quality Control (see section Statistical Quality Control).

Responsibility for FMEA

The analysis can be performed by either the Design, Manufacturing or Quality Engineer, but the most suitable is the person who knows the system, product or process best. The Design Engineer is the person most likely to conduct this analysis as having the most complete knowledge of the product, therefore can best anticipate the failure mode and the effect of the failure modes. The FMEA technique can be completed by an individual but is best carried out as a team exercise led by the engineer responsible for the product or sub-assembly. The team could include the Designer, Quality Engineer, Manufacturing Engineer, Customer and where appropriate any sub-contractors.

Some benefits of the application of FMEA can be:

A.   Identifying potential and known failures
B.   Identifying the cause and effect of such a failure mode
C.   Ranking the identified failure modes in terms of risk factor
D.   Following up or taking action on the potential failure modes
E.   Providing detailed documentation for the purpose of quality audit
F.   Checking on the FMEA decisions in the event of a major failure
G.   Making clear the accountability for the system, product or process

Limitations of FMEA

FMEA involves a considerable amount of time and labour resource in performing the study but in any case this is only time that would need to be spent in order to satisfactorily evaluate the design. Conducting an FMEA does require the completion of paperwork but at the end of the analysis documentary evidence is available proving an assessment was performed. Even after completing an FMEA, it may be that the key design failures may have been overlooked by the team and failures still occur, however the likelihood of such an event has been reduced. It may also be that after completing the FMEA no action is taken regarding the potential failures identified. This may be the case but clear responsibilities for taking action will have been established.

Guidelines for FMEA

The key stages in any failure mode and effects analysis on a design, product or system are detailed below and should be followed in conjunction with **Table 32** shown at the end of this section.

1. Logistics

    The system, sub-system or item and the FMEA team members need to be selected. All the relevant information needs to be collated: examples, drawings, customer brief, field failure information etc.

2. Header details

    Complete the details at the top of the form including name of the Engineer who performed the study and is responsible for the design. Include the revision status of the drawing and the FMEA. *Note, if the study was performed by a team then the name of the team leader.*

3. Part, Process or System name and number

    Complete details regarding the part, process or system name and number.

4. Describe the function

    The engineer must identify as briefly as possible the function of the part, component or the system being analysed. The question needed to be asked is: "What is the purpose of this part?"

5.   Describe the anticipated failure mode

The engineer must consider how this part could fail to complete its intended function? For example, could it break, bind, corrode, wear, deform, leak, short, etc. It is important at this stage that the engineer should be asking the question: "How could it fail?" not whether or not it will fail.

6.   Describe the effects of failure

The engineer must describe what the effects of failure on the final component or the assembly would be. The question, "What will happen as a result of the failure mode described?" needs to be posed. Will the component or assembly be inoperative, intermittent or noisy, inefficient, not durable, inaccurate etc?

7.   Cause - describe the cause of failure

Anticipation as to the cause of failure is necessary at this stage. What is being sought is which set of conditions or factors can bring about the failure mode? e.g.

o   could a foreign body jam the mechanism?
o   would poor or wrong material cause the mechanism to break?
o   would poor soldering cause the wire to short or cause an open circuit?
o   made outside specification or unable to achieve specification?

The engineer must analyse what conditions could bring about the failure mode.

8.   Estimate the frequency of occurrence of the failure

Here it is necessary to estimate the probability that a failure mode will occur. This estimation will be evaluated on a scale of 1 to 10. A one would indicate a very low probability of occurrence, ten would indicate near certainty of occurrence. The engineer needs to assess the probability of an occurrence based on his knowledge and experience of the product. The following evaluation scale is used:

1	=	1 in 1,000,000 Chance of occurrence
2 & 3	=	1 in 100,000 Chance of occurrence
4 & 5	=	1 in 10,000 Chance of occurrence
6 & 7	=	1 in 1,000 Chance of occurrence
8	=	1 in 100 Chance of occurrence
9	=	1 in 10 Chance of occurrence
10	=	100% Chance of occurrence

9.   Estimate the severity of failure

At this stage it is necessary to determine the likely severity of failure and again the scale of 1 to 10 is used, where a one would indicate a minor nuisance and ten would indicate severe consequences such as a high voltage shock. An estimate must be made of the severity of the failure. The engineer must consider the consequence of failure using the following severity scale:

1	=	unlikely to be detected
2	=	25% chance of service call
3	=	50% chance of service call
4	=	75% chance of service call
5	=	100% chance of service call
6	=	failure on installation or first use
7	=	failure results in customer complaint
8	=	failure results in a serious customer complaint
9	=	failure results in a fire, accident or injury
10	=	failure results in non-compliance with statutory safety standard or a fatality

10. Estimate the detection of failure

An estimate must be made of the probability that a potential failure will be detected before it reaches a customer. Again the evaluation scale of 1 to 10 is used. A one would indicate a very high probability that failure would be detected before reaching the customer and ten would indicate a very low probability that the failure would be detected in-house and therefore is likely to be experienced by the customer. E.g. If a 100% conclusive test is performed on the component, it is unlikely that the fault will reach the customer and is therefore assigned one. Alternatively if no checks are performed then it is highly likely that, if faulty, the defective product will reach the customer and is therefore assigned ten.

1	=	failure will be detected
2	=	80% chance of detection
3	=	70% chance of detection
4	=	60% chance of detection
5	=	50% chance of detection
6	=	40% chance of detection
7	=	30% chance of detection
8	=	20% chance of detection

9	=	10% chance of detection
10	=	no chance of detection

11. Calculate the risk priority number

By multiplying together the assessed likelihood of occurrence, the severity and the detection of the risk priority number (rpn) is found. The highest number being 1000, the smallest number being 1. From this number it is possible to determine which the high priority items are in terms of failure mode. The higher the risk number the more critical the component or item failure is.

12. Corrective action

The basic purpose of failure mode and effects analysis is to highlight the potential failure mode so that the engineer can take steps to eliminate or reduce the risk. At this stage it is necessary to analyse the risk number and determine what appropriate action is necessary. Obviously a high risk number would indicate immediate action, a low risk number may be ignored or could require some minor checks to be included.

13. Follow up

Having determined what the appropriate corrective action should be it is now necessary to perform a further FMEA to ensure that the resulting risk number has been reduced to an acceptable risk. It is also advisable to confirm at some future date that the proposed action has been successfully and effectively implemented.

Table 32 FMEA Form

Product: Component Name: Component Number: Revision Number: Effect on Purchasing: Yes/No										Engineer: Dates: Report Number: Sheet of Sheets: Revision Number: Last Updated:
Part, Process or system name & number	Function	Possible Failure Mode	Effect of Failure	Cause of failure	Occ	Sev	Det	Risk	Remarks/ Action taken	

Other Risk Assessment Techniques

FMEA is not the only risk assessment technique, although possibly the most popular, there are many other approaches that can be employed. In line with the objective of producing attractive products, organisations need to continually strive to improve, not only the range and performance of the product, but also evaluate new techniques that prevent any possibility of customer problems (safety).

There are various approaches to hazard analysis that could be evaluated. Listed below are some of the more commonly used techniques:

Hazard and Operability study (HAZOP)
Hazard Analysis Critical Control Points (HACCP)
Failure Mode and Effects Analysis (FMEA) sometimes known as Failure Mode, Effects and Criticality Analysis (FMECA)
Fault Tree Analysis

a.   Hazard and operability study (HAZOP)

This technique tends to be applicable to the operation of facilities and plant, detailing the controls necessary to ensure the continued safe operation of the facilities. The HAZOP study is carried out by using guide words. These words are to identify all deviations from the objectives of the facility or plant, which will have undesirable effects on safety or operability. The overall aim of the study is to identify any potential hazards.

The HAZOP study report should contain:

i   Technical information about the facility or design and operation of the plant or installation.
ii   Details on how safety will be managed.
iii   Information about the particular hazards of the plant or installation. These hazards will need to be systematically identified and documented by means of safety studies.
iv   Information about the safety precautions taken to prevent major accidents, together with the emergency provisions that should be taken if a safety problem or accident occurs. The object then is to reduce the effects of such accidents or safety problem.

This study will require the compilation of operating manuals. These operating manuals will need to describe:

i   Operation, control and safety procedures and instructions, including procedures for the management of changes in technology, operations and equipment.
ii   Adequate maintenance and monitoring of key operations.
iii   Adequate inspection and repair.
iv   Proper training of workers and contractors.

Part of the study will also be to determine the possible causes of accidents. This analysis of hazards should lead to the identification of potential hardware and software failures, process and design deficiencies and human error. The study should also determine what action is necessary to counteract these failures (including abnormal/normal operation, e.g. start-up and shut-down).

Such causes could include: component failure, corrosion, temperature, malfunction of control and safety devices, deviations from normal operation, failure in the monitoring of crucial process parameters, human and organisational errors, incorrect repair or maintenance work, etc.

A HAZOP study should be performed by a multi-disciplinary expert group, always including personnel familiar with the installation.

One problem with this (HAZOP) approach is that it tends to concentrate on the plant and facilities and not the process or the product. It does not provide the ability to identify areas of waste and inefficiency.

b.   Hazard Analysis Critical Control Points (HACCP)

Hazard analysis like the other analysis techniques is a preventive approach aimed at avoiding problems. The approach for Hazard Analysis Critical Control Points (HACCP) consists of:

i   Description and assessment of the hazards associated with all stages in the process from raw material to delivery of the finished product.
ii   Identification of the critical control points.
iii   Establishment of procedures to monitor and regulate the critical control points.

One major problem of this analysis is that no account is taken of the likelihood of occurrence, the seriousness of the operation, and the likelihood of detection. The analysis also does not rank the risk or exposure to problems, not just health and safety problems but also problems of waste, inefficiency and rejects. The technique also tends to concentrate on the process and there is a need to analyse the product as well. The technique was used to identify any possible health or safety problems with the product and it's method of development, production and delivery. While this technique is successful in helping to catalogue logically, the issues surrounding health and safety, it is felt that the analysis could go further, not only in terms of ensuring health and safety but possibly improving the overall performance of the product and process - FMEA?

Histograms or bar charts

Introduction

A histogram is a method of representing data in a bar chart format. These diagrams can be used when gathering and analysing data.

The data may be discrete categories of data. This could be used to analyse numbers of customer complaints against the reason for the customer complaint or the hours spent on inspection of each operation or product.

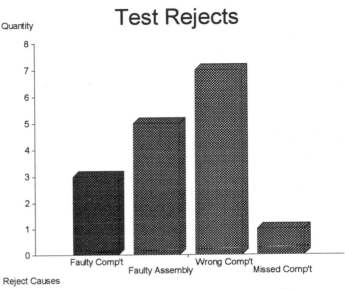

Figure 47 Histogram

The diagram **Figure 47** opposite shows the number of rejects for each fault type. This type of histogram can be employed when performing a Pareto Analysis, in this case the causes of rejects would be listed in descending order.

Alternatively, the histo gram could show data spread over a period of time or over a range of dimensions or sizes. There are numerous ways

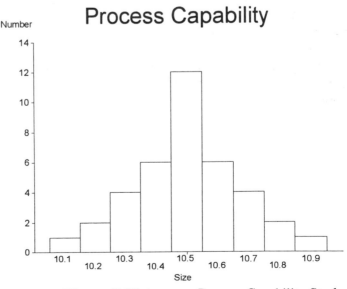

Figure 48 Histogram - Process Capability Study

in which histograms can be usefully employed, two examples are:

To analyse the change in the cost of quality of a company by displaying the total cost of quality on a month by month basis over the past year.

Or as in the diagram **Figure 48** opposite the number of components manufactured between a particular range of sizes (10.1 to 10.9mm). This type of histogram is particularly useful when performing a process capability study.

Guidelines for Creating Histograms

a.   Determine the factors to be analysed and collect the data (possibly by the use of check sheets).

b.   Rank the data in ascending or descending order.

c.   Establish the appropriate horizontal scale by determining the number of columns required (normal 6 to 8 is adequate) and the width of each column.

$$Width\ of\ each\ column\ =\ \frac{Largest\ Value\ -\ Smallest\ Value}{Number\ of\ Columns}$$

(2)

Establish the vertical scale. The vertical scale is often cost, quantity or frequency of an event.

Non-Value Added Activities

Introduction

The objective is to identify and eliminate non-value adding activities; i.e. those activities that do not contribute towards the customer requirements. This involves continually attacking and eliminating wasteful activities and unnecessary complex processes. A non-value activity is an activity which is costing money but does not add value to the item or service, an activity which is not a direct requirement of the customer and is usually the consequence of poor planning or systems. Value added activities, however, are activities that the customer is prepared to pay for. This is because the customer accepts their efforts as value obtained for the money; the customer is prepared to pay for the product.

Guideline procedure for Non-Value Added Activities

There are four phases involved in identifying and eliminating non-value added activities shown in the table:

Table 33 Phases Associated with Non-Valued Added Analysis

Phase 1	Elimination of Non-Value Added Activities
This phase requires a review of the processes within an organisation or department. What are the activities associated with the process? Who are performing the activities? What activities are people performing? How many people are involved in the process? In which department are the activities being performed? For which customer? Departmental purpose analysis, process flow charts and Pareto analysis can be used to help answer the above questions. Using these techniques to establish the value adding activities, enabling identification and elimination of the non-value adding activities.	

Phase 2	Simplify Remaining Activities
It may not be possible to eliminate all non-value added activities, so all attempts must be made to simplify the remaining activities. I.e. Simplification of the activities that cannot be eliminated. Again process flow charting may help in simplification of the activities.	

Phase 3	Organise into Natural Cells
In simplifying the activities it may be possible to reduce or minimise the number of non-value added activities and to reorganise the remaining activities into Natural Cells*. Reducing the overall number of steps and making responsibilities for activities clear. * Natural Cells are where the organisation is based on the task or project rather than grouping people on the basis of their specialism or skills.	

Step 4	Technology improvements
The application of the latest techniques can be employed to carry out the remaining activities more efficiently, for example the introduction of Material Planning Computer Systems.	

Pareto Analysis

Introduction

Establishing the factors that together make up all the various causes of rejects invariably means that a considerable number of problems are discovered. To tackle all these problems at one go would require enormous resources and in many cases some of the problems may be trivial and not worth pursuing for the time being.

A technique invaluable in singling out those problems which have the greatest influence on the total reject quantity or costs is Pareto Analysis.

Very often when this type of analysis is conducted, the results show that when placed in order of importance out of a given number of causes, only a small percentage, usually around 20%, account for 80% of the total problem. For this reason the concept is often known as the 80 - 20 rule.

As an example of this technique the reasons for rejects or scrap from a process were recorded over a convenient period of time. This

Table 34 Scrap records

Operation	Dept Resp	Scrap Qty	Cause	Value	Total Cost
Saw	105	50	Wrong Size	0.30	15.00
Turn	105	61	Wrong O.D.	0.40	24.40
Mill	103	87	Flat Position	0.50	43.50
Drill & Tap	120	230	Hole Position	0.60	138.00
Heat Treat	110	239	Wrong Case Depth	0.80	191.20
Cyl. Grind	110	320	Wrong O.D.	0.90	288.00
Bore Grind	103	616	Wrong I.D.	1.00	616.00
Hone	103	701	Over Size	1.50	1,051.50
Lap	103	1991	Surface Finish	2.00	3,982.00
Total		4,295			6,349.60

information has been tabulated. **Table 34** opposite shows the number of scrapped components found by inspection at each operation.

215

This information can been arranged in order and a graph plotted of the results, see **Figure 49** Graph Pareto Analysis. Examination of this graph reveals that approximately 20% of the causes of reject items are responsible for 80% of the total cost of rejects.

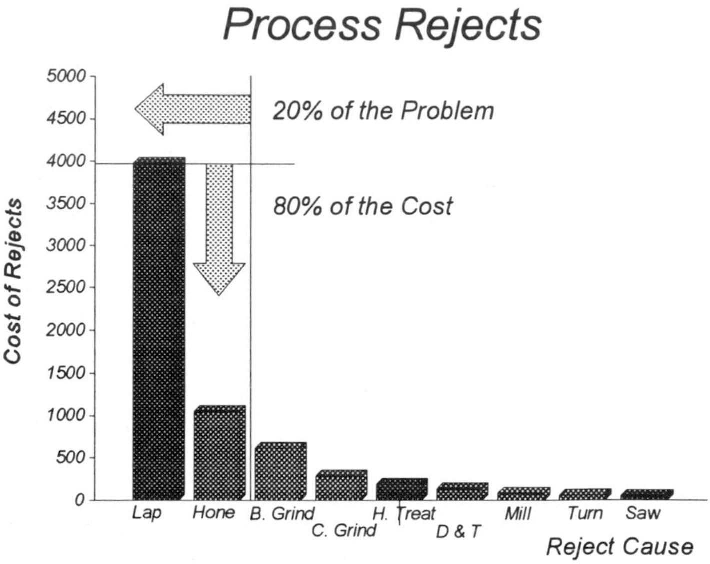

Guidelines for Pareto Analysis:

Figure 49 Pareto Analysis Graph

Select the factor to be analysed. Determine how the data is to be collected (possibly by the use of check sheets) and what the duration of data collection will be.

Rank the data in ascending order.

Establish the appropriate horizontal scale and vertical scale.

Table 35 below shows other criteria which can be analysed using the Pareto technique depending on the nature of the problem.

The object of Pareto Analysis is to identify 'THE IMPORTANT FEW' with a view to avoiding 'THE TRIVIAL MANY'. Thus it is possible to make an 80% improvement by tackling and eliminating only 20% of the problems.

Table 35 Pareto Graph Axis

HORIZONTAL AXIS	VERTICAL AXIS
Part No./Machine No./ Operator or Dept. No.	Cost of defectives
Supplier	Goods inwards inspection rejects
Reasons for warranty returns	Quantity of warranty returns
Reasons for test failures	Quantity of test failures
Reasons for rework	Quantity of rectification work

Performance Measurement/Bench Marking

Introduction:

All organisations need to establish and quantify the key factors with which to monitor their quality performance. It is not enough to believe that the organisation's quality performance has always been satisfactory. Agreement needs to be reached as to what the key factors are by which to judge the organisation's quality performance. What is the organisation's current performance against these factors and how can the current quality performance be improved? If measures of Quality Performance are not established and monitored then adverse and possibly catastrophic trends may not be identified with possible dire consequences for the organisation concerned. Juran talks about breakthrough and control to new levels of quality performance; organisations that can achieve this objective will always be successful because they will continually be making never-ending improvements.

Quality Performance measures need to be established, not only at a corporate level but at all levels throughout the organisation, even down to an individual unit or person. Quality Performance measurement is one of the most important ways of improving the quality performance of organisations. If the current quality performance is not known then improvements can only be subjective and not quantifiable.

Having established and measured an organisation's or department's performance indicators these values need to be compared (bench marked) against recognised leaders or pacesetters. This is to determine if the current performance is of the correct standard (*World Class*).

Guidelines for Bench Marking:

Firstly, there is a need to agree the necessity for establishing quality performance measures by senior management. The necessity of establishing quality performance measurement then needs to be communicated to all levels throughout the organisation to gain commitment and understanding for the need to continually make improvements in quality performance. Departmental Purpose Analysis and Customer/Supplier investigations can be used to help convince personnel of the need for quality performance measurement. The TQM team need to agree the Performance Measurement.

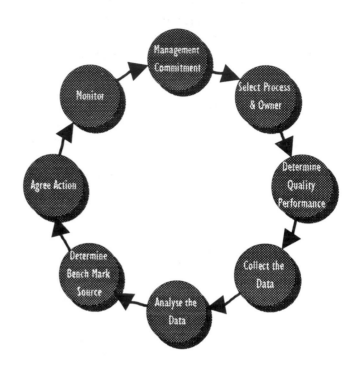

Figure 50 A Bench Marking Sequence

Next, the actual processes that need to be monitored have to be established and agreed. Having established the process to be monitored then the factors critical to success need to be determined.

These critical success factors or quality performance measurements should be:

    a.   Suitable for the particular process, department or organisation evaluated.

    b.   Consistent, so that there is no doubt about the method of calculation of the performance measure and so that the data for performance measurement can be accurately and reliably obtained.

    c.   Clear and rest with a particular group or cell so that responsibility or ownership for achieving the performance criteria understood.

Quality Assurance Management

d. Easily and regularly calculated, usually numbering between 3 and 7 performance measures.
e. A clearly defined start and finish.
f. A defined direction not a solution.
g. Achievable and within the groups capability.
h. Possibly determined from the customer/supplier relationship and the department purpose analysis.

The performance measurement categories can be broken down into two main categories, quantifiable "Hard Standards" and non-quantifiable (subjective) "Soft Standards". These categories can be broken down again within these categories in terms of:

o customer satisfaction; product and service performance, reliability, complaints and claims
o process efficiency; scrap, rejects, wasted time, change, rework, labour and process utilisation
o environmental losses; pollution, unsatisfactory performance, disposal and decommissioning, waste of resources human and energy.

"Hard Standards" are measurable such that an agreed performance target can be set. Examples of such standards could be:

Cost	a.	Costs/item, transactions/employee
Quality	b.	Number of rejects, failure rates, complaints
Service	c.	Average response and down time, lead time, delivery time

"Soft Standards", although not always directly measurable these standards are as equally important as hard standards. These soft standards can make the difference between an existing customer returning, obtaining a new customer or placating a dissatisfied customer.

An example of soft standards could be the way in which the service engineer deals with the customer. This can often make the difference between the customer renewing their service contract and the customer advising possible new customers of the excellent service the customer has received. Alternatively the poor service the customer has received and may result in the customer not returning and advising possible future customers of the unsatisfactory service.

Soft Standards can include:

Personnel style	a.	Friendly, helpful, positive approach
Efficient Service	b.	Anticipate needs, be flexible, provide clear information, professionalism
Concern	c.	Manage problems - when troubles do occur understanding the customer's difficulties and help to resolve the problem.

Data collection: Having determined the quality performance standards that need to be monitored the next stage is to agree how to quantify the current performance level and to start to collect the data on a regular basis. The data collected could include:

o   customer satisfaction which could be quantified by surveys of both existing and potential customers (see example of the customer satisfaction survey). Surveys of competing products and services. Analysis of service and product performance in terms of reliability, numbers and types of complaints and claims.

o   process efficiency; by monitoring scrap, rejects and rework levels. Analysis of processes to determine wasted time, labour and process utilisation, examination of the number of changes. (See Cost of Quality).

o   environmental losses; waste of resources, human and energy, could be quantified and monitored by employee surveys, interviews (e.g. exit or leaving interviews) and energy audits.

Analysis: With the current performance level determined the TQM team or departmental personnel need to agree new targets. These new targets can either be agreed with the customer (internal or external), or alternatively, the targets may be based on other recognised leaders or pacesetters - the organisations who are seen as being World Class or best in class. This information can be obtained from: surveys (customer and competition), technical journals, review of advertisements etc.

Obtaining the Bench Mark Source: There are a number of possible bench mark sources. *Internal bench* marking against a similar national or international division. This is the easiest as access to the required information should be relatively straight forward. Industrial Bench Marking against the competition. This is obviously more difficult as competitors are unlikely to be keen on releasing commercially sensitive information. However, Trade Associations can be helpful but information scientists can provide useful information. Alternatively recruiting staff from the competition could provide a more effective route. There are also best practice clubs now available which share approaches and information.

Action Plan & Monitoring: Having obtained what is seen as being a suitable target then work can commence towards establishing an action plan for improving the performance to meet the new performance criteria.

Process Flow Charts

Introduction

Process Flow Charting and Document Flow Charting are techniques that can be employed to provide a visual representation of a procedure. Flat text can be boring and an uninteresting way of describing a process; the reader is likely to lose interest and concentration. A picture can tell a thousand words - it can convey, in certain circumstances, a better graphical indication of the sequence and methods employed within a process. The flow chart can be used to describe a number of activities, sequence of tasks, the way documents flow around an organisation, a computer program etc. Once the chart has been completed, the Process Flow Charts can be employed to analyse all the activities involved in processes or system. This may be used to explain why a process is done in a particular sequence or why a particular route was taken. The flow chart will also show the suppliers and customer of a particular task or activity. The flow charts can be used to determine the stages that require special quality control activities. With the flow chart being a comprehensive description of the process, identification of value added and non-value added activities, any unnecessary transportation and delays, becomes much easier. Boundaries can be added to the flow chart to denote when a responsibility for a particular set of activities changes from one person to another.

There are a number of different standards that can be used for the process flow symbols. ISO5807 contains the most generally accepted symbols.

Process - Identifies the activity or task and contains a brief description of the work performed.
Decision - the point where a decision is made and the flow chart can slip into two paths. The paths are labelled true/false yes/no etc. depending on the outcome.
Terminator - identifies the beginning or end of the process.
Document - where a document is required, used or created then this symbol can be employed.
Flow lines - Used to represent the next step in the process, connecting activities and tasks.
Connector -
Visual - When a computer is used to convey information this symbol can be used.

Guidelines for Process Flow Charting

1.   Select the process or system to be examined.

2. Complete the Process Flow Chart **Table 36** representing each of the activities diagrammatically with the appropriate symbol (See **Figure 51**). The table needs to be completed by discussion with the person most knowledgeable about the process under investigation (the person doing the job?)

Table 36 Process Flow Chart Form

Operation: Department: Name: Date:			
Stage	Symbol	Description	Remarks

Symbol	Activity
◯	Operation
⊘	Redundant Operation
▷	Delay
△	Unfile
▽	File
⇨	Transport
☐	Inspection
◇	Decision

Figure 51 Process Symbols

Table 37 Activity Summary

Activity	No. of Activities	
	Current	Proposed
Operations		
Redundant Operations		
Delays		
Unfile		
Files		
Transports		
Inspections		
Decisions		
Total		

3.   Critically analyse the chart to identify:

a.   Whether the objectives of the process are being met? (Are there any omissions or duplications?)

b.   Whether the activities are necessary? (Use the activity summary to show the number of current and proposed activities)

c.   Whether the process is under control? (Where could the process go wrong and have all the necessary reviews or checks been included and are they being performed?)

d.   Whether all the resources and information are available to perform the activities?

e.   Whether there are any redundant operations and unnecessary delays.

f.   Whether there are any non-value added activities (see section Non-Value Added Activities).

4.   Complete **Table 37** indicating the current proposed number of activities, showing the savings made.

5.   The finally agreed flow chart then needs acceptance and approval by the appropriate authority.

Document Flow Charting

Introduction

This technique is very similar to Process Flow Charting but as its name implies is used for the analysis of paperwork systems. The technique can also be used as a way of describing or mapping an administrative procedure.

Guidelines for Document Flow Charting

1.   Select the process to be examined.

2.   Complete the Document Flow Chart - **Figure 52**.

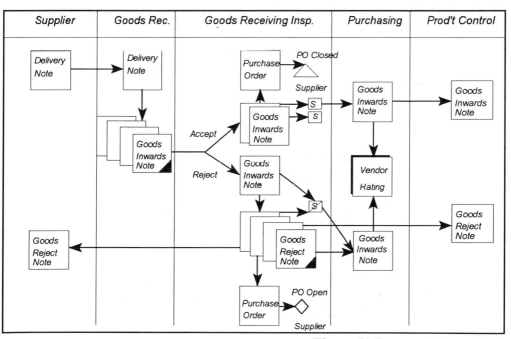

Figure 52 Document Flow Chart

Enter the name of each department, section or operator at the head of each column. Complete the chart by using a symbol to denote each stage and document employed. An arrow is drawn between the stages to indicate the flow of information around the departments.

3.   Analyse the Chart to identify:

a.   Are the objectives of the procedure being met? (Are there any omissions or duplications?)

b.   Are all the activities/documents necessary?

c.   Is the procedure under control? (Where could the process go wrong and have all the necessary reviews or checks been included and are they being performed?)

d.   Are all the resources and information available to perform the activities?

e.   Are there any redundant operations/documents and unnecessary delays.

f.   Are there any non-value added activities (see section Non-Value Added Activities).

Quality Function Deployment

Introduction

As a project or design progresses the greater becomes the possibility of overlooking specific customer's needs and expectations. In order not to neglect or overlook "the voice of the customer", the technique of Quality Function Deployment (QFD) has been developed. This initial development work took place in the Kobe Shipyard of Mitsubishi Heavy Industry. The QFD Technique is similar to value analysis as both techniques seek to understand the basic function or customer requirements and determine how best these functions can be achieved. The analysis is performed in a very structured way considering each customer need and how the need is best realised.

The aim for QFD is to identify the key customer needs and translate these needs into controls. This is achieved by establishing what the customer requires and throughout the various stages of QFD how these various requirements will be realised. QFD is not intended to determine the function of the quality department but to provide better quality planning. QFD is not only applicable to product engineering, it can also be applied to manufacturing processes and the service industries e.g. hotels, airlines etc.

Some of the benefits derived from QFD can include:

A.   Reduction in the number of design changes
B.   Reduction in design time
C.   Reduction in the development and start up costs
D.   Reduced warranty claims

Guidelines for Quality Function Deployment

The first stage in performing QFD is to list the customer's requirements, not necessarily in terms of a product specification but in fairly general terms. E.g. the customer may require a ball point pen, giving as their requirements that the pen must write smoothly. This requirement would need to be converted into "company speak" or something the organisation manufacturing the pen can understand. Normally these requirements would be translated by means of the design or manufacturing specification, but with QFD this means translating the customer requirements into what and how. For the pen example, writing smoothly could be translated into the ball and clasp design and target values set for the ball and clasp dimensions and durability. This relationship between what (customer requirements) and how (features), will eventually become very complicated.

227

The basic QFD tool is a matrix chart which can be employed to simplify and represent the relationship between what the customer wants and how these needs will be achieved. See **Table 38** QFD matrix chart.

Table 38 QFD Matrix

	Cus-tomer Rating	Means to achieve (HOW)		
		Target Values		Competi-tion Rat-ing
Customer Requirements (WHAT)				
Importance Rating				

The matrix is relatively simple but does provide a disciplined way of representing the customer's needs and how they are to be achieved.

Completing the matrix

Completion of the matrix would normally be completed by a team of people which could be drawn from the design, marketing, production, purchasing and quality departments. The role of the team is to establish all the key customer requirements and complete the QFD matrix. These requirements would be listed down the left-hand side of the QFD matrix. How these requirements are to be achieved would be listed along the top of the QFD matrix.

Stages

1.   Establish the *Customer Requirements* - list what the customer requires from the product. Note, different customers may require different features so the list needs to be reasonably comprehensive. For the pen example this could include: write smoothly, reliable, long life, cheap etc.

2.   Having established the customer requirements, these requirements need to be given a *Customer Rating*. This rating is quantified by selecting a number between one and ten - an essential customer requirement is given a ten, a minor requirement is given a one. It may be that the weighting will vary for different customers i.e. house wife, bulk buyer etc. For the example, write smoothly may be considered to be very important and therefore given a ten, easy to grip is usually not quite important and given a five.

3.   How the customer requirements are to be achieved are detailed along the top of the matrix *(Means to achieve (How)). The means to achieve should be quantified if possible by detailing Target Values below each "how." The Target values* provide objective figures for the design to achieve. For the example the means of achieving the customer requirements include: ink viscosity, number of colours, ball & clasp tolerance, ink volume etc. For ink volume the target value could be 10cc +1cc/-0cc etc.

4.   Working from the customer requirements and how the requirements are to be achieved, numbers can be added to the matrix. The number selected indicates the relationship between the factors. A one to ten scale is used; selecting a ten would indicate a strong relationship, five a medium relationship and a zero no relationship. In this way all the customer needs can be fully addressed ensuring that no customer need is overlooked. For the example there is a strong relationship between write smoothly and the ball & clasp tolerance, but no relationship between no leaks and the clip.

5.   The right-hand side of the matrix *Competition Rating* is used to evaluate and appraise the competitions' ability to achieve the customer requirements. The number chosen is in direct proportion to the competition's ability to meet the customer requirements ten fully met, five partly met, zero not met. Having completed this stage then analysis of the figures can provide an estimate of whether the competition is ahead or behind. This information can be used to identify where

product improvements need to be made, to improve the design or alternatively to extend an existing lead.

6.   The *Importance Rating* can then be calculated by multiplying the Customer Requirements by the Relationship Number and then summing each column. This number given is the Importance Rating for each feature. By applying the Pareto principle to the importance rating the key features can be established. Identification of the key features suggests where to concentrate resources (money, time and engineering effort). For the example the key features would appear to be Seals & Joints 290 and Ball & Clasp tolerance 244.

Table 39 shows the QFD analysis performed on a ball pen.

Means to achieve (How) A=Ball & Clasp tolerance, B=Ink Viscosity, C=Ink volume, D=Number of colours, E=Seals & Joints, F=Shape & Size, G=Surface Finish, H=Clip

Table 39 Completed QFD Matrix

Customer Requirements	Customer Rating	A	B	C	D	E	F	G	H	Means to achieve (How) Target Values Competition Rating
Write Smoothly	10	10	2	0	2	0	3	0	0	
Reliable	10	5	1	0	4	10	0	0	4	
Long Life	7	2	8	10	3	10	2	0	0	
Colours	7	0	2	0	10	0	0	1	0	
No leaks	10	8	2	3	1	10	0	0	0	
Easy to grip	5	0	0	0	0	0	10	9	0	
Retractable	5	0	0	0	0	0	8	0	4	
Aesthetics	5	0	0	0	10	4	10	8	9	
Importance Rating		244	120	100	211	290	184	92	105	

Due to the labourious arithmetic associated with QFD, it may be appropriate to use a computer (spread sheet) to perform these calculations. The above analysis would suggest that the important features which require special attention are Seals & Joints (290) and Ball & Clasp tolerance (244). The analysis would also suggest that the designer and manufacturer need to pay particular attention to these features. This may include a review to ensure that the design can achieve the requirements and manufacturing is capable of meeting the design specification.

Some organisations believe that establishing the key features has a significant effect as it provides new ways of thinking about their products. It also provides for better understanding between departments such as marketing, quality and engineering. Having realised these benefits some organisations stop at this stage, however, it is possible to continue the QFD process.

QFD can be continued throughout the various stages in the design/ manufacturing process, from the customer/marketing requirements all the way through to the quality control methods. At each stage the key features (Importance Rating) are identified and selected for use in subsequent stages. If all the features identified are used, then the next stage of analysis will become bigger than the last. If this continues throughout the stages the analysis can then become very extensive and unwieldy, however,

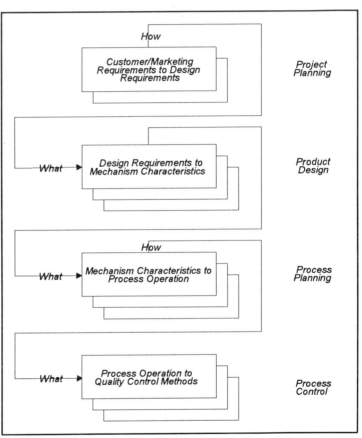

Figure 53 Voice of the Customer

this depth of analysis may on occasion be essential. To limit the amount of work at subsequent stages only the key features may be chosen.

Using the QFD matrix for each process stage can establish the key features and each feature's relative level of importance in satisfying the customer requirements. See **Figure 53**. The QFD can now be redrawn indicating these features throughout each stage as shown in the diagram - "Voice of the Customer". Compilation of this diagram involves the repeated application of QFD for each project stage.

For example the Project Planning Stage; using the QFD approach to interpret what the customer requires into how the design achieves these customer requirements. Next the Product Design Stage, using QFD to interpret the Design Requirements or Functional Requirements into Detailed Design or Mechanism Characteristics. This process continues until finally (in the example shown) the Process Operations stage interpreting the Process Operation into Quality Control Procedures and Methods. In this way the "voice of the customer" is heard all the way through the project and finally interpreted into specific quality controls. This would ensure that the voice of the customer is heard at the very point of manufacture so that personnel clearly understand which are the important features needing to be consistently and reliably maintained.

Note: Organisations may find completion of the first stage (Customer Requirements to Design Requirements) relatively simple but moving on to the subsequent stages may involve considerably more resource.

Quality Planning

Introduction

Every stage of a process or project is a possible source of poor quality, the objective of Quality Planning is to anticipate possible sources of poor quality and to arrange for means of identifying such failure and preventing them from occurring.

A Quality Plan tends to be a project or product specific document which defines the Quality Assurance tasks to ensure meeting specific customer requirements and time scales. It enables the identification of preventive activities to provide early warning of any possible problems occurring or becoming major. It allows anticipation of any project or product risk areas and for the opportunity to take appropriate action to eliminate or mitigate any such difficulties. This differs from a Quality Manual which is project or product independent and a Quality Programme which usually describes the implementation of the Quality Manual.

A Quality Plan identifies any existing and additional procedures or activities that may be necessary. Often Quality Plans are required on large capital cost projects such as construction projects or the launch of a new product or software development etc. - where main contractors need to control the activities of sub-contractors. The Quality Plan can be used as model or method of describing the Quality Assurance activities so that everyone can comment on, criticise and develop the plan ensuring their involvement in project achievement.

Normally the project manager or project controller is responsible for the generation of the Quality Plan; the plan would then require approval by the project team and possibly the customer.

The stages involved are:

Defining the process - this can often be established by drawing a flow chart of the process showing each of the key stages and the sequence.

The next stage is to identify which parameters or key stages require control, specifying the criteria for judging conformity, deciding on the means of control, deciding on the means of assessment, preparing the appropriate documentation and monitoring the effectiveness of the plan.

Guidelines for Quality Planning

How to complete a Quality Control Plan:

a.   The sequence to follow in the compilation of a Quality Control Plan is first to select a process, project or operation, e.g. a manufacturing or servicing sequence, processing a customer or purchase order, processing documentation, a project etc.

b.   Identify the process or project owner or person responsible for the process. Ensure that there are adequate resources to complete the process satisfactorily in terms of:

          Labour (quantity, skills, ability etc.)
          Facilities (equipment, assets, buildings etc.)
          Time
          Budget
          Materials

c.   Draw the chosen process as a flow chart. Include all stages and activities (transfer, store, inspect, test etc.)

d.   Transfer the flow chart on to the Quality Control Plan Form.

     i.   Numbering and describing each stage.

     ii.   Selection of the appropriate quality control activities - trials, design reviews, project reviews, tests etc. Determination of when in the project sequence such quality control activities should take place.

     iii.   *Source of Information*: Describe the source of information for the person performing the task e.g. Quality Manual, Work Instruction Number 1234 etc. The work instruction would need to include: the activity or task description, the sequence, the resources necessary to perform the task i.e. quantity of people, skills, materials, equipment (both process and measuring), the process standard and tolerance to be achieved.

     iv.   *Responsibility*: Who is responsible of performing the task?

     v.   *Record*: What records (if any) will be maintained showing successful completion of the task.

     vi.   *Check by*: Who carries out (if anyone) the check on the task confirming if successfully completed and what inspection and records will be maintained of this check?

     vii.   *Overseen by*: Who oversaw (or audited or reviewed) the check of the task confirming successful completion and what inspection and records were maintained of this check?

e.   Re-assess the process or project commitments in the light of the information gained from the review of the necessary resources availability, the creation of the flow chart and the quality plan. Gain agreement and approval of the overall process or project quality plan from the project team members, key managers and customers.

There follows two examples of a Quality Control Plan Flow Chart, one for a Service Organisation (shown in **Figure 54**) and the other for a Software Process (shown in **Figure 55**). Both the Flow Charts have been developed into Quality Plans. (The Service Organisation is shown in **Table 40**). (The Software Process is shown in **Table 41**).

Service Quality Plan

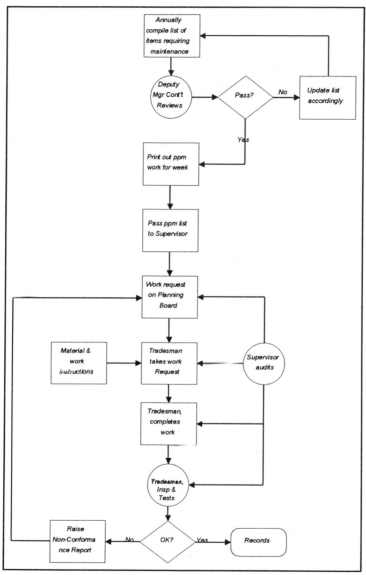

Figure 54 Flow Chart - Service

The numbers in the Quality Plan Flow Chart correspond to the stage numbers in the Quality Plan Table. This Quality Plan is for a Service organisation involved in providing Planned Preventive Maintenance (ppm) on electrical and mechanical equipment and buildings. The Flow Chart represents the initial review of the yearly overall maintenance programme for the facility or organisation. Once the programme has been agreed, the subsequent stages of the Flow Chart show the undertaking of the maintenance programme. This is with the tradesman completing the work as required by the maintenance programme and being responsible for the quality of their own work. The supervisors audit the work completed by the tradesman to ensure the work has been performed in a satisfactory manner. This Flow Chart has been developed into a Quality Plan. Having agreed the activities, stages and sequence of the Flow Chart (no easy task!) the next step is to establish:

- Where the information (work instructions) will be found to explain how to perform each stage e.g. Quality Manual, Labour Management System Operation Handbook. For stage 1 the instruction for conducting the review of the annual maintenance programme are to be found in section 3 of the Quality Manual.
- Who is responsible for completing the stage and meeting the quality standard. For stage 1 the person responsible for holding the review is the Deputy Manager of the organisation.
- What records need to be maintained, the format of the records and where the records will be kept. For stage 1 the records will be kept on the completed contract review check list. This check list is used as an aide-memoire during the contract review process (see ISO9001 paragraph 4.3). The check list will be signed by the Deputy Manager indicating satisfactory completion of the contract review stage.
- The check is performed by the Deputy Manager.
- In this case there is no need for anyone to oversee that the stage was performed satisfactorily.

Table 40 Quality Plan for a Service Process

#	Description of Stage	Source of Info.	Respon-sible	Re-cords	Checked by	Over-seen by
1	Contract Review for Planned Preventive Maintenance (ppm)	QM Section 3	Deputy Mgr	Check List	Deputy Mgr	
2	Weekly print of all equipment requiring ppm	Labour Mgt System (LMS)	Clerical Officer	Weekly List		
3	Pass list to supervisor		Super-visor			
4	Pass ppm Instruction to Tradesman	QM Section 8	Super-visor			
5	Tradesman draws material, starts work and updates job card	Ppm & stores Procedure	Trades-man	Job card	Trades-man	Super-visor
6	Tradesman carries out work as per job card	Service Manuals and job card	Trades-man	Signs ppm	Trades-man	Super-visor
7	Final Inspection & Test (sample)	QM Section 9	Super-visor	Com-pletes Audit Form	Deputy Mgr	
8	Raise Instructions for any defects found	QM Section 8	Super-visor	Instruc-tions	Super-visor	
9	Raise Non-Conformance Report	QM Section 12	Super-visor	NCR Report	Super-visor	
10	Ppm instruction to Planners for closing & updating (if necessary)	LMS	Planner	Note on ppm	Deputy Mgr	
11	Modify ppm (if necessary)	QM Section 4	Super-visor	Change Note	Deputy Mgr	

#	Description of Stage	Source of Info.	Respon-sible	Re-cords	Checked by	Over-seen by
12	Ppm to Planner for computer feedback Statistics	LMS	Planner	Com-puter Re-cords		Deputy Mgr
13	Records updated on weekly list		Super-visor	Weekly List		

Figure 55 shows a Flow Chart outlining the process of software development. The flow chart starts with a review of the order. Having accepted the order the specification is detailed and the project reviewed. The software application is then developed and approved. On completion of the software development the software is installed and tested - on completion of successfully testing the software the project is again reviewed. The proprietary hardware and software is purchased and the developed software integrated on to the customer system. The user and maintenance manuals are created and a final project review is conducted prior to final installation and commissioning on the customer site.

With the completion of the flow chart the quality plan can be developed. The following table shows the development of the Flow Chart into a full Quality Plan. The plan includes:

o A detailed description of the various stages.
o Quality criteria and reference documents that contain the procedures to be observed.
o The responsibilities for observing the procedures and the records to be maintained.
o Identification of the responsibilities for approvals.

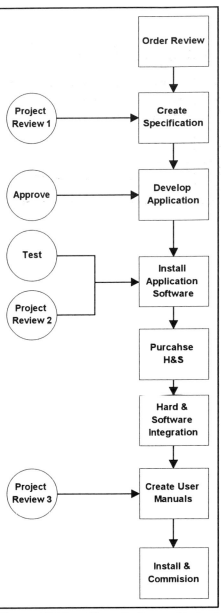

Figure 55 Flow Chart Software Project

Table 41 An example of a Quality Plan for Software Development

Quality Plan		
Client Name: **Client Order Number:**	**Plan Description:**	**Prepared by:** **Approved by**:
Client Address: **Client Telephone/Fax Number:**	**Plan Number:**	**Date of Issue:** **Rev**:

#	Stage Description	Quality Criteria	Reference Documents	Resp.	Record	Approvals	
						Org	**Cust**
1.	Order Acceptance	Contract Review	Order review procedure QM Section 3	Project Manager	Order File	DR-100%	
Project Mobilisation							
2.	Create Contract Specific Project & Quality Plan	Design/ Project Input	Standard Project Plan Format QM Section 4 & 5	Project Manager	Project Plan	DR-100%	
3.	Project Review 1	Design/ Project Verification	Project Review Minutes Check List	Project Manager	Project Review Minutes		
Develop Application Software							
4.	Develop Prototype Application Specification	Design/ Project Input	Standard Application Specification Format	Project Manager	Application Specification	DR-100%	

#	Stage Description	Quality Criteria	Reference Documents	Resp.	Record	Approvals	
						Org	Cust
5.	Create Acceptance Specification	Design/ Project Input	Standard Acceptance Specification Format	Project Man-ager	Accep tance Spec-ifica-tion	DR-100%	
6.	Develop Application Software	Design/ Project Process	Codes of Practice Application Development	Pro-gram-mers	Code	DR (Sam-ple)	
7.	Install Application Software in house. Records of acceptance will be shown on the Acceptance Specification document, copy retained of acceptance in project file	Design/ Project Process	Codes of Practice for Installation	Pro-gram-mer	Accep-tance Spec-ifica-tion	DR-100%	
8.	Acceptance of Application Software. Records of acceptance will be shown on the Acceptance Specification	Design/ Project Verifica-tion		Pro-gram-mer	Accep-tance Spec-ifica-tion	DA (ind)	
9.	Project Review 2	Design/ Project Verifica-tion	Project Review Minutes Check List	Project Man-ager	Project Review Min-utes		
	Hardware & Software Procurement						
10.	Purchase Proprietary Hardware & Software	Purchasing Control	QM Section 6 Hardware & Software Schedules Approved Supplier List	Purch-asing	Pur-chase Order	DA	
11.	Hardware & Software delivered	Verifica-tion	QM Section 10	Goods In-wards	Deliv-ery Note	Insp	

#	Stage Description	Quality Criteria	Reference Documents	Resp.	Record	Approvals	
						Org	Cust
12.	Hardware & Software Integration		Hardware & Software Integration Procedure				
13.	Hardware & Developed Software Acceptance	Verification	QM Section 4	Programmer	Check List & Acceptance Specification	DA	Wit
14.	Create User & Maintenance Manuals	Design/ Project Control	Standard Format for User Manuals QM Section 9	Programmer	Standard format	DA	
15.	Dismantle for Shipment		QM Section 9	Tech Services	Check List	Insp	
16.	Project Review 3	Design/ Project Verification	Project Review Minutes Check List	Project Manager	Project Review Minutes		
17.	Site Survey		QM Section 9 Site Survey Procedure	Project Manager	Check List	Visit	Wit
18.	Installation & Commissioning	Verification	QM Section 9 & 10 Installation & Commissioning Procedures	Project Manager	Acceptance Specification	Insp (Full)	Wit

#	Stage Description	Quality Criteria	Reference Documents	Resp.	Record	Approvals	
						Org	Cust
19.	Customer Acceptance/ Handover		Handover Certification QM Section 9	Project Manager	Handover Certificate	Insp (Full)	Wit
20.	Software & Documentation Archiving	Records	Archiving QM Section 9	Project Manager	Various		
21.	Final Report	Records	Project Control QM Section 4	Project Manager	Project Summary	DA	

Description of Check		
Key	Explanation	Approved or checked by
Cust.	Customer	
DR100%	100% Examination of documentation for Review & Approval	Peer
DR(sample)	Sample Examination of the documentation for approval	Peer
DA(ind)	Independent approval of document	Project Mgr. & Peer
DA	Approval of document	Peer
Insp	Inspection activity	Peer
Insp(Full)	Full Inspection & Test of System	Project Mgr.
Org.	Organisation	
Visit	Visit Customer & Inspection	Project Mgr.
Wit	Witnessed by customer	Project Mgr. & Customer

Stratification

Introduction

Stratification or sampling is a technique where a small sample is taken from a large sample or batch, usually to determine the quality of the large sample.

Sampling can be used for attribute data (pass/fail) or variable data (measured). The advantages are that it provides a quick method of determining the state of the batch without having to examine every item. Often, examining every item can result in mistakes, possibly through boredom or inattention of the checker. To determine the correct sample size to use, sampling tables such as BS6001 can be employed. The diagram

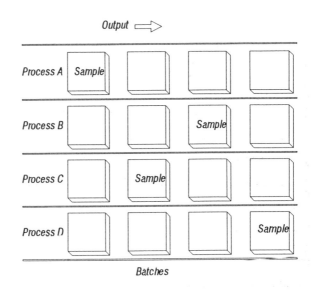

Output ⇒

Process A	Sample			
Process B			Sample	
Process C		Sample		
Process D				Sample

Batches

Figure 56 Sampling from batches

Figure 56 shows how a sample could be randomly taken from four processes.

Guidelines for Stratification

Stratification involves:

Planning to identify the batch to be examined and the sample size to be taken.

Data collection by randomly selecting the sample and examine the selected sample. The diagram shows random selection of samples from a number of processes.

Analysis of the results of sampling.

Scatter Diagram

Introduction

Scatter diagrams are used to examine if there is a relationship between two factors or variables. These diagrams can be employed in gathering and analysing data, problem solving, and testing solutions

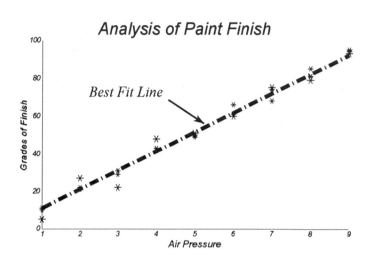

Figure 57 Scatter Diagram

When analysing a problem, it is sometimes necessary to determine if there is a relationship between two factors. For example, measurements taken by two inspectors, tool life and cutting speed or, as shown in **Figure 57**, air pressure and paint finish.

Guidelines for Scatter Diagrams

To perform this analysis:

Planning to determine the factors to be monitored, possibly using the horizontal axis for the cause and the vertical axis for the effect.

Data collection of approximately 50 or more results.

Analyse the graph and draw the 'best fit' line through the points. (There are statistical techniques which can be employed i.e. Regression Analysis to determine the best fit line).

It is important to ensure that the relationship is real, remember there are lies, damn lies and statistics. With statistics, it is probably possible to prove a direct relationship between the number of new Methodist Ministers and the number of unmarried Mothers. This relationship is obviously (hopefully) faulty, but with statistics it may be possible to demonstrate such a relationship, so care needs to be taken when attempting to determine a relationship between two variables. If there is a relationship between the factors then it should be possible to fit a line between the points plotted and consequently make predictions regarding the cause and effect. Using **Figure 57** as an example an experiment was set up to determine if there was any relationship between paint finish and pressure of the spray gun. As can be seen from the graph, the results tend to suggest a relationship. If the variable pressure is increased then there is a corresponding improvement in grade of finish. Presumably there would be a limit to this relationship - continuing to increase pressure would eventually not improve the paint finish. But within the limit of the graph shown above the paint finish grade does improve. From this data it should be possible to determine the optimum setting for the air pressure.

Tally Sheets

Introduction

Tally sheets or check sheets are used to gather and record data. The data may be numerical but check sheets can also be used for audit purposes, i.e. listing audit questions to be asked and recording the responses. The tally list provides the facility to record data to establish a clear picture of the situation. **Table 42** shows an example of a tally sheet used for recording the number of rejects produced each week.

Table 42 Tally Sheet

Test Rejects	Number per day					Week Total
	M	T	W	T	F	
Voltage	II	IIII	IIIIIIII	I	III	17
Power	II	IIII	I	IIIIII	II	15
Speed	I	I	I	IIIII	II	10
Torque	IIII	I	IIIIII	0	IIIIIIIIII III	24
Total	9	10	15	12	20	66

Guidelines for Tally Sheets

Plan: Determine the reasons for collecting the data. Establish which factors are to be monitored (Brain Storming or Cause and Effect Diagrams may help). When (how frequently and sample size) and how the data is to be collected.

Implementation: Collect the data and record the quantities on the tally sheet

Analysis: Total the result over the predetermined duration. Analysis of the data can be accomplished by the use of Pareto Analysis or Scatter Diagrams

Value Analysis

Introduction

The aim of Value Analysis (VA) is to investigate the function of a system, process or equipment with the objective of achieving the intended function at the lowest overall cost. The technique is a logical, disciplined approach that can be applied from individual components or stages up to complete systems or processes. It consists of five basic phases:

A. Information phase
B. Function phase
C. Speculation phase
D. Evaluation phase
E. Implementation phase

Sometimes, when systems or products are designed, certain key customer requirements can be overlooked, also not all the design options may have been considered. VA provides the opportunity for a team of people to critically review the system or product design to establish simpler, cheaper and more effective ways of achieving the design's intended function. This technique has provided some astounding successes in reducing the design and manufacturing costs. Savings of tens of thousands of pounds per month is not unusual. It is particularly successful where the system or product has never been Value Analysed before.

Guidelines for Value Analysis

Value Analysis is a team approach, although the first stage (information) may be completed by one person, subsequent stages are a team effort.

Information Phase: This phase involves gaining as much information as possible about the item under evaluation to enable a complete understanding of

Table 43 Sheet 1 - Information Form

INFORMATION PHASE	
Basic Data	Information
Title Drawing Number and issue no.	
Design Data Design Material Quantity	
Process Data Process Costs Volumes/batch sizes	Materials Labour Sub-Contract

the system being studied. This can include: obtaining drawings and parts lists, diagrams and photographs, descriptions of the process, flow diagrams, customer specifications, costs, budgets, time scales or quantities. It may be that some of this information is sketchy or unavailable. This phase can be a very lengthy stage involving a number of man hours (100 man hours is not unusual). See **Table 43**.

Function phase: **Table 44** Sheet 2 - Function Form

This phase involves defining the basic function of the item under evaluation.

The function being the purpose for which the item exists, the purpose for which it was designed and manufactured. The function can be broken down into two parts - the basic and secondary function.

Purpose	Information	
What does the item do? Operation & Performance Is this task necessary Can another method or component perform this function		
Function Basic Secondary	Verb	Noun
Are all these functions necessary		
Other major design requirements		

The basic function is the specific feature which must be attained. It may be that the item has two basic functions to perform.

The secondary function is the features other than those which must be attained. To help in clarifying the basic and secondary function, it may be helpful to express the function of the item in terms of a verb and a noun. This ensures an exact understanding and statement of the function of the item, which provides the opportunity for exploring many possible approaches to achieving the function. (See **Table 44**)

Table 45 Screw driver

Table 45 opposite shows this function definition. Using a screw driver as an example the basic function is to convey torque (including the handle) and the secondary function is to aid friction. If the screw driver were an electrician's screw driver then another basic function would be to protect the user/electrician.

Function	Verb	Noun
Basic Function	Conveys	Torque
Secondary Function	Aids	Friction

Speculation phase: This phase involves speculating as many problem solutions as possible. Often this phase is called Brain Storming. Brain Storming can be used to generate possible solutions and latterly to develop possible action plans.

Brain Storming

Firstly, a full understanding of the function of the item will have been gained by the completion of the information and function phases. Having clearly stated the function the next stage is for the team to propose as many different solutions as possible. To get accustomed to the concept of brain storming it may be helpful for the team to brain storm a trivial problem like "different uses of a brick?" before moving on to the actual problem. It is important that this speculation is performed freely with no evaluation or criticism of the proposed solutions or approaches. During the Brain Storm all of the team's suggestions are written on a flip chart with the objective that the team may develop other ideas.

Evaluation phase: Having generated a list of possible solutions these solutions require evaluation to determine the most appropriate approach.

The list of solutions is initially reviewed to remove ones which can obviously be rejected. Next, the list is rewritten and the team awards marks for each suggestion in terms of cost, simplicity, ease of application and introduction. A scale of 1 to 10 can be used. For example:

Highest cost award 1, lowest cost award 10
Most Complex award 1, most simple award 10
Difficult to implement award 1, easy to implement award 10

These numbers can be multiplied together to give an overall score for each suggestion.

Table 46 Sheet 3 - Evaluation Form

This should reduce the list down to the final few where upon the Evaluation Form can be employed. Each of the remaining solutions are listed on the left-hand side of the form. On the right-hand side each solution's good and bad features are listed e.g. costs (material and manufacturing) etc. At this stage other information may be required (costings, feasibility studies etc) and action may need to be taken away from the VA team's meeting. (See **Table 46**)

Evaluation Phase		
Possible Solution	Advantages	Disadvantages

At any time during the Evaluation phase it may be appropriate to return to the Speculation phase to refine some of the ideas but it is important to remember not to criticise or evaluate while speculating.

Implementation phase: This is probably the most difficult of all the phases discussed, but the most important as the Value Analysis Team has not completed its task until the proposed solution has been implemented. There will be numerous reasons (or negative attitudes) put forward as to why the proposed solution will not

Table 47 Sheet 4 - Approvals Form

Implementation Phase		
Features	Proposed	Current
Cost Analysis Material Cost Labour Cost Sub-contract Cost		
Implementation Cost Detailed Design Product Development Equipment Design & Manufacture Other Costs		
Approvals Quality Purchasing Design Marketing Customer Service Production		

work or not be acceptable. "We've done it before, the customer won't accept it, too difficult, too expensive" etc. All of these problems need to be addressed before implementation can be achieved. Many key people will need to be convinced of the viability of the proposed solution. The Approvals Form **Table 47** shown opposite is one method of clearly listing the benefits gained by the implementation of the solution. The Approval Form can also be used to record acceptance of the approach by the relevant personnel.

A clear implementation programme is required and again the Brain Storming techniques can be employed. (**Table 48** - Implementation Form may be used to provide guidance in establishing the Implementation Programme.)

Table 48 Sheet 5 - Implementation Form

Implementation Phase		
Stage	Date	Duration
Submit VA proposals		
Approve VA proposals		
Produce Specification		
Review & Approve specification		
Design FMEA		
Produce prototype		
Test prototype (Lab & field)		
Produce process plan		
Process FMEA		
Produce Inspection & test plan		
Process Approval		
Purchase items		
Process capability studies		
Produce		

Business Process Analysis

Introduction

Organisations are full of processes, not only manufacturing processes but processes for purchasing, warehousing, handling orders etc. These processes can involve moving and manipulating data and information as much as material. They can also involve various departments and specialists in completing tasks and activities, making decisions, filling out forms, filing and retrieving information. The processes can also involve complex parallel and serial activities interconnected and dependant on tasks being completed satisfactorily. Very often these processes have evolved as the organisation has grown, sometimes keeping pace, sometimes overwhelmed by the sheer size of the organisational growth. To solve growth problems - such as maintaining the throughput, quick fix solutions may be used e.g. increasing the labour resource rather than improving or overhauling the process. Sometimes this can just make the situation worse. (If it takes one man one day to dig a hole - then one hundred men can dig the hole in one hundredth of the time - Oh I wish).

Not only can processes be very complex and involved but they can also be very inefficient; responsibility ownership can be unclear.

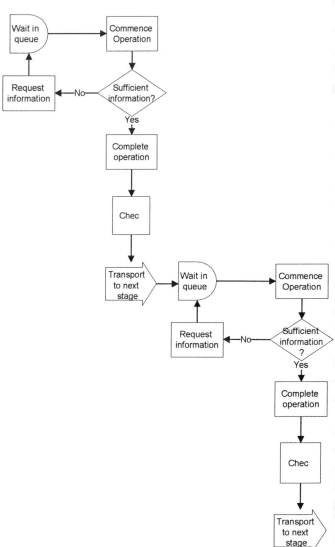

Figure 58 Typical process

This is because it can be very difficult to understand, control and manage all the tasks involved in a process from start to finish.

Analysis has suggested that the way to make processes more efficient is to break them down to their most simple tasks or stages. In this way the process tasks can be completed by unskilled labour. Having sufficiently de-skilled the tasks, then the work can be distributed to a team of semi-skilled people so that the work is equally shared between each team member. (Adam Smith - Wealth of Nations)

The de-skilling and fine balancing of the tasks between the workers involves many specialists and technicians who analyse the process and determine the most efficient way to complete the process. To purchase the equipment, install and commission to make the process run successfully. This divides responsibility between several specialists:

o   engineers to develop the process
o   engineers to plan the process
o   engineers to develop the equipment or identify the supplier of the required equipment
o   buyers or purchasers
o   trainers to train the process operators
o   managers or supervisors to coordinate the labour, material, equipment, process output, transportation etc.
o   inspectors or checkers or approvers to check the process and allow it to run and confirm the output is to requirements

This may seem efficient, as it breaks the process down to its smallest element, allowing the specialists (knowledgeable in their particular field) to decide the best way to do things. One problem is however, that the responsibilities for the process can be become unclear. Taking a small example of this can be, who is responsible for the quality of the output? Is it the engineer who designed the process and provided the equipment? The purchaser who supplied the material? The operator who produced the item? The supervisor responsible for the process? The inspector who checked the output?

Ownership is just one problem with this specialisation approach. Another problem can be the total process itself which can be very slow and unwieldy, as it can involve several sequential operations, each operation with its own inherent delays and transportation between each stage (see **Table 49**). The actual action (value added) time for each of the process tasks can be very small compared with the waiting and transportation time. Waiting, queuing and transportation can take up a significant proportion of the time to complete the whole process. The process tasks can consist of three basic elements; wait (queue), action and transport - performed by four departments. See **Figure 59**.

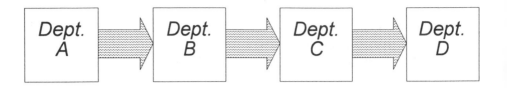

Figure 59 Typical Process

Table 49 Process Time Table

Activity	Department A	Department B	Department C	Department D	Total Time
Queue	500 mins	500 mins	500 mins	500 mins	2000 mins
Action	5 mins	5 mins	5 mins	5 mins	20 mins
Transport	20 mins	20 mins	20 mins	20 mins	80 mins
Total	525 mins	525 mins	525 mins	525 mins	2100 mins

Table 50 Total Process Time taken

So for this process the work or value added time is 20 minutes but completion of the process will take some 360 hours to complete. If the process was completed efficiently, it could be completed in 20 minutes.

Activity	Total (Min)
Total waiting/reconciliation time	2000 (≈ 4 days)
Total transport time	80 (≈ 0.17 day)
Actual work time	20 (0.04 day)
Total Process Time	2100 (≈ 4 days)
Possible World Class Time	20 (0.04 days)

Note, the waiting/reconciliation time could consist of:

- o Reconciliation of various pieces of information. For example Goods Inwards Data, Invoice and Delivery Note
- o Resolving any problems concerning inaccurate data etc.

Why is Business Process Analysis Important?

The previous section described some of the reasons why Business Process Analysis is important (ownership and responsibility, improvement in lead time, reduction in the amount of reconciliation work etc.) but there are other factors that may be the motivation for embarking on a Business Process Analysis exercise.

i. *Customer focus - Customer Focus In All That We do*

The aim of customer focus is to continually understand the customers' needs and expectations. Using our customers' perceptions to guide our improvement activities. *The customer* is not necessarily an external customer but could equally be an internal customer i.e. one who within the organisation is the recipient of your product or service. Business Process Analysis helps in ensuring that the customers receive timely, defect free products and services that meet or exceed their expectations. Improving the processes to reduce variation and waste. Providing flexible and responsive processes that respond quickly to customer demands and consistently meeting the customers' expected delivery target.

Some spin offs from these process improvements are better teamwork, communication, and training.

Quality is judged by the customer and the judgements the customer makes are: Value, Satisfaction and Preference. It is therefore essential that the customer has:

- Trust and confidence in products and services
- Unique product-service combinations
- Sensitivity to customer and market information
- Rapid response to requirements

Business Process Analysis is the process improvement catalyst that can be used to focus attention on these issues.

ii. *Non-Value Added Activities*

The objective with Non-Value Added Activities is to identify and eliminate those activities that do not contribute towards the customer requirements. With many processes there can be activities which may be considered worthwhile but may not add any value to the finished product or service. Consequently these

260

Quality Assurance Management

activities will not be something the customer wishes to pay for. Unfortunately these activities do have to be paid for and will become an overhead to the running of the process. A non-value added activity is an activity that is costing money but does not add value to the item or service and an activity that is not a direct requirement of the customer and usually the consequence of poor planning or systems. Value-added activities, however, are activities that the customer is prepared to pay for. This is because the customer accepts their effect as value obtained for the money.

Business Process Analysis, with its detailed analysis of the key process, gives the opportunity to identify any activities that may be considered Non-Value Adding.

iii.   *An organisation provides its external customers through a small number of key processes*

Although there are many processes running in and through organisations there are only a few (possibly four[13]) which are key in delivering the organisation's product or service. These processes often provide 80% of a business turnover but only constitute 20% of their costs.

The processes running through an organisation can be complex, cross functional and sometimes wasteful. This waste can manifest itself in terms of:

- Cost to run the process (number of transactions per employee).
- The length of the time to get from one end of the process to the other (lead time).
- The quality of the service provided e.g. errors, response or delivery times.

Organisations structured along functional lines do not always reflect the needs for efficient process flow.

---

[13]   Bidding to Winning - Enquiry/Quotation to Customer Order
Product or Service delivery - Providing the product or service
Product or Service Development - Product or Service Improvement
Supplier Development - Improving the Performance of Suppliers

Other Business Processes

Order Processing

Figure 60 shows the sequence of events associated with processing an order. Initial enquiry into the Sales Department. Sales will need to review the enquiry, identify if there are any special requirements that they cannot deal with and compile a quotation. If there are special requirements then the Technical Department may need to be involved to advise on the solution. Once the order arrives, then again the order will need to be reviewed but this time initially by the Order Processing Department. Then the Technical (technically correct), Financial (credit worthiness and

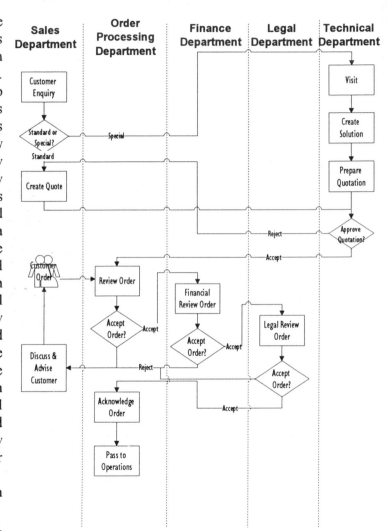

Figure 60 Current Order Processing Process

payment terms) and Legal (penalties, consequential damages and insurance) Departments will re-review the order. Having completed these stages the order can be acknowledged and fulfilled. Note, throughout this process the people completing the individual tasks are probably working hard and efficiently as they can in isolation. The process works vertically - functionally based rather than horizontally - process based.

What now needs to happen is a complete review of the process. What are the process objectives? Who is best placed to achieve these objectives? Who in this process adds value? Who is responsible for the complete process? Is the process being completed correctly? What errors are made when completing the process? Full use needs to be made of techniques and methods such as information technology, process cost modelling, ownership, skills levelling etc. to Process Re-engineer the process.

Figure 61 shows what the new process diagram might look like after Business Process Analysis. Order Processing now handles all the stages and tasks associated with processing a customer enquiry and order. The process has been re-engineered to make it the central focus, rather than the departments or functions which were previously the central focus. The process is now not about single tasks but single process and multi-tasking.

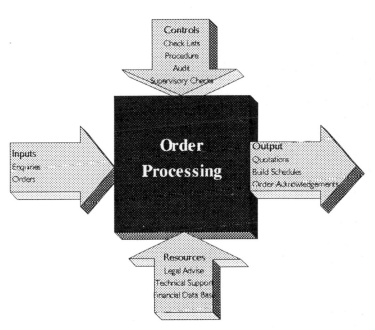

Figure 61 Order Processing Re-engineered

Changing the process into its natural order rather than its functional order. This gives the opportunity to combine jobs, getting the workers to make the key decisions - real empowerment. Managers often emphasise empowerment but this approach gives the chance to change talk into action. Managers are understandably nervous regarding empowerment, as it can be seen to give the power to make change without the responsibilities for the consequences of change. The functional manager will still be responsible and held accountable for the resulting mess. The process can be organised on its natural process lines with the emphasis on results rather than transactions. (Results - Average time to place orders, Transactions - Number of Orders handled per Individual). Results are the process performance rather than the performance of individuals within the process. The performance of individual activities may be seen as unimportant, as it is the performance of the complete process that counts. The workers will be responsible for both the decisions and the consequences of that decision - Ownership.

However, there are certain implications with this new approach. The order processors will need all the skills, training and facilities to fulfil this new approach. Procedures and check lists will need to be created which describe the tasks to be completed. Checks and monitoring will need to be carried out to ensure the tasks are being completed in a satisfactory manner.

Product Development

When developing a new product, the sequence associated can be lengthy and complex. Usually the development of a new product can involve the development of various product sub-systems. For example, when developing a new Overhead Projector, the lens system, the electrical system and the mechanical arrangement of all the parts' will need to be considered.

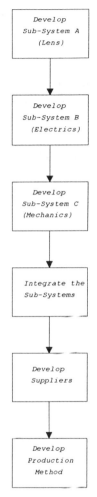

The development sequence can look like development of the lens system first, then the electrical system and finally the mechanical box to hold all the elements in place. These sub-systems will then require integrating to form the completed overhead projector. Suppliers of the various parts then need to be identified and the production or build and testing method established. The figure shows such a sequence.

The problem with this process is that it can be difficult to coordinate - one team not knowing what the other team is doing. Management is difficult because if one team falls behind the whole project will be placed in jeopardy. There is a technique that is gaining favour called concurrent engineering which means instead of doing the stages in series some elements can be completed in parallel.

The examples are two totally different approaches to re-engineering the process. The approach necessary to arrive at these solutions would also have been unique for each situation. There is no one approach to review and re-engineer processes, each situation must be evaluated according to the process needs. However there is a general shape to Business Process Analysis that can be adopted. Business Process Analysis could be a zero based approach - tear it up and start again, or an attempt to optimise the process using techniques such as Information Technology, Automation, Special Skills (up skilling) etc.

Figure   62
P r o d u c t
Development

Procedure for Business Process Analysis

The figure opposite shows a typical overview of implementation of Business Process Analysis. Additional detail on the sequence is shown in **Table 51** .

Figure 63 Business Process Analysis Overview

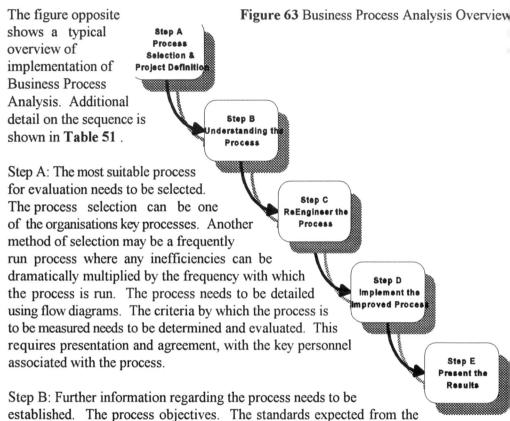

Figure 63 Business Process Analysis Overview

Step A: The most suitable process for evaluation needs to be selected. The process selection can be one of the organisations key processes. Another method of selection may be a frequently run process where any inefficiencies can be dramatically multiplied by the frequency with which the process is run. The process needs to be detailed using flow diagrams. The criteria by which the process is to be measured needs to be determined and evaluated. This requires presentation and agreement, with the key personnel associated with the process.

Step B: Further information regarding the process needs to be established. The process objectives. The standards expected from the process need to be agreed, e.g. the quality standards of the quotations - levels of detail, quantity of information etc. What are the inputs, outputs, controls and resources required to run the process? What are the projected new targets that should be achieved following the re-engineering of the process? E.g. What is the ideal number of people to run the process?

Step C: All this information now needs to be evaluated, discussed and agreed, with a view to establishing a better solution - brain storming, tree diagrams and other problem solving techniques.

Step D: The new agreed solution now requires implementation, with all the necessary Project Plan, Procedure Writing and training to ensure successful start of the re-engineered solution.

Step E: Finally, and most importantly, recognition via presentation to management to show changes, successes and failures with the new process.

The above sequence has been described in greater detail in **Table 51**. The table shows the stage number and objectives; what the inputs to completing the stage are and the output expected from satisfactory completion of that stage.

Table 51 Procedure for Business Process Analysis

#	Stage	Inputs	Outputs
I	Identification of the Organisations Key Processes and determination of the process current status A Key Process[14]. i.e. A process that is regularly repeated (e.g. Order Processing) or a project that follows a series of similar activities (e.g. Research Projects).	Process Scope[15] Process Boundaries[16] Process Bench Marking[17] Process Requirements Process Customer Process Problems[18] Process Support Process Procedures Process Custom & Practice[19] Process Versions or Variety[20]	A Business Process Analysis Team (BPAT)

---

[14] Often the key processes are; Enquiry to Order Acceptance, Product or Service Development, Supplier Development, Product or Service Delivery

[15] Process Scope can include the geographical or physical location, products or services delivered and the aim of the process etc.

[16] Process Boundaries: Identification of the start and end point of the process e.g. receipt of an enquiry to Contract Acceptance. It may assist in determining this point by identifying the finished product at the successful completion of the process?

[17] Identification and measurement of the key factors to measure the performance of the process and then to quantify these factors e.g. cycle times, lead times, response time etc.

[18] Process problems need to embrace not only the obstacles and difficulties with existing process (common mistakes, inadequate information, rejects, rework etc.) but also problems with suppliers and customers. These problems will need to categorised in order to identify the important few from the trivial many (Pareto Analysis)

[19] Custom & Practice could be the various methods of offering customer discounts

[20] Process Versions: These can be categorised in a number of ways. Repeaters or jobs which are effectively the same e.g. repeat orders. Runners or projects which involve a number of other functions or disciplines. Stranglers or jobs which clog up the process to the detriment of the other jobs. Alternatively the process version may be categorised into Small - a job which can be completed in the normal way. Medium - a job which requires a project manager to progress the job and Large - a job which requires the formation of a project team.

#	Stage	Inputs	Outputs
2	Commitment to the future objectives and vision for the process	Understanding of the Process Current Status	Establish and confirm process objectives and vision Process Owner Establishment of targets Development of possible approaches Establish the process control and resource requirements Service Level Agreements - Measures & Targets
3	Short term solutions	Process objectives and vision Process targets Possible approaches	Identify areas for short term improvements in the process performance
4	Re-engineering the Process	Process objectives and vision Process targets Possible approaches Value and Non-value added activities	Business Process Analysis Solution Process inputs, outputs, control and resource requirements[21] Cost Benefits System Model Information Model Documented Procedures Validated Process Logic[22]
5	Agreement to Change	Process Re-engineered Solution	Agreed solution management Communicated
6	Implement Solution	Agreed solution management Communicated	Training Migration Plan System: Specification Testing New Technology: Specification Prototype & Test Install & Commission Organisational Responsibilities: Effects Interfaces Skills Structure Management Reporting System: Service Level Agreements Source of data and method or recording and reporting Method of review
7	Project Review	Changes and Benefits	Presentation to Key Personnel

---

[21]   In the style of the input/output diagram
Identifying any non-value added activities

[22]   Taking due account of commercial, political and cultural changes that may be necessary

QUALITY AWARDS SCHEMES

The European Quality Award

Introduction: In the 1980's companies began to realise that their only way of surviving in business was to pay much greater attention to quality. In many markets, quality has already become the competitive edge. This is not confined only to the quality of a product or a service. It also applies to delivery, administration, customer service and every other aspect of a company's activities.

Total quality encompasses all the ways in which an organisation meets the needs and expectations of its financial stakeholder, its customers, its people and the community in which it operates. This total quality habit enables organisations to strive for business excellence.

In recognition of this opportunity, fourteen leading Western European companies took the initiative of forming the European Foundation for Quality Management (EFQM) in 1988. By July 1993 there were more than 280 members from most Western European countries and most business sectors. Recognition of achievement is a feature of the policy of the EFQM. In line with this policy, 1992 marked the inaugural presentation of a major new European business award - The European Quality Award. This award is presented to the most successful exponent of Total Quality Management in Western Europe. The Trophy is held nominally for one year by the recipient. The national bodies like the British Quality Foundation and other similar organisations promote and manage the award, training and promotion.

Self-assessment: It is not necessary to enter the award scheme. Most organisations use the award scheme model to assess themselves (self-assessment). This contrasts with the approach often adopted for ISO9000 where third party certification is usually the case. With EFQM the assessment can be performed internally. The technique of quality self-assessment can be a powerful tool for organisations wishing to develop and monitor their quality culture. It is the systematic review and measurement of the organisation's operations which give management a clear picture of the activities of the Total Quality Management system. Self-assessment allows the organisation to ascertain the strengths and areas for improvement by analysing the relationship between the organisation's people, processes and results. In a quality-conscious organisation self-assessment should ideally be a regular activity.

Self-assessment can be based on any number of different models; ISO9000, Deming Prize, etc. In the following explanation the European Model for Total Quality Management will be used. The EFQM model is based on people, processes and results. By Processes is meant the means by which the organisation harnesses and releases the talents of its people and other resources to produce results. In other words, the processes, people and resources are the enablers which provide the results. A graphical display of the principle is shown in **Figure 64**.

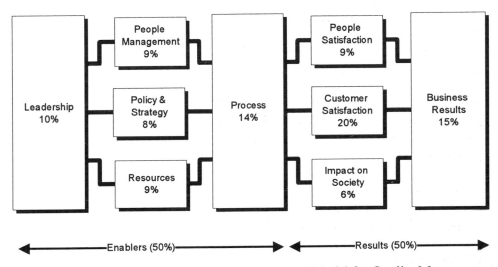

Figure 64 Graphical representation of the European Model for Quality Management

The main principles are that performance in customer satisfaction, employee satisfaction and impact on society is achieved through the quality of leadership. This leadership is driven through the chosen policy and strategy, people and resource management and processes. This consequently will, if applied successfully, lead ultimately to excellence in business results. The **Enablers** drive the processes which provide the results. The processes are grouped with the enablers as the vehicle, to provide the results. **Results** are what the organisation has achieved as a consequence of these enablers - each is valued at 50%.

The Assessment Process: The first step as with any Quality Initiative is to obtain the full and unequivocal commitment from the Management Team to conduct an EFQM assessment. Without this commitment the assessment team and process will have no authority or value and the assessment process may even be counter-productive. This commitment is only to the study element. Once the study findings are available, further commitment and consensus will be required on the strategy to adopt, as a consequence of the assessment report.

Once the management agreement has been obtained planning the assessment can begin. The assessment team requires selection. This team could be unit managers or quality staff. Guidelines for the assessment will need to be established and the people selected will need to be trained in the assessment guidelines, process and technique and briefed on the assessment task. The business areas for assessment will need to be identified, including the boundaries or scope of each business unit. A pilot business unit may be used. Communication with the business unit on the time, date and duration of the assessment will need to take place.

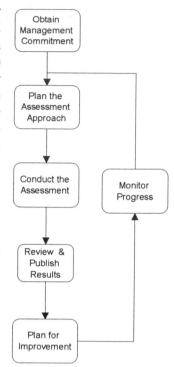

Figure 65

The self-assessment can be conducted using a matrix (the matrix shown in **Table 53** is based on the British Gas plc method but adapted for more general use), workshop, peer or questionnaire approach.

Taking the matrix approach as an example, each team member can conduct the assessment by rating each of the business units against the matrix (see **Table 53**). The rating should be based on actual or documentary evidence, rather than anecdotal evidence (show me) and the results recorded.

The results are then discussed and reviewed by the assessment team at a consensus meeting and the business units performance calculated. These final results can then be discussed with the Management Team to determine what action (if any) to take to improve the performance of the business units. This action plan will require general acceptance and then communication for agreement and commitment.

Table 52 Typical EFQM Assessment Matrix

Enablers					
Leadership	Policy & Strategy	People Management	Resources	Processes	Mark/ Step
Managers are visibly (proactive) involved in steps one to nine.	The Business Units Mission Statement, Goals & Plans are understood & contributed to by everyone.	Management can show extensive use of team & individual empowerment.	Resources allocation is changed to reflect the needs of the business policy & strategy.	Future process evaluation objects set.	10
Managers show commitment by participation in external TQ initiatives.	The competition's business strategies have been SWOT[23] analysed.	Use is made of empowerment - driving out fear.	Use or resource is compared with business policy & strategy.	Project Reviews performed and compared with best practice.	9
Managers have consistently operated steps one to seven.	A process of bench marking is in place.	A human resource plan[24] is activity operated.	Evaluation of new sources of resource is regularly performed.	Solutions implemented.	8
Managers are recognising & rewarding TQ effort at all levels.	There is regular testing, evaluation & reviewing of business plans.	The natural flair & creativity of all employees is encouraged & used to its full extent.	Resources are made available to ensure business goals are achieved.	Agreement to changes agreed.	7
Manager can demonstrate their support of the TQ process (Including resourcing).	The Mission Statement & Quality Goals reflect EFQM & ISO9000.	Improvement teams are in full operation.	Waste of resources is identified & reacted to. Including quality costs.	Evaluation & action plan determined.	6
Managers attend regular, documented meetings with employees, customers & suppliers.	Policy & Strategy is regularly tested evaluated & reviewed.	Complete Training Matrices are available.	Regular reviews of these resources is performed.	Key Business Process Analysis performed.	5
Managers can show (by example) to be visibly working towards the TQ initiatives (Role Models).	Personnel are clearly advised & understand the mission, goals and plan.	Documented Team & individual appraisals are regularly performed.	A process is in place for optimising each resource.	Consideration to implication of change.	4

---

[23]   Analysis of the Strengths, Weaknesses, Opportunities and Threats

[24]   Human Resources Plan covers recruitment, development, and career progression

Enablers					
Leadership	Policy & Strategy	People Management	Resources	Processes	Mark/ Step
A management communication process communicates both to & from employees.	Feedback process is available from external sources to confirm Quality Goals suitable.	Bottom up communication is active & encouraged.	Suppliers & managers of these resources have been identified.	Commitment given to future process objectives & targets.	3
Managers have a process in place to increase employee TQ awareness.	Feedback process is available from internal sources to confirm Quality Goals suitable.	Team Improvement is actively encouraged.	This information is accurate & regular collected.	Processes have been charted & owners identified.	2
Managers have a process in place to increase their own TQ awareness.	There is established a Mission Statement & various Quality Goals[25].	Employee opinions are regularly obtained & acted upon.	Information is available on: finance, facilities, material, people & technology resources.	Key Business Processes have been identified.	I

---

[25]   Sometimes Critical Success Factors

Table 52 Continued

Results				
Customer Satisfaction	People Satisfaction	Impact on Society	Business Results	Mark/ Step
Results confirm real achievement is being made in delighting the customer.	Evidence is available to confirm that positive trends for all employees satisfaction factors.	Results confirm real achievement, over the last two years, is being made in environmental & societal standards.	50% of targets have shown improvement over a two-year period.	10
Results confirm real achievement is being made in satisfying the customer.	Evidence is available to confirm that 75% of all employees feel that their contribution is valued.	75% of target met.	75% of targets being met.	9
Customer delight factors are understood & acted upon.	Preventive action is taken regarding employee satisfaction and dissatisfaction factors.	Some targets are being met.	Some targets are being met.	8
Customer satisfaction factors are understood & acted upon.	Results are being achieved regarding the action plan.	Performance regularly monitored.	Action plans in place.	7
Customer dissatisfaction factors are understood & acted upon.	Employee satisfaction & dissatisfaction factors are understood, measured & regularly reviewed. Reviews available.	Employee & society views solicited.	Targets set.	6
Processes are in place to avoid potential customer complaints (preventive action).	Employee satisfaction & dissatisfaction factors are understood, measured & acted upon. Plans available.	Awareness amongst employees & the local community is measured.	Trends plotted.	5
Some targets set are being achieved.	Employee satisfaction factors are understood & measured.	Targets set.	Reviewed & understood by all employees.	4

275

Results				
Customer Satisfaction	People Satisfaction	Impact on Society	Business Results	Mark/ Step
Customer complaint targets are set, reviewed & acted upon (corrective action).	Employee dissatisfaction factors are understood & measured.	Trends plotted.	Openly communicated to all employees.	3
Customer complaint trends are recorded.	Employee satisfaction factors are understood.	Factors[26] effecting the organisations impact on the local community have been identified.	Performance is regularly reviewed.	2
Customer complaints are recorded and individually acted upon.	Employee dissatisfaction factors are understood.	Factors[27] effecting the organisation's environmental impact on society have been identified.	Results of the key performance indicators are published.	1

Note 1: People Satisfaction can include such factors as: health & safety, people development, reward mechanisms, labour utilisation etc.

Note 2: The above table is an interpretation of the EFQM criteria. Reference could be made to the original EFQM document.

---

[26] Local community factors including: charity, education and training, sponsorship, links

[27] Environmental factors include: pollution, health performance, disposal and decommissioning, recycling, waste of global resources e.g. energy

Calculating the Score:

Table 53 EFQM Score Sheet

Use the matrix to determine both the individual category scores and the total score. For each square where documentary evidence can be provided which substantiates the claim of compliance, a point can be awarded. The points are then added up for each step completed below a blank square. The calculation would be then as shown in **Table 53**. The total score being 168.

Category	Value	Weighting	Score
Leadership	1	10	10
Policy & Strategy	2	8	16
People Management	1	9	9
Resources	2	9	18
Processes	1	14	14
Customer Satisfaction	1	20	20
People Satisfaction	2	9	18
Impact on Society	3	6	18
Business Results	3	15	45
		Total Score	**168**

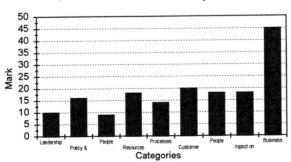

Figure 66 Graphical Representation of the EFQM Results

Action Planning: From the matrix potential weaknesses and areas for improvement can be clearly identified. These improvement areas, need to be addressed and the self-assessment process repeated to determine what advances have been made towards increasing the score.

EFQM Exercise

Find an interested Manager and using the above check list determine the Business Unit's score.

Hint: Agree how the results will be used beforehand.
Ask the Manager to be as honest and open as possible.
Avoid the Manager becoming defensive.
Anecdotal evidence is not acceptable.
Determine in each case the approach adopted, current status and results achieved.

Scores

500 to 1000	Quite exceptional, very difficult to achieve
300 to 499	Extremely good
200 to 299	Good
50 to 199	The norm for the first attempt
0 to 49	Oh dear!

The Deming Prize

Introduction: It probably will not come as any surprise to learn that Japan holds the highest number of QC conferences in the world. It is the view of Dr. Ishikawa that these conferences have been one of the key factors in the advancement of Japan's Quality Control activities. It was at the first QC Annual Conference in Japan that the first Deming Prize was awarded in 1951. Since that time the Union of Japanese Scientists and Engineers (JUSE) has continued to handle the business affairs of this conference including the awarding of Deming Prizes.

The Deming Prize has been divided into categories. There are categories for individuals, organisations or industries who have contributed to Japanese Quality Control statistical methods. As well as these categories there are also application prizes for divisions and quality control awards.

To qualify for the Deming Prize top management of a company must make an application. This application is reviewed by the experts in the Deming application prize sub-committee. These experts will be involved in visiting the company and performing an audit to determine the state of their quality control. As a consequence of this audit they will assign grades to the company.

Although this is a competition the purpose of it is not necessarily to achieve winning the Prize, the purpose of application is to promote the means of total quality control and statistical quality control within the organisation. Dr. Ishikawa believes that the application procedure will rejuvenate the management of an organisation.

There are a number of different types of audit that can be performed, i.e.:
Audit by Consultant
Audit by the Managing Director
Audit by the Department Head
Audit by the Quality Department
Mutual Auditing

The final four audits are considered internal audits. Possibly the most powerful of these is the audit by the Managing Director, giving him an opportunity to find out what he believes happens in good faith is actually happening in practice.

Quality Control Audit for Deming Prize and Japanese Quality Control Medal

For the Deming Prize there is a check list which can be used to assist the audit process. Following is a typical check list based on the Deming Prize Application.

1. ***Policy and objectives***; *The direction of the organisation regarding their Deming Prize Initiative*
   a. Policy and objectives regarding management, quality, and quality control
   b. Methods for establishing policy and objectives
   c. Appropriateness and consistency of the policy and objectives
   d. Utilisation of statistical methods
   e. Dissemination and acceptance of objectives
   f. Checking policy and objectives and their interpretation
   g. Policy and objectives relationship with long-range and short-range plans

2. ***Organisation and its operation***; *The coordination of the organisation's Deming Prize Initiative*
   a. Clear lines of responsibilities
   b. Delegation of power (where appropriate)
   c. Teamwork between divisions
   d. Activities of committees
   e. Utilisation of the staff
   f. Utilisation of QC circle activities
   g. Quality control audit

3. ***Education and its dissemination***; *The organisation's Training Initiative*
   a. Education plan and achievement
   b. Understanding regarding quality and quality control
   c. Education concerning statistical concepts and methods, and application
   d. Education for sub-contractors and outside organisations
   e. QC circle activities
   f. Suggestion system

4. ***Assembling and disseminating information and its utilisation***; *Communication of the Strategy*
   a. Gathering outside information
   b. Communication of information between divisions
   c. Speed in communicating information
   d. Analysis (statistical) of information and its utilisation

5. ***Analysis***; *Problem Solving*
   a. Selection of problems and themes
   b. Appropriateness of the analytical method

280

c. Utilisation of statistical methods
d. Integration with engineering technology
e. Quality analysis, process analysis
f. Utilisation of analysis results
g. Degree with which suggestions for improvement have been embraced

6. *Standardisation; Obtaining consistency within the organisations*
a. System of standards established
b. Methods of establishing, revising, and withdrawing standards available
c. Records showing establishing, revising, and withdrawing standards available
d. Contents of standards acceptable

7. *Control; Establishing of the Quality Control System*
a. Control systems for quality
b. Control points, and control items established
c. Widespread use of statistical methods such as the control chart
d. Contributions of QC circle activities
e. Current status of control activities
f. Current status of control system

8. *Quality assurance; Establishing the QAMS*
a. Procedures for new product development
b. Quality development and quality function
c. Safety and product liability prevention
d. Process control and improvement
e. Process capabilities
f. Measurement and inspection
g. Control of facilities/equipment, sub-contracting, purchasing, services etc.
h. Quality assurance system and its audit
i. Utilisation of statistical methods
j. Evaluation and audit of quality

9. *Effects; Obtaining the Results from the Deming Prize Effort*
a. Measuring effects (results)
b. Visible effects on; quality, serviceability, date of delivery, cost, profit, safety, environment etc.
c. Invisible effects
d. Comparison between predicted effects and actual results

10.   ***Future plans****; The next step*
   a.   Understanding of the present condition and its stability
   b.   Policies adopted to solve shortcomings
   c.   Plans for the future
   d.   Relations with the company's long-range plans

The Malcolm Baldrige Award

Introduction: The Malcolm Baldrige National Quality Award is an annual award to recognize U.S. companies that excel in quality achievement and quality management. The objectives of the award are to; promote quality awareness as an increasingly important element in competitiveness. To improve the understanding of the requirements for quality excellence. To share of information on successful quality strategies and the benefits derived from implementation of these strategies. There are three eligibility categories of the award, manufacturing companies, service companies and small businesses.

The Award Scheme: The examination categories comprise seven categories. These categories represent (as far as the Malcolm Baldrige Award is concerned) the major components of a quality management system. These categories are:

- o   Leadership
- o   Information and Analysis
- o   Strategic Quality Planning
- o   Human Resource Utilization
- o   Quality Assurance of Products and Services
- o   Quality Results
- o   Customer Satisfaction

Below is detailed an examination of each of these categories.

1.   Leadership (worth one hundred points)

The leadership category assesses how well management creates and sustains clear quality values. Also, whether management provides a management system to guide all activities of the company toward quality excellence. The leadership category also examines how directors and senior management demonstrate the organisation's quality leadership in the external community and how the organisation integrates its public responsibilities with its quality values and practices. The leadership category can be broken down into the elements:

- a.   Senior Management leadership
- b.   Quality values
- c.   Management for quality
- d.   Public responsibility

2.   Information and analysis (worth seventy points)

The information and analysis category assesses the scope, validity, use and management of data and information. How this data is analysed to support a responsive, prevention-based approach to quality and customer satisfaction. The information and data category can be broken down into:

a.   Scope and management of quality data and information
b.   Competitive comparison and bench marking
c.   Analysis of quality data and information

3.   Strategic quality planning (worth sixty points)

The strategic quality planning category assesses the organisation's planning process aimed at achieving quality leadership. The integration of quality improvement planning into overall business planning. Also, included in this category are the organisation's short-term and longer-term plans for quality leadership.   The strategic quality planning category can be broken down into:

a.   Strategic quality planning process
b.   Quality goals and plans

4.   Human resource utilization (worth one hundred and fifty points)

The human resource utilization category assesses the effectiveness of the organisation's efforts to develop and realize the potential of the work force. Maintaining an environment conducive to participation, quality leadership and personal and organisational growth. The human resource utilization category can be broken down into the elements:

a.   Human resource management
b.   Employee involvement
c.   Quality education and training
d.   Employee recognition and performance measurement
e.   Employee well-being and morale

5.   Quality assurance of products and services (worth one hundred and forty points)

The quality assurance of products and services category assesses the approaches used by the organisation for assuring quality of goods and services. This is based upon design control and procurement control. The category also assesses the integration of these process control with continuous quality improvement. The quality assurance of products and services category can be broken down into the elements:

a.   Design and introduction of quality products and services
b.   Process quality control
c.   Continuous improvement of processes
d.   Quality assessment
e.   Documentation
f.   Business process and support service quality
g.   Supplier quality

6.   Quality results   (worth one hundred and eighty points)

The quality results category assesses the quality levels and quality improvement achievements. This based upon objective measures derived from analysis of the business operations. This includes a comparison of current quality levels in relation to those of competing organisations. The quality results category can be broken down into the elements:

a.   Product and service quality results
b.   Business process, operational and support service
c.   Quality results
d.   Supplier quality results

7.   Customer satisfaction (worth three hundred points)

The customer satisfaction category assesses the organisation's knowledge of the customer needs and it's ability to meet requirements and expectations. Also, examined are current levels and trends in customer satisfaction. The customer satisfaction category can be broken down into the elements:

a.   Determining customer requirements and expectations
b.   Customer relationship management
c.   Customer service standards
d.   Commitment to customers
e.   Complaint resolution for quality improvement
f.   Determining customer satisfaction
g.   Customer satisfaction results
h.   Customer satisfaction comparison

The scoring system

The scoring system is designed to facilitate feedback and give an opportunity to compare organisations' results. The scoring is based on evidence and duration with which the quality system has been in place and the degree to which the quality system has been accepted and implemented. **Table 54** shows a typical range of scores when organisations have been assessed using the above Malcolm Baldrige assessment criteria.

Table 54 Typical range of scores for the Malcolm Baldrige Award

Range of Scores	Remarks
0 to 125	Only just developing a strategy to address some of the basic categories
126 to 250	Implementation of the strategy to address some of the basic categories
251 to 450	Significant gaps in application. However, effective results are being obtained from the early application of strategy.
451 to 550	Strategy in most areas effective as indicated by good results
551 to 750	Strategy now being refined as a consequence of good deployment of the approaches. Good results in most categories. Probably an industrial leader.
751 to 875	Approaches deployed as confirmed by excellent results in all categories. An industry leader.
876 to 1000	Outstanding approaches and results. A world leader.

PART C

Supplier Quality Assurance

> *"For the want of a nail a horseshoe was lost,*
> *For the want of a horseshoe a horse was lost,*
> *For the want of a horse a rider was lost,*
> *For the want of a rider a battle was lost,*
> *For the want of a battle a kingdom was lost."*

There is a wide range of approaches and techniques that can be adopted in controlling suppliers, (Supplier Quality Assurance) from the fairly basic approach as described in ISO9001 (section Purchasing Control) to a comprehensive approach, such as QS-9000 the Automotive Quality System Standard. Both approaches have features that make them attractive to Buyers; the simple approach will be less demanding in terms of resource but may be considered too vague and not sufficiently product or service specific.

A Basic Purchasing Control System

a)   *Assessment of suppliers:*

This could include an audit against the requirements of a recognised Quality Assurance System Standard like ISO9001 and assessing the supplier's ability to meet the customer's requirements. (See section on Auditing).

Selection of the supplier from an approved list of suppliers. This may be an internally created list produced as a result of Vendor Rating or from commercially available lists of companies of assessed capability provided by organisations such as BSI or the Department of Trade & Industry.

Sending questionnaires to existing or prospective suppliers requesting information about the supplier's Quality Assurance Management System.

Examination of the supplier's historical performance by the use of techniques such as Vendor Rating.

Vendor Rating: Views on suppliers performance can be very subjective when making a decision on the selection of a supplier. The supplier may be selected on the basis of one person's judgement of a particular supplier's performance. This judgement may be on the basis of price alone. Price alone is not a good criteria on which to place an order. Many organisations would willingly (and do) pay a price premium for supplies that are to the correct quality and delivered on time. In fact studies have shown that the customer is willing to pay up to a 30% price premium if the perceived quality standard is higher than the competitors.

There are a number of factors which may be considered other than price alone, although price does need to be included when making a judgement on suppliers performance. These factors can include:

Price

The rating needs to include price as a factor but because there are various types of supplier (e.g. suppliers of apples and suppliers of pears) comparing the price of apples with the price of pears is not appropriate. Also, often the items are obtained from a single source so comparing different suppliers on the basis of price is impossible. One way of overcoming the problem of comparing suppliers with suppliers can be to monitor changes in price from the original order price to current order price.

On time Delivery   Number of deliveries on time against the number of late deliveries.

Quality

i)   The number of batches rejected against the number of orders accepted (this can include any subsequent problems found with deliveries at a later date).

ii)   The results of any external assessment by giving the supplier a rating on a scale from zero - poor to ten - excellent.

Service   A subjective judgement on the supplier's ability to react to problems (quality, schedule changes, technical support etc.). This may require discussion with buyers and engineers to determine the quality of service provided using a rating scale of zero - poor to ten - excellent.

Each of these factors needs to be given a weighting say:

Price   30%
Delivery   20%
Quality   30% (if no audit rating figure)
             15% for rejects + 15% for external audit rating (the audit rating is a numerical interpretation of the results of an external audit)
Service   20%

Note: This weighting may need to vary for different industries.

Table 55 An example of Vendor Rating Analysis

Factor	Weighting	Formula	Supplier A	Supplier B
Price	30%	$\dfrac{\text{Original Price}}{\text{Current Price}} * 30\%$	$\dfrac{10}{12}*30\%=25$	$\dfrac{12}{15}*30\%=24$
Delivery	20%	$\dfrac{\text{On time delivery}}{\text{Total no. of Deliveries}} * 20\%$	$\dfrac{54}{60}*20\%=18$	$\dfrac{50}{50}*20\%=20$
Quality	30%	$\dfrac{\text{No of batches accepted}}{\text{Total no of batches}} * 15\%$ + $\dfrac{\text{Audit Rating}}{} * 15\%$	$\dfrac{32}{60}*15=8$ + $\dfrac{6}{10}*15=9$	$\dfrac{45}{50}*30=27$ (No audit)
Service	20%	Service Rating $* 20\%$	$\dfrac{5}{10}*20=10$	$\dfrac{9}{10}*20=18$
Rating	100%		70	89

It is important to remember to keep the analysis relatively simple as the Vendor Rating is only a guide to the supplier's performance and does not replace communication, discussion and generally working with the supplier towards the common objective of improving the overall quality performance.

b)   *Purchase Order:*

Ensuring that the Purchase Order contains all necessary information for the supplier to satisfactorily fulfil the customer's requirements.

The order could contain:

Identification, description and technical (drawing specification etc.) information.
Any Inspection and Test criteria (including certification) or Quality Standards to be applied.
Delivery instructions.
Review of the order (checking and approval).

c)   *Goods Receiving Inspection (GRI):*

Almost all organisations perform some form of GRI. It may take the form of a complete inspection and test of the items received against a specification, possibly employing a sampling scheme such as BS6001. Alternatively, GRI may consist of a check only on quantity, documentation, identification and damage.

Although it may be considered important to perform a dimensional or functional inspection or test at the Goods Receiving stage, the decision to carry out a formal GRI requires careful consideration. For example, take a typical company, say they receive one thousand different batches per month, containing on average one thousand components, each component may have approximately twenty different features that could be checked. If all components are checked, then the number of checks will be:

> 1000 different batches per month * 1000 components per batch * 20 features per component
> = 20,000,000 features to be checked per month - (This will obviously require a considerable inspection resource)

Due to the number of checks involved the organisation may decide:

o   Not to check every batch or type, but who decides which batch to check, the inspector?
o   Not to check 100%, this can be reduced by sampling (BS6001) but there are a number of risks with sampling.
o   Not to check all the different features on an item - only the key features, but again who decides what a key feature is, the inspector?

Say the above gives a 1000% reduction giving 20,000 features per month to be checked, even at one minute per feature this is still approximately two inspectors' work per month. Is it any wonder that organisations are often complaining that GRI does not stop poor quality entering the factory?

The above basic approach to Purchasing Control may be considered inadequate when considering large orders for one off contracts or for high volume supplies. In these circumstances other approaches may be appropriate. One such approach could be the application of a Purchase Control System such as QS-9000. QS-9000 is the standard developed and adopted by Chrysler, Ford, General Motors and a number of lorry manufacturers. This standard replaces Chrysler's - Suppliers Quality Assurance Manual, Ford's Q101 and General Motors Target for Excellence. The QS-9000 standard is based on an interpretation of ISO9001 for the Automotive Industry, with additional elements for sector (automotive) and customer's specific needs. The sector specific requirements include:

- o   Product Approval Process
- o   Continuous Improvement
- o   Process Capabilities

This standard may be considered only applicable for the Automotive industries - that would be rather short sighted. While this standard is aimed at volume suppliers, it is equally applicable to one off high cost projects. The standard also provides an invaluable insight in to how influential customers view supplier quality assurance.

Supplier Quality Assurance

Introduction

Although there are numerous approaches that can be adopted regarding supplier quality assurance (SQA), the approach outlined below is initially fairly general but the latter section concentrates on one influential supplier quality assurance standard, namely QS-9000.

Possibly the typical stages in managing the supply chain are:
  a. analysing the requirements
  b. supplier selection & management
  c. market testing and tendering
  d. negotiating
  e. contracting and partnership sourcing
  f. cost reduction.

Analysing the Requirements: The objective of this stage is to collate, analyse and prioritise all the key information relevant to the product or service being purchased. This can include the methods by which the purchase order or tender specification is established and agreed.

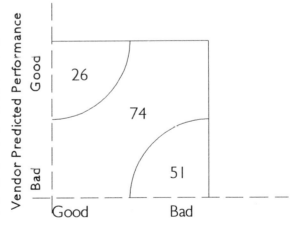

Supplier selection & management: Selection of the supplier can be assisted through the use of supplier questionnaires to determine initial suitability. Use of a vendor rating system can also help to ensure that the supplier's historical performance is satisfactory. Visits and quality surveys can be employed to establish supplier suitability. However, there can be serious short comings with vendor quality surveys. A study carried out by Mr. E H Brainard in *"Quality Assurance"* gave the results shown in the graph. Of 151 vendors, the vendor survey correctly predicted

Vendor Actual Performance

Figure 67 Vendor Surveys

77 vendors. I.e. 26 vendors predicted good were good and 51 vendors predicted bad were bad. But, more seriously 74 vendors were wrongly predicted. (Either predicted good and actual performance was bad or predicted bad and actual performance was good.) This may

confirm what many people have always thought, that vendor surveys are not good at predicting vendor performance and should not be solely relied on.

Supply positioning is a technique which can assist in ensuring that the buyers concentrate effort on the *important* suppliers and also so that the buyers' organisation is not exposed to any risks associated with any particular supplier. To determine the importance of any particular supplier Pareto analysis (probably completed on the basis of cost) can be employed to identify the important few suppliers. Resource and time can then be spent concentrating on the important few suppliers rather than the trivial many. One of the problems with this approach is cost is not the only criteria. Some purchased products and services, while cheap, can have a disproportionate effect (if they break down) on the buyers' organisation. "For the want of a nail....." Also this Pareto analysis approach does not take into consideration the implications of single or multi suppliers.

If, rather than a Pareto analysis, a supplier position analysis is performed then a much clearer picture of the key suppliers emerges (see **Figure 68**). The supplier position analysis is completed by plotting risk of exposure against relative cost. Relative cost is the cost expenditure per annum, not the individual item cost, which can be misleading. The buying objectives for the suppliers in **Figure 68** would seem to be:

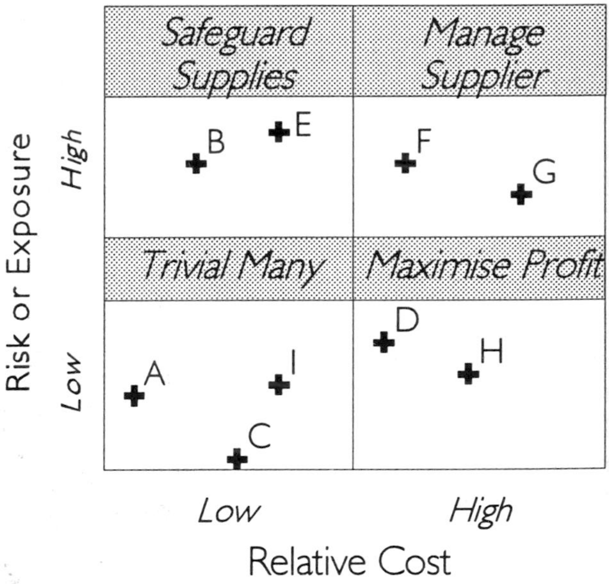

Figure 68 Supplier Position Analysis

For Suppliers B & E, although the relative cost is low, the risks are high and alternative sources of supply may be needed to safeguard supplies.

For Suppliers F & G, both the relative cost and the risks are high, these suppliers will need careful management.

For Suppliers D & H, the risks are low and the costs high, so driving for lower prices would seem appropriate.

For suppliers A, C & I, the risks and costs are low and these suppliers can be generally ignored.

Partnership Sourcing has a role to play in developing the organisation's supplier quality assurance strategy. Developing relationship with suppliers to ensure that they understand the customer's specific requirements and needs. Reducing the number of suppliers to provide better control. Fostering a mutually beneficial climate of continuous improvement. This climate can be used to prevent defects, reduce variation and waste in the supply chain. Often customers will link this continuous improvement and waste reduction to cost and price reduction. I.e. the customer has actively guided and assisted suppliers in reducing waste and improving efficiency. Now, is it unreasonable for the customer to expect some price benefit? It is this (price reduction) side of partnership sourcing and SQA, which is difficult for the suppliers to accept. Customers acting as consultants and telling suppliers, what is good for them, under the name of improving quality performance and then asking for a price reduction is hard for suppliers to accept. Never the less this should not detract from what is a widely accepted and respected approach to supplier quality assurance.

Quality System-9000

The key elements of a Supplier Quality Assurance System are often based on the interpretation of ISO9000 for a particular industrial sector, together with some additional customer specific requirements. QS-9000 is no exception to this. There are three elements.

Supplier Quality Assurance

Based on QS-9000

ISO9000 Based Requirements

Sector Specific Requirements

Customer Specific Requirements

Figure 69

The first is based on ISO9000, the second Sector or Industry Specific requirements and the third on Specific Individual Customer requirements.

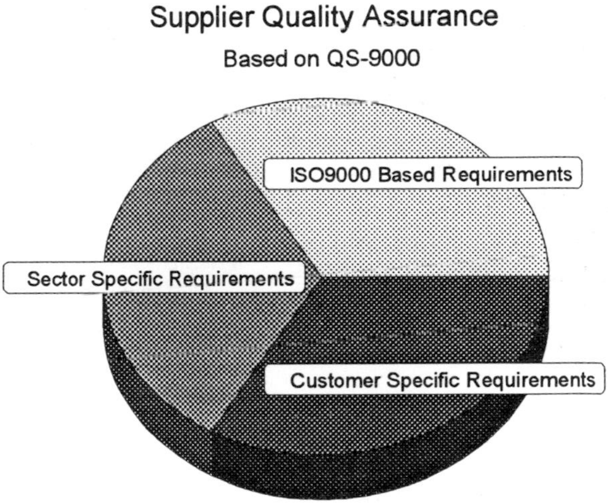

These key elements can form part of an approach to ensuring supplier quality, even to the extent that the standard is made part of the contractual conditions contained in the Purchase Order.

One of the main criticisms of ISO9000 is that the standard is not sufficiently product or process specific. I.e. ISO9000 is too general and does not describe specific quality controls to the product or service that are needed to guarantee satisfactory supplies. The application of the following approach should ensure the identification and implementation of very specific quality control actions. This approach may be seen as augmenting ISO9000 as the chosen Quality Assurance Management System of the organisation.

An overview of QS-9000

ISO-9000 Based Requirements

The interpretation of ISO9000 for the automotive industry, is very similar to the original document, with the following main additions:

Management Responsibility
    Business
       Planning
    Customer
       Satisfaction
Quality System
    Quality Planning
    Failure Mode and Effects Analysis
Design Control
    Quality Function Deployment
    Value Engineering
    Design of Experiments (Taguchi)
    Design for Production

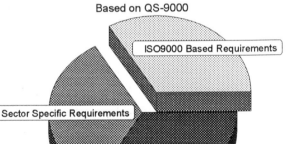

Supplier Quality Assurance
Based on QS-9000

ISO9000 Based Requirements

Sector Specific Requirements

Customer Specific Requirements

Figure 70

Reliability Engineering
Purchasing Control
100% on time delivery
Process Control
Safety & Environment Regulations
Planned Preventive Maintenance
Process Capability Studies
Statistical Techniques
Application of fundamental statistical process control

Most of the above requirements can be found by reference to the relevant section of this book. The main theme behind these additions is prevention and quality improvement. In fact these themes are enlarged still further with the next element - Sector Specific Requirements.

Sector Specific Requirements

The Sector Specific Element of QS-9000 covers such issues as:

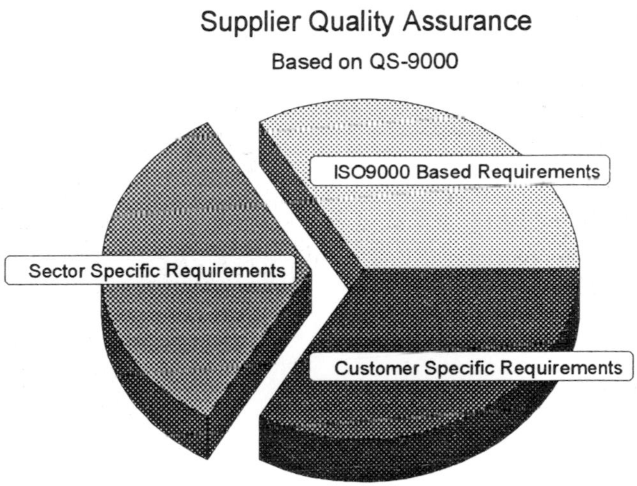

Product Approval: This usually involves the submission of product approval data and results. These results can be obtained either by self-assessment or from some recognised third party (possibly a

Supplier Quality Assurance
Based on QS-9000

ISO9000 Based Requirements

Sector Specific Requirements

Customer Specific Requirements

Figure 71

test house, see NAMAS). These results could include process capability data from preproduction trials. This data should confirm the processes ability to reliability and consistently produce the product to specification, usually within ±four standard deviations of the product specification.

Continuous Improvement: Having demonstrated the processes ability to consistently produce to specification, the next stage is to improve the processes quality performance and reduce variation. Techniques such as Just in Time and Process Cost Modelling are suitable methods to be employed to improve quality and productivity. Reduction in process variation and continuous improvement may be achieved by the use of Statistical Quality Control and other typical Quality Circle techniques.

Manufacturing Capability: This aspect of QS-9000 is concerned with optimising and quality assuring the processes, resources and facilities. One example of this could be such as fool-proofing equipment to ensure that mistakes cannot be made when operating the equipment. (In Japan this is known as Poka-Yoke).

Customer Specific Requirements

The Customer Specific Element of QS-9000 is concerned with issues key to that i n d i v i d u a l customer's needs. For example in Ford's case, one of the main requirements is the introduction of a *Quality Operating System* (QOS). This is a very simple technique and one which employs techniques which are well known but in an immensely powerful way.

Supplier Quality Assurance
Based on QS-9000

ISO9000 Based Requirements

Sector Specific Requirements

Customer Specific Requirements

Figure 72

The Quality Operating System is a simple problem solving tool which can be used to drive the continuous improvement programme. It is based on collecting and analysing data in a consistent way and can, in certain circumstances, be used as an alternative to Statistical Quality Control (SQC). Some organisations have great difficulty in applying SQC to their processes. (The sheer volume of processes or variables to monitor, is usually cited as the most difficult problem).

QOS can be broken down into four phases: Measurement & Targets, Pareto Analysis, Action Planning and Performance Monitoring. There is nothing new in these phases but applied consistently it provides a common method of assessing quality improvement projects progress. Also this assessment can be contained on one sheet of paper and be quickly understood and analysed by almost anyone.

Figure 73 Phase One - Measurement & Targets

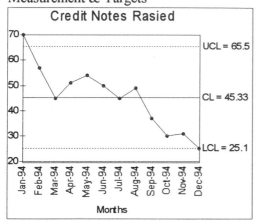

Table 56 Phase Three - Action Plan

Problem	Action	% Completed				Date
		¼	½	¾	1	
Misinterpretation	Training for Sales men	▓	▓	▓		Jul 94
Price Error	Create Pricing Procedure	▓	▓	▓	▓	Mar 94
Wrong Customer Details	Up date data base	▓				Jul 94

Figure 74 Phase Two - Pareto Analysis

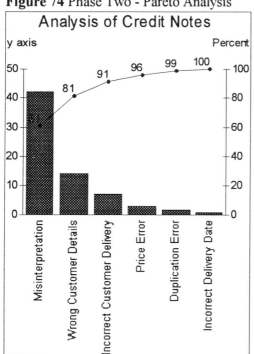

Table 57 Phase Four - Performance Monitoring

Jan	Feb	Mar	Apr	May	Jun	Jul	Aug	Sep	Oct	Nov	Dec
42	34	27	31	33	30	27	30	22	18	19	15
14	12	9	11	11	10	9	10	8	6	6	5
7	6	5	5	6	5	5	5	4	3	3	3
3	3	2	2	2	2	2	2	2	1	1	1
2	2	1	2	2	1	1	1	1	1	1	1
1	1	1	1	1	1	1	1	1	0	0	0
69	56	45	52	55	44	45	49	38	29	30	25

Figures **Figure 73** & **Figure 74** and tables **Table 56** & **Table 57** show an example of a completed QOS sheet. Phase one, the measurement and targets, shows the monitoring of performance with time. In this case the number of credit notes issued monthly. Phase two, is a Pareto analysis of credit note data to identify the important few reasons for raising credit notes. From this Pareto analysis, an Action Plan (Phase three) has been established in an attempt to reduce and eliminate the specific causes for issuing a credit note. Phase four is the raw data collected on a monthly basis detailing the breakdown of the reasons for issuing credit notes. Included in phase four are flags which indicate that one of the items on the action plan has been implemented. The effect of this action should be seen (hopefully positively) on the measurement and targets chart.

Implementing QS-9000

To see this QS-9000 as an overall process **Figure 75** has been drawn. The figure represents typically the sequence that could be followed in achieving QS-9000 (assuming ISO9000 certification has already been achieved).

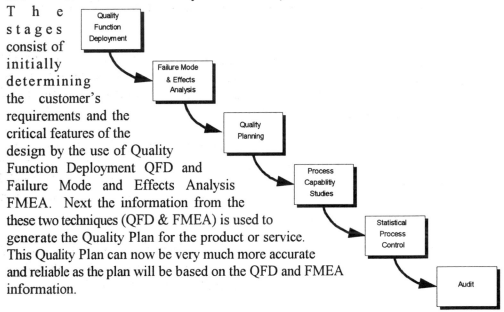

The stages consist of initially determining the customer's requirements and the critical features of the design by the use of Quality Function Deployment QFD and Failure Mode and Effects Analysis FMEA. Next the information from the these two techniques (QFD & FMEA) is used to generate the Quality Plan for the product or service. This Quality Plan can now be very much more accurate and reliable as the plan will be based on the QFD and FMEA information.

The Quality Plan can detail the quality control elements and records that will be needed at each stage in the production of   **Figure 75** Supplier Quality Control Steps

service process. Examples of the sort of controls specified in the Quality Plan may be Process Capability Studies or Statistical Quality Control (variable or attribute control charts) etc.

Finally, instead of what may be considered a rather nebulous audit as required by ISO9000, a product or process based specific audit can be performed against the precise requirements of the Quality Plan.

Quality Function Deployment: As a project or design progresses, the greater the chance that specific customer's needs and expectations are overlooked or not satisfied. In order not to neglect or overlook *"the voice of the customer,"* the technique Quality Function Deployment (QFD) has been developed. The aim for QFD is to identify the key customer needs and translate these needs into controls. This control is achieved by establishing what the customer requires and through the various stages of QFD how these requirements will be achieved. (See section Quality Function Deployment).

Failure Mode and Effects Analysis: This technique is used to identify and eliminate possible causes of failure. The technique requires a sequential, disciplined approach by engineers to assess systems, products or processes. The technique involves establishing the modes of failure and the effects of failure on the system, product or process. This ensures that all possible failure modes have been fully identified and ranked in order of their importance. (See section FMEA).

Quality Control Planning: Having completed the QFD and FMEA an excellent understanding of the customer needs and expectations will have been gained. Any potential system or product failures will also have been identified. Consequently, the process or project can be properly planned.

Process capability studies: Processes can be subject to variation. This variation may be small and insignificant. Alternatively, the variation could be excessive allowing products to be manufactured outside the specification. It is therefore important to understand the extent to which a process will vary before starting manufacture, thereby avoiding costly scrap or start/stop manufacture.

One method of determining a process's ability to meet specification is by conducting a Process Capability Study, where the process is statistically evaluated for the processes ability to conform to specification. (See section Statistical Quality Control).

Statistical Quality Control SQC: Having determined the process's ability to meet specification, controls need to be applied which continually monitor the process for quality and to make continuous improvements to product quality. This involves taking regular measurements of process variation and comparing these observations with predetermined control limits of variation. This comparison can best be accomplished graphically on control charts. The application of SQC gives the opportunity to implement operator quality control, assisting in reinforcing the operator's responsibility for the quality of their own work and gives a sense of pride in their work. (See section Statistical Quality Control).

Problem Solving: The use of the seven stage approach is a powerful tool in problem solving.

      i.   Use the team approach.
      ii.   Understand the problem.
     iii.   Implement and confirm provisional corrective action.

iv.   Establish and verify the root cause.
v.   Confirm the viability of permanent corrective action.
vi.   Implement permanent corrective action to prevent recurrence of the problem.
vii. Recognise the team's achievements.

Assessment, review and evaluation: Having established a product specific Quality Control Plan, then perform an audit to confirm compliance with the agreed Quality Plan including the application of SQC. Review and evaluate the results of the assessment to identify any areas for possible improvement.

As can be surmised, time resource for such a programme is considerable, but the final analysis must be - how seriously is supplier quality assurance to be taken.

Just in Time

Introduction

Just in Time (JIT) is an approach to ensuring that the customer's requirements in terms of quality and service (deliveries and quantities) are exactly matched. The customer receives the precise quantities

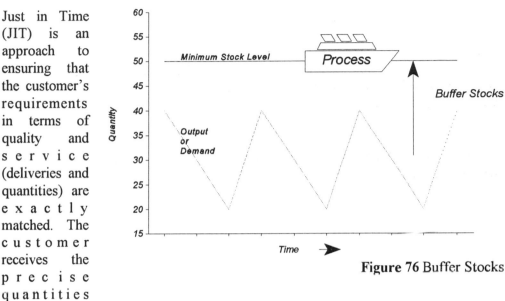

Figure 76 Buffer Stocks

required (no more no less) at the time required. It involves the implementation of a programme that affects all aspects of the product or service from the purchase of raw material through to on time delivery. Many of the techniques described in TQM can be usefully employed in the introduction of JIT. JIT by its very nature has significant effect on buffer stocks, work in-progress etc, reducing these stocks levels to a minimum. The consequence of this stock reduction is where allowances could be made for late or faulty deliveries by the use of the "slack in the system," using the buffer stocks to solve inefficiencies in the system; post JIT these buffer stocks are no longer available, allowances can no longer be made for late or faulty deliveries.

The diagram **Figure 76** shows how the process can negotiate the vagaries of the process in terms of output and demand by holding excessively high, inefficient and expensive stock levels. The process and output can be maintained by holding excessive buffer stocks which can be used to overcome system problems.

Figure 77
shows that the
implementation
of JIT should
hopefully
achieve a
reduction of
stock levels. If
the system
problems are
not resolved,
then with the
reduction of
these stock
levels the
inefficiencies in
the system will
be exposed and

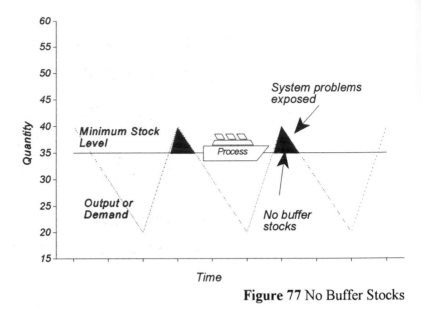

Figure 77 No Buffer Stocks

the process as a consequence will suffer stoppages and material shortages.

JIT needs to focus not only on how to reduce stock levels but also on how to resolve problems of inefficiency within the system.

The concepts and philosophy behind JIT includes:

Kanban - This is the method employed to pull work through the system rather than the usual approach of pushing the work through the system. Often the phrase is heard from a Manager "I am the highest paid progress chaser in this company," meaning that much of management time is spent chasing (pushing) work through the system, as opposed to being pulled through the organisation by a system of Kanban Cards. Kanban Cards are used by the customer to let the supplier know more material is required (internal as well as external customers). The objective is that only the absolute minimum required quantities are made and that the operator is involved in progressing the work through the organisation. The Kanban card is the trigger to release work and work cannot be released unless a Kanban Card is received. Work travels in one direction, Kanban Cards in the other.

WORK MOVES IN THIS DIRECTION

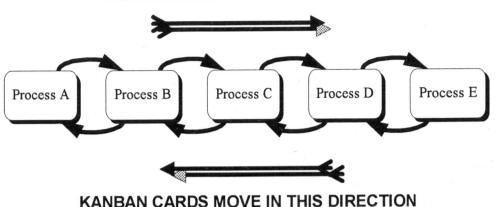

KANBAN CARDS MOVE IN THIS DIRECTION

Figure 78 Kanban Cards

The Kanban Card can be attached to the container that carries the work. The card will contain the following information: Quantity, Identification, Inspection Status (on leaving), Source and Destination. Often the quantities requested will be much smaller than usually expected, in order to maintain productivity at the correct level the process switch-over times will need to be radically improved.

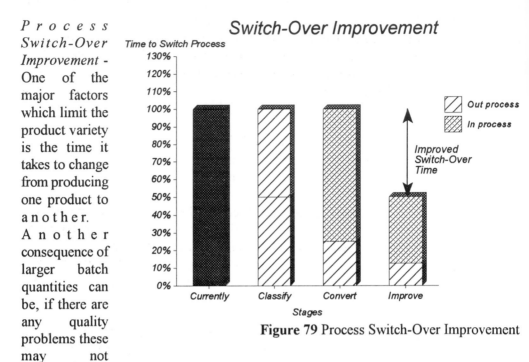

Process Switch-Over Improvement - One of the major factors which limit the product variety is the time it takes to change from producing one product to another. Another consequence of larger batch quantities can be, if there are any quality problems these may not become apparent until the batch has labouriously and finally reached the assembly stage. If smaller batch quantities could be employed and consequently quicker process switch-over then the time to discover a quality problem is greatly reduced. JIT, because it works on much smaller batch sizes, means that any inefficiencies or bottle necks in the system are quickly exposed.

The procedure (see **Figure 79**) that can be followed in improving process switch over times can be:

To investigate the CURRENT situation, Pareto Analysis could be usefully employed to determine which processes take the longest to changeover and what factors have the greatest influence on the changeover time. **Figure 79** shows the current situation to be 100% of the time is spent completing tasks while the process has stopped. Some of these tasks could be performed while the process is running. The tasks could be: obtaining material, equipment, labour, work instructions, stopping the process, changing the equipment over (i.e. removing the existing equipment and installing the following equipment) and restarting the process. Detailing the correct or approved changeover method.

Having established the current situation the factors involved in process switch-over need to be CLASSIFIED into out process (activities that could be performed while the process has stopped) and in process (activities that could be performed while the process is running). Analysis of what actually happens as opposed to what should happen may be appropriate. **Figure 79** shows the classified (actual) situation to be 50% activities with the process stopped, 50% of the activities with the process running. The actual situation could be determined by the use of activity sampling.

The out process activities now need CONVERTING into in process activities so that the process waiting time is minimised. **Figure 79** indicates 30% more of the activities could be or should be performed while the process is running.

Finally, the overall activities can be analysed to determine if it is possible to complete the process switch-over more effectively and efficiently; IMPROVING the overall process switch-over time. This may involve closely examining the logistics associated with the process switch-over involving the coordination and management of activities, design of equipment for ease of switch-over, fool-proofing the equipment etc. **Figure 79** indicates a further 50% saving, reducing the out process time still further.

If the group in charge of process switch-over were told to achieve a 300% improvement in switch-over time, it may be interpreted as needing to work 300% harder. What the above example suggests is that they work 300% smarter. *Work smarter, not harder!*

Supplier Development - Mass production industries used to vertically integrate the supplier into their own manufacturing facilities by buying the supplier. Today it is considered better to develop a continuous process/supplier improvement relationship with supplier, where the supplier is seen as a key element in the overall process, thereby ensuring that the supplier completely understands the customer's particular requirements and needs. The section Purchasing Control describes some of the techniques which can be usefully employed.

Some other techniques involved in JIT are: Flow Charting, Continuous Improvement, Material Planning Resources (all of these techniques are described in other sections of this book).

Statistical Quality Control (SQC)

Introduction

Most activities, when analysed, form some type of process or sequence, e.g. office paper work, manufacturing, construction, service or maintenance processes. All of these processes will require some form of monitoring to ensure that the process is not going out of control and to identify the causes of variation and thereby improving the overall process performance. SQC can be used as a means of process monitoring to assist in identifying causes of variation and improve process performance.

The skill of starting RIGHT! - All processes are subject to variation. This variation may be small and insignificant, alternatively the variation could be excessive causing products to be produced outside the specification. It is therefore important to understand the extent to which a process will vary before production starts, thereby avoiding costly scrap or start/stop production. To determine the extent of process variation a study can be performed measuring the amount by which processes vary. These measurements can subsequently be statistically analysed, providing a clear indication of the process's ability to meet specification, i.e. a Process Capability Study (see diagram Process Capability Study Chart).

The skill of keeping the process RIGHT and making the process world class! - Having determined the process's ability to meet specification, controls need to be applied which continually monitor the process for quality and which allow continuous improvements to be made to product quality - (Statistical Quality Control, SQC). This involves taking regular measurements of process variation and comparing these observations with predetermined control limits of variation. This comparison can best be accomplished graphically on control charts. The application of SQC gives the opportunity to implement operator quality control, assisting in reinforcing the operator's responsibility for the quality of their own work and gives a sense of pride in their work. Reinforcing the need for all concerned to achieve a process of world class standard.

Guidelines

Statistical Quality Control

Process Capability Studies (PCS) - *The skill of starting RIGHT!*

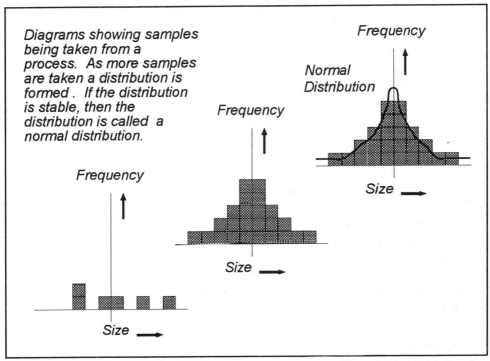

Figure 80 A Distribution

As explained, processes are subject to variation which can affect the process's ability to meet process specification. One method of determining a process's ability to meet specification is by conducting a Process Capability Study. The diagram **Figure 80** shows how data from a process can be collected and plotted on a chart. As more data is collected a picture starts to form; if the process is stable then this picture will form the shape of a normal distribution. The following procedure describes how to gather the data and to produce a picture that represents the way in which the process is performing for quality.

Pre-study Guidelines

A.   Determine the process to be studied - this may be on the basis of:

1.   analysis of scrap or rework - internal failures
2.   analysis of customer complaints - external failures
3.   a modified process which has never been run before or the acceptance of a new process i.e. new capital equipment
4.   the first off after setting a process

B.   Determine the features to be studied - possibly on the basis of a Failure Mode and Effects Analysis* results or after producing a cause and effect diagram or just the inspector/setter's judgement on which are the key feature/s.

      *See section Failure Mode and Effects Analysis

C.   Ensure that all the key factors are correct against the relevant process instructions and drawings. Parameters such as pressures, temperatures, settings, equipment etc.

D.   Confirm that operations carried out prior to the process under investigation have been satisfactorily completed. I.e. That the previous processes met specification and therefore will not have any detrimental effect on the process undergoing consideration. For example, excessive variation in the location dimension could have a direct effect on the result of the study.

E.   It is advisable that the number of samples taken is at least 25.

F.   The measuring, gauging or transducer accuracy is usually expected to be within 10% of the process specification.

G.   Communicate the reason for conducting the study to all personnel concerned.

During the study

The samples should be measured in the order that they are produced, otherwise trend cannot be observed. If multiple processes are being studied, then each product should be identifiable to a particular process. Should the process be reset during the study this should also be noted. Any abnormal conditions should be noted if they are likely to produce variation in the product e.g. size.

If a product is found to be 'way out of line' with the others during the study, it should be examined for an assignable cause or non-random effect which would account for its condition. Only then can the product be discarded.

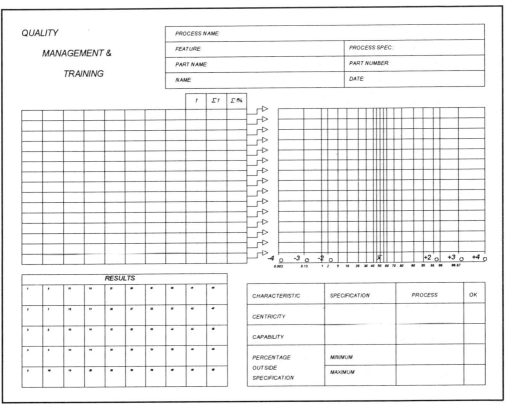

Figure 81 Process Capability Chart

Completing the Process Capability Study Form

STEP   ACTION

1.   Enter the process details (see **Figure 81** Process Capability Chart).

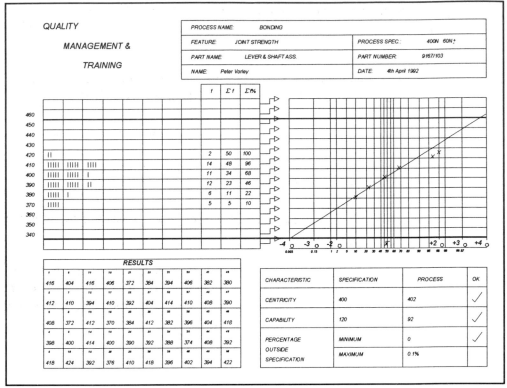

QUALITY		PROCESS NAME:	BONDING			
MANAGEMENT &		FEATURE:	JOINT STRENGTH		PROCESS SPEC.:	400N 60N±
		PART NAME:	LEVER & SHAFT ASS.		PART NUMBER:	9167/103
TRAINING		NAME: Peter Vorley			DATE: 4th April 1992	

Figure 82 Completed Process Capability Chart

2.   Enter the process results in the sequence that they were produced.

3.   Determine the scale to be used. Experience has shown that the formula below can be used as a guide.

$$\frac{Largest\ Reading\ -\ Smallest\ Reading}{8} = Class\ Interval \qquad (3)$$

In the example (see **Figure 82** Completed Process Capability Chart)

$$\frac{424 \ - \ 370}{8} \ \approx \ 6.7 \ \textit{rounding up gives class interval of } 10N$$

(4)

4. Draw in the tolerance or process specification limits in a thick black line across the complete width of the chart. Enter the results on the tally chart.

5. Enter the frequency of each result in the column 'f' (zero if no value is found).

6. Working upwards in column '$\sum f$' calculate the cumulative frequency (Note $\sum$ means the sum of or cumulation).

7. Convert the cumulative frequencies '$\sum f$' into percentages of the total and enter the result in column '$\sum f\%$'.

8. Noting the bottom figure in column '$\sum f\%$' follow the arrow until the corresponding point on the probability graph is found. Mark this point with a cross. Repeat this exercise until the 100% figure is reached. To avoid losing this last number the average of the last two figures can be plotted e.g.

$$\frac{\textit{Last Reading} \ + \ \textit{Second to Last Reading}}{2}$$
$$\frac{100+96}{2} = 98$$

(5)

plot as 98% @ 425N

9. Draw the best fit straight line through all the points (extend the line to the extremities of the graph paper). If a reasonable fit cannot be found (your own judgement is required here), then the data may contain some non-random effect or be zero limited. In these circumstances either identify the non-random effect or use special skewed distribution paper.

Interpretation of Results

10. **Figure 83** Interpretation of PCS Results indicates the desired process performance.

    The process setting should fall within 2 standard deviations. The symbol x bar is a measure of the location or setting of the process.

    The process specification should be less than or equal to

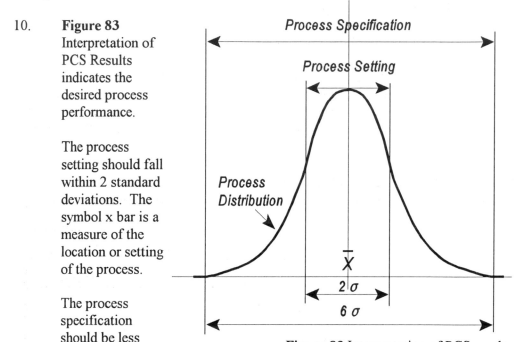

Figure 83 Interpretation of PCS results

the process capability (6 standard deviations). The symbol σ means standard deviation and is a measure of the spread or width of the distribution.

11. Locate the 50% or x bar point on the probability paper and read off the average value from the left-hand scale. This average value will be adjacent to the intercept point on the graph *(in the example 402N)*. This gives an indication of the setting of the process and is sometimes termed the **CENTRICITY** value.

12. Enter the specified (required) centricity and process (actual) centricity in the box. *(In the example 400N & 402N respectively)*.

13. Determine from the chart the distance that will correspond to 6σ (±3σ); this is termed **CAPABILITY**. Enter the values for specified and process capability in the box. *(In the example 120N & 92N respectively)*.

14.   Determine the number of items likely to be produced outside specification. *(In the example, the intersection of the best fit line and the process limits, i.e. minimum 0% and maximum 0.1%).*

Benefits of Process Capability Studies (and uses of a PCS)

Having gathered the data regarding the process, it is then possible to determine the extent to which the process holds the specification. In the previous example (**Figure 82**) if the process specification was changed from 340N/460N to 380N/460N then the predicted reject level will be approximately 10%. This would provide the data for a process improvement programme.

If there were a number of processes to choose from:

The decision on which process to choose can be on the basis of quality and price.

Table 58 Process Selection

Characteristic	Process A	Process B
Cost	£0.50 per piece	£0.25 per piece
Output Rates	10 per hour	10 per hour
Predicted reject quantities Minimum	0	10%
Maximum	0.1%	0.1%

The PCS data and graph provides the means of assessing the process faults and the causes of any rejects.

It may be possible to establish the frequency with which the process needs to be monitored and adjusted.

A PCS could form the basis of acceptance trials for the purchase of capital equipment. If the features to be monitored were determined prior to ordering capital equipment then a PCS could be performed prior to acceptance. This PCS could be performed either by the supplier or customer to confirm the process's ability to meet specification.

As a process matures then the process's ability to meet specification can become impaired. If the original process capability was known it may be possible to predict when the process requires repair or replacement.

Statistical Quality Control

The skill of keeping the process RIGHT and making the process world class!

The previous section described how to determine whether it is possible to make it right. Having established that the process can make it right, then the next stage is to keep it right and make it world class. Sometimes the PCS establishes that the process cannot produce correctly, thus in these circumstances, it is even more important to apply SQC.

The application of SQC can be used to monitor and improve the performance of the process.

Before Introducing SQC

Communication: Ensure that all personnel are aware of the need for, and the benefits of using SQC. The personnel involved in collating and analysing the data should be suitably trained.

Characteristic: Determine the features or characteristics to be controlled using SQC. From past experience it may be known which features or parameters present the most problems. Alternatively, the features may be established on the basis of:

A.   Performing a Pareto analysis, identifying "the important few", internal or external quality problems e.g. scrap, rectification, rejects, customer complaints or warranty returns.
B.   Key Features - Features that could cause financial or reputational damage if they are not maintained within certain limits.
C.   Features identified as a result of performing a Failure Mode and Effects Analysis*.

Measuring: Establish testing, checking, measuring or gauging methods to be employed, ensuring that the equipment will be sufficiently accurate, (approximately 10% of the drawing requirements should be adequate).

Decide on the inspection criteria:

1.   Check that drawings and specifications contain realistic quantifiable standards.

2.   Check that the specifications are appropriate (designers have been known to set unrealistic specifications on rare occasions).

318

3.   Check that the acceptance criteria are clearly defined.

4.   Check that the reference standards, gauges, visual aids such as samples or photographs etc. are available.

5.   Check that operator/inspector possesses the appropriate faculties (e.g. good eyesight) and necessary skill.

6.   Check correct environment for task (e.g. good lighting).

Logistics: Install the chart holders and control charts in a prominent position, preferably adjacent to the process and within easy reach of the personnel controlling the process.

Sampling: Select an appropriate sample size and frequency for monitoring the process. It is not essential, but if a PCS has been performed the results can give a good indication of the sample size and frequency.

Select: Decide on the most appropriate charting method to use.

Chart Selection

Various types of chart are available, described below are some of the more commonly used charts, together with examples of where the charts can be usefully employed. See **Figure 84**.

VARIABLE DATA; X/R Chart (Average and Range) these charts will be used when the data is measured, i.e. readings from measuring device such as a volt meter.

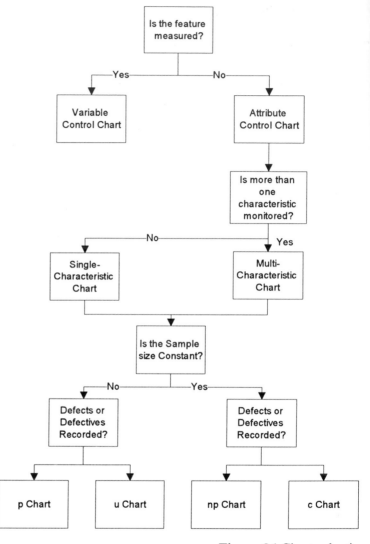

Figure 84 Chart selection

ATTRIBUTE DATA (see **Figure 84**) Single characteristic chart or Multiple characteristic chart. These charts will be used in go/nogo, pass/fail situations.

A.   The p chart for proportion of Defectives where the sample is not necessarily of constant size.

B.   The np chart for Number of Defectives where the sample size is constant.

C.   The c chart for Number of Defects where sample size is constant.

D. The u chart for Number of Defects per Unit where the sample size is not necessarily constant.

Table 59 Attribute Chart Selection

Sample Size Varies	Sample Size Constant	Fault Type	Description
Proportion	Number		
p	np	Defectives	Accept or Reject
u	c	Defects	Number of different flaws

Note: An item may have 4 different flaws, in which case there are 4 **defects** in the item, but there is still only one **defective** item. (See **Figure 85**)

Examples in the use of single characteristic charts may be:

For p and n types charts
○ pass or fail light bulb test
○ go or nogo hole size
○ correct or incorrect torque loading
○ accept or reject weld strength

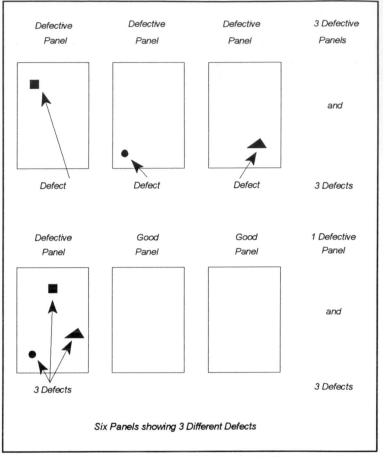

Figure 85 Defectives or Defects

For c or u type charts
○ porosity or number of holes in a casting
○ number of paint blemishes on a panel
○ number of flaws in a sheet of glass
○ number of errors on a printed circuit board
○ number of faults with a washing machine

In the latter two examples (printed circuit board and washing machine) each board or machine may contain various defects.

In the case of the printed circuit board the characteristics could be: a component missing, bad soldering, wrong component, defective components.

Or in the case of the washing machine: leaking, fails to start, motor defective, heater defective etc.

In these circumstances it may be appropriate to employ a multiple characteristic chart. With this type of chart, each of the above characteristics will be monitored individually. The result of this monitoring is then collated and the total number of defects is plotted.

Implementing SQC

This step consists of 3 key elements

STAGE 1:   Gather the data

STAGE 2:   Determine the control limits

STAGE 3:   Data analysis and variation reduction

These 3 stages are ceaselessly repeated for continuous improvement in process performance.

Variable Charts and data

The procedure to be observed when SQC is applied to variable data is described below.

STAGE 1 Gather the data

1.   Complete the process details on the Statistical Quality Control Chart (see **Figure 86** SQC Chart) using the Statistical Quality Control Chart and from the Process Capability Study determine an appropriate scale for the average x and range R.

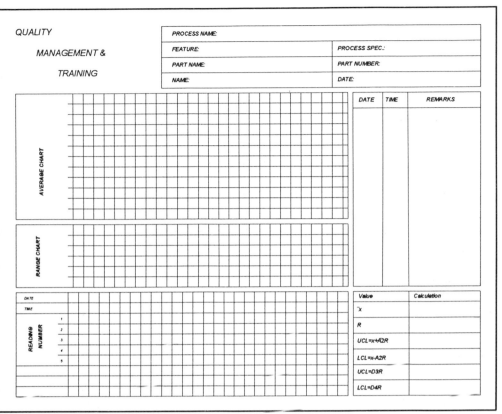

Figure 86 SQC Chart

For the average and range chart this can be approximately 2 * Process specification

2.   Obtain first set of readings and record date, time and results. Circle or highlight any readings outside process specification.

3.   Calculate average and range for each sample taken.

$$Average\ \bar{x} = \frac{\sum x_i}{n} \tag{6}$$

Where Σx_i = the summation of each individual reading 1,2,3,...i
       N   = number of readings
and   R   = range, the difference between the highest and lowest value

Record x bar & R at the bottom of the chart

$$\textit{For the first example } \bar{x} = \frac{51.7}{5} = 10.34$$
$$R = 10.4 - 10.3 = 0.1$$

(7)

See **Figure 87** *Completed SPC Chart*

4.   Plot the value for average and range on the control chart directly above the date and time. Join the points together with a straight line.

Now repeat this exercise until approximately 25 samples or 100 readings have been obtained.

STAGE 2 Determine the control limits

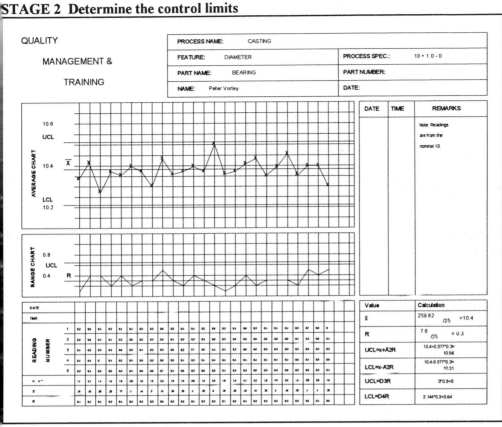

Figure 87 Completed SQC Chart

5. Calculate the average range value R.

$$\overline{R} = \frac{\sum R_i}{k} \tag{8}$$

Where $\sum R_i$ = the summation of each range value
and   k   = the number of samples taken

$$\bar{R} = \frac{7.6}{25} = 0.304 \qquad\qquad (9)$$

Draw $\bar{R}$ on the range chart as a thick line

6.   Calculate the control limits for the range chart.

The control limits are used as a guide to determining process performance. The use of the control limits is described in the section - STAGE 3 Data Analysis & Variation Reduction (Page 225).

In order to calculate the control limits it is necessary to use certain constants. In **Table 60** Control Limit Constants are the sample size and the other constants A_2, D_3 and D_4 which are used in the control limit calculations.

Table 60 Control Limited Constants

n	2	3	4	5	6	7	8	9	10
A_2	1.880	1.023	0.729	0.577	0.483	0.419	0.373	0.337	0.308
D_3	0	0	0	0	0	0.076	0.136	0.184	0.223
D_4	3.268	2.574	2.282	2.114	2.004	1.924	1.864	1.816	1.777

The first constant to be used is D_4 which can be found in **Table 60** by locating on row 'n' the sample size and read off the value for D_4. Record the value of D_4.

Calculate Upper Control Limit for ranges.

where $UCL_R = D_4 * R$

In the example $UCL_R = 2.114*0.304 = 0.642$

Draw UCL_R on the range chart as a thick line.

Calculate the Lower Control Limit for ranges.

328

$LCL_R = D_3 * R$

D_3 is given in **Table 60** and is found in a similar way to D_4.

In the example $LCL_R = 0*0.304 = 0$

Draw LCL_R on the range chart as a thick line.

7.   Calculate the process average.

$$Average \; \overline{\overline{x}} \; = \; \frac{\sum xi}{k} \tag{11}$$

Where $\sum xi$ = the summation of each individual sample average

$$e \; example \; (Completed \; SQC \; Chart) \; \overline{\overline{x}} \; = \; \frac{259.62}{25} \; = \tag{12}$$

Draw x bar on the average chart as a thick line

8.   Calculate the control limit for average charts.

Determine the value for A_2, where A_2 is given in the table; it is found in a similar way to D_4.

Calculate Upper Control Limit for averages

$$UCL_x \; = \; \overline{x} + (A_2 * R) \tag{13}$$

In the example (Completed SQC Chart) $UCL_x = 10.38 + (0.577*0.304)$

Draw UCL$_x$ on the average chart as a thick line

Calculate the Lower Control Limit for averages

$$LCL_x = \bar{x} - (A_2 * R) \tag{14}$$

In the example (Completed SQC Chart) LCL$_x$ = 10.38 - (0.577*0.304)

Draw LCL$_x$ on the average chart as a thick line

STAGE 3 Data Analysis & Variation Reduction

One of the key purposes of using control charts is to improve quality, by reducing variation. Consequently techniques need to be employed which can help identify any sources of variation. One such method is to identify the presence of a non-random effects, and if possible eliminate it. Non-random effects can be recognise by applying the following tests when examining the charts.

TEST 1　　　　**Any point outside the control limit**

TEST 2　　　　**A series of 7 points above or below the average**

TEST 3　　　　**A trend of 7 points up or down**

TEST 4　　　　**Any other cyclic pattern**

Once a non-random effect has been identified, its source should be investigated to determine what action is necessary to a) correct the non-conformity and b) prevent it recurring. As an aid to trouble shooting when non-random variations occur, it is important to keep a log of any changes such as resetting, change of shift, material or equipment changes.

TEST 1

Points outside the control limits. The control limits have been calculated using the constants (A_2, D_3 and D_4). These constants are calculated so that there is only a 1 in 1000 chance of points lying outside the Control Limits. It is reasonable, therefore, to presume that a non-random effect has caused the change.

A point outside the control limit (either above or below) could indicate that:

A.　　　The point has been wrongly plotted
B.　　　The control limit has been incorrectly calculated or plotted
C.　　　The process has worsened or improved
D.　　　The inspection standard has changed

TEST 2

A series of 7 points above or below the average. A change in the process average could indicate that the average has moved and stabilised at a new higher or lower level. A run of 7 points above the average could indicate that, on the average chart, the accuracy or process average has worsened. On the average chart - a run of 7 points below the average could indicate that the accuracy or process average has improved.

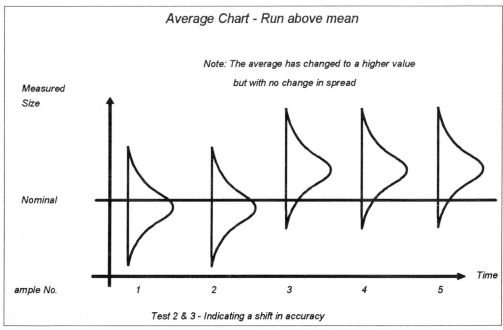

Figure 88 Average Chart - a run of points

The effect on the process distribution is shown in the diagram **Figure 88**. The spread of the process has not changed but the setting has undergone a change, resulting in a shifted average and stabilising at a new higher level.

On the range chart - a run of 7 points above the average would indicate the repeatability or spread of the process has worsened. Or the inspection standard or measuring system has changed.

On the range chart - a run of 7 points below the average would indicate that the repeatability or spread has improved. Or the inspection standard or measuring system has changed.

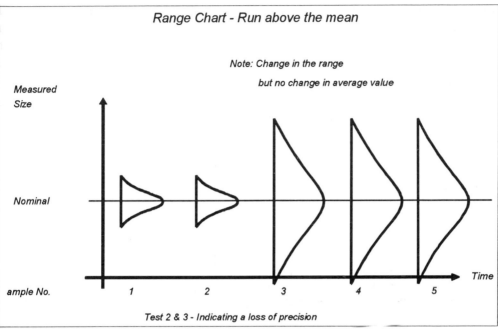

Figure 89 Range Chart - a run of points

The effect on the process spread of a run of points above the average on the range chart is represented in the diagram **Figure 89** above. The location of the spread has not changed but the width of the spread has increased. Consequently, there will be greater variation between the individual process values.

TEST 3

Any trends within the control limits (even when all points are within the control limits) should be investigated as it may be an indication of conditions which, if ignored, could lead to the process moving outside the control limits, or an improvement opportunity that should be encouraged.

Trends - on the Average Chart.

A run of 7 points where each point is higher or lower than the previous may indicate that the accuracy or process average is changing, possibly worsening. The inspection standard or measuring system could be changing.

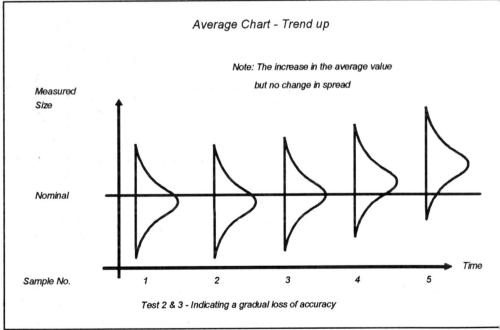

Figure 90 Average Chart - Trend

The above diagram **Figure 90** represents the effect on the process distribution as a result of a run of points on the average chart. There is no change in the process spread but a shift upwards of the process setting or location.

Trends - on the Range Chart.

A run of 7 points where each point is higher than the previous could indicate that the repeatability or spread has worsened and is still deteriorating. A run of 7 points where each point is lower than the previous could indicate that, the repeatability or spread has improved and is still improving - investigate and encourage this trend.

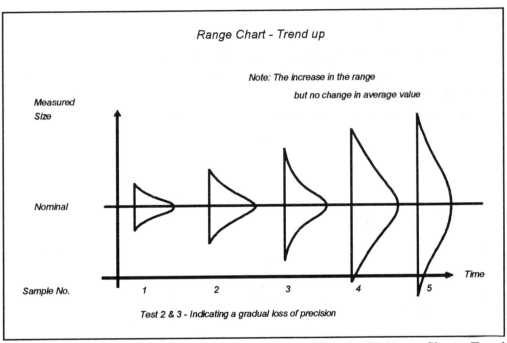

Figure 91 Range Chart - Trend

The above diagram **Figure 91** represents the changes to the process distribution as a consequence of a run upwards of points on the range chart. The spread of the distribution is deteriorating and there will be a steadily worsening variation between individual process values.

TEST 4

The control limits are such that approximately 2/3 of the data points should lie within the middle third region of the control limits. About 1/3 of the data points should lie in the outer two thirds of the control limits

Cyclic patterns may be due to plotting points from samples taken from different conditions e.g. different processes, different shifts, different batches.

Variation Reduction

Identify and Remedy: Once a non-random cause of variation has been investigated and remedied, the process should have improved. If subsequent data points are consistently below the previous average (confirming the improvement) then the control limits can be re-calculated for the new improved process performance.

Continuous Process Improvement: The data should continue to be collected, plotted on the chart and analysed to identify further process improvements. It may be appropriate to use the techniques detailed in the section on Total Quality Management to assist in achieving process improvements, particularly Pareto analysis and cause and effect diagrams.

Attribute Charts and Data

The previous section described the procedure to be observed when SQC is applied to variable data. This section shows how to apply SQC when attribute data is collected. Prior to following the procedure outlined below, check that the steps stated in the section *Before Introducing SQC* (Page 217) have been observed.

The data will need to be divided into samples or sub-groups of 'n' items. The number of items in each sample should preferably remain constant (although this is not essential). The interval between each sample should be chosen on the basis of production frequency, the importance of the operation or process. The samples need to be sufficiently large to allow defectives to appear (although hopefully none). The samples should be taken from one process otherwise it will be difficult to identify the source or cause of any defectives. I.e. separate charts should be kept for different processes.

STAGE 1 Gather the data

1.   Decide on a sample size in accordance with the above rules.

2.   Record the number of defects/defectives in each sample. See **Figure 92**.

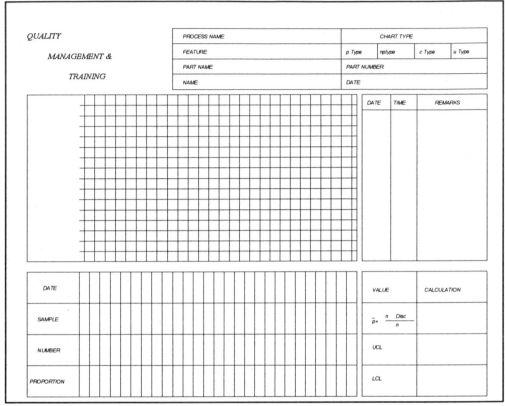

Figure 92 SQC Chart for Attributes

3. The proportion or number of defects/defectives on the vertical axis and the sample identification (hour, day etc.) on the horizontal axis. The vertical axis should extend from zero to about 1.5 times the highest point expected.

4. Depending on the chart type selected, plot the value of p, np, c or u for each sample on the chart.

STAGE 2 Determine the control limits

i)   **The p chart for PROPORTION OF DEFECTIVES (NON-CONFORMING UNITS)**

The proportion of defectives is p i.e. the number of defectives (np) divided by the number in the sample.

$$p = \frac{np}{n} \qquad (15)$$

Calculate the average number of defectives for the process

$$p = \frac{Total\ number\ defectives}{Total\ number\ inspected} \qquad (16)$$

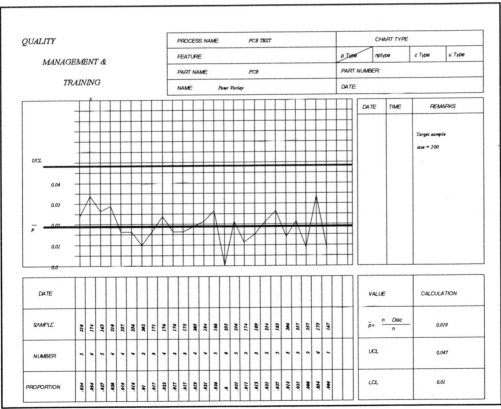

Figure 93 Completed SQC Chart for Attributes

Calculate the Control Limits (UCL, LCL).

$$UCL_p = \bar{p} + 3 * \sqrt{\frac{\bar{p}(1-\bar{p})}{\bar{n}}} \qquad (17)$$

$$LCL_p = \bar{p} - 3 * \sqrt{\frac{\bar{p}(1-\bar{p})}{\bar{n}}} \qquad (18)$$

Draw the process mean (p bar) and control limits on the chart and label (p, UCL_p and LCL_p).

Note 1: As the sample size can vary with p charts then this can affect the control limits. Therefore, it may be necessary to recalculate the control limits. Once calculated the new control limits should be plotted on the control charts.

Note 2: If the LCL is negative then ignore this control limit since it is not possible to have less than zero defectives. (See **Figure 93** Completed SQC Chart for Attributes).

ii)   **The np chart for NUMBER OF DEFECTIVES**

The number of defectives is np i.e. the number in the sample multiplied by the proportion of defectives in the sample.

Calculate the average number of defectives for the process

$$\bar{np} = \frac{np_1 + np_2 + np_3 + \ldots np_n}{m} \qquad (19)$$

Where np_1, np_2 etc. are the number of defectives in each of m samples inspected.

Calculate the Control Limits (UCL, LCL).

$$UCL_{np} = \overline{np} + 3 * \sqrt{\frac{\overline{np}(1-\overline{np})}{\overline{n}}} \qquad (20)$$

$$LCL_{np} = \overline{np} - 3 * \sqrt{\frac{\overline{np}(1-\overline{np})}{\overline{n}}} \qquad (21)$$

Draw the process mean and control limits on the chart and label (np, UCL_{np} and LCL_{np}).

Note: If the LCL is negative ignore this control limit since it is not possible to have less than zero defectives.

iii) The c chart for NUMBER OF DEFECTS (NON-CONFORMITIES)

The number of defects is c.

Calculate the average number of defects for the process

$$\overline{c} = \frac{c_1 + c_2 + c_3 + \dots c_m}{m} \qquad (22)$$

Where c_1, c_2 etc. are the number of defects in each of m samples inspected.

Calculate the Control Limits (UCL, LCL).

$$UCL_c = \overline{c} + (3 * \sqrt{\overline{c}} \qquad (23)$$

$$LCL_c = \overline{c} - (3 * \sqrt{\overline{c}} \qquad (24)$$

Draw the process mean and control limits on the chart and label (c, UCL_c and LCL_c).

Note: If the LCL is negative ignore this control limit since it is not possible to have less than zero defectives.

iv) The u chart for NUMBER OF DEFECTS (NON-CONFORMITIES) per unit

The number of defects per unit is u.

Calculate the average number of defects per unit for the process

$$\bar{u} = \frac{u_1 + u_2 + u_3 + \dots u_m}{n_1 + n_2 + n_3 + \dots n_m} \tag{25}$$

Where u_1, u_2 etc. are the number of defects per unit in each of m samples inspected.

Calculate the Control Limits (UCL, LCL).

$$UCL_u = \bar{u} + 3 * \sqrt{\frac{\bar{u}}{n}} \tag{26}$$

$$LCL_u = \bar{u} - 3 * \sqrt{\frac{\bar{u}}{n}} \tag{27}$$

Draw the process mean and control limits on the chart and label (u, UCL_u and LCL_u).

Note 1: As the sample size can vary with u charts then this can affect the control limits. Therefore it may be necessary to recalculate the control limits with the new sample size varies. Once calculated the new control limits should be plotted on the control charts.

Note 2: If the LCL is negative then ignore this control limit since it is not possible to have less than zero defectives.

v)   Multiple Characteristic Charts

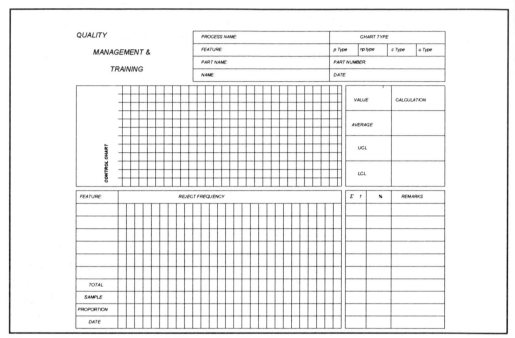

Figure 94 Attribute Control Chart - Multiple Features

With any of the above p, np, c and u charts it is only possible to monitor one characteristic. With all of these charts (p, np, c, and u) it may on occasion be necessary to monitor more than one characteristic or feature. In this situation a multiple characteristic chart can be employed which enables several characteristics to be recorded on the one chart. Thus giving a more comprehensive picture of the process performance and assisting with identifying the causes of variation (see **Figure 94** Attribute Control Chart - Multiple Features). Note that a Pareto Analysis (see section Pareto Analysis) of the various characteristics can be performed on the data calculated on the right-hand side of the chart.

STAGE 3 Data Analysis & Variation Reduction

One of the key purposes of using control charts is to improve quality by reducing variation. Consequently techniques need to be employed which can help identify any sources of variation. One method of reducing variation is to identify the presence of a non-random effect and if possible eliminate this non-random effect. Non-random effects can be recognise by applying the following tests when examining the charts.

TEST 1   **Any point outside the control limit**

TEST 2   **A series of 7 points above or below the average**

TEST 3   **A trend of 7 points up or down**

TEST 4   **Any other cyclic pattern**

Once a non-random effect has been identified its source should be investigated to determine what action is necessary to a) correct the non-conformity and b) prevent it recurring. As an aid to trouble shooting when non-random causes of variations occur, it is important to keep a log of any changes such as resetting, change of shift, material or equipment changes. The previous section - Stage 3 Data Analysis & Variation Reduction (for Variables) described interpretation of the four "Tests".

Benefits of SQC: Monitoring a process by the use of control charts provides the means of a process improvement programme. Giving the operators the opportunity to use their abilities to the full in controlling and improving the process performance - (world class performance), facilitating the process improvement for better quality, lower costs and greater productivity. SQC assists communication and discussion regarding the process performance, giving a better understanding of the requirements and processes ability to meet requirements.

Limitations of SQC: Although there are major benefits from the introduction of SQC there can also be some limitations and problems.

The organisation may operate a piece work scheme which may prevent the operator having the time to complete the control chart. *One solution to this is for the inspector to complete the control chart - this should be avoided at all costs as it defeats one of the main objectives of SQC - getting the operator involved with the quality of the work produced. The operator needs to be provided with all necessary facilities to perform SQC.*

The operator may not be capable of understanding or using SQC and may not wish to be involved. Not possible to gain appropriate commitment from all areas.   *If SQC is properly explained then there will be no problems in understanding or gaining commitment - it is only when the reasoning behind SQC is not fully explained that problems will be encountered.*

There will be certain expenditure associated with the introduction of SQC: resources to implement, equipment (measuring, chart holders and charts etc.), additional time completing and analysing the charts *-but there are savings as well (quality, productivity etc.).*

The process may not be capable of meeting specification therefore SQC cannot be applied. *Applying SQC will help identify the reasons for non-capability of the process and assist in establishing conformance to specification.*

The process may have too many features that need control. *Failure Mode and Effects Analysis may assist in identifying the key features that need control. Alternatively Multi-feature Attribute Charts could be employed.*

Not applicable on certain processes, i.e. no measurements are taken, only pass or fail. *Attribute control charts can be used for go/nogo situations.*

Statistical Tolerancing

Introduction

Statistical Tolerancing is a method of avoiding specifying unnecessarily tight tolerances. When assemblies consist of several mating components the designer will usually select tolerances for the individual components that will make tolerance clashes impossible. This is an understandable decision as it avoids any problems in assembling the finished product. However, in practice the designer is worrying unnecessarily because the chance of such a tolerance clash condition actually occurring is very remote.

An example of this could be a lamination assembly.

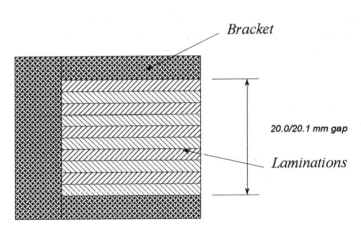

Figure 95 shows a bracket which contains 10 laminations. The 10 laminations fit inside a bracket with a 20/20.1mm gap. If the designer uses arithmetical tolerances then the following equation would apply.

Figure 95 Lamination

$$\frac{Total\ tolerance}{Number\ of\ Components} = Component\ Tolerance = \frac{0.1}{10} = 0.01mm \qquad \textbf{(28)}$$

In effect this means that each lamination must be between 2.00 to 2.01mm in size. In practice the probability of requiring this tolerance condition is very remote. This is because this tolerance allows for the assembly being fitted with all top limit laminations, which is a very unlikely event.

Statistical tolerancing takes into consideration that this is a very unlikely event. If statistical tolerancing was applied to this example then the tolerance could be much greater.

From the section on Process Capability Studies it was suggested that for process capability the process specification should be equal to or greater than 6 standard deviations.

$$Tolerance = 6 * \sigma \qquad\qquad (29)$$

Statisticians have shown that the sum of the individual variance equals the total variance. As standard deviation equals the square root of the variance then:

$$\sigma_t = \sigma_1^2 + \sigma_2^2 + \sigma_3^2 + \sigma_4^2 + \dots\dots\dots \ \sigma_n^2$$

Where $\sigma_1^2, \sigma_2^2, \sigma_3^2, \sigma_4^2, \dots\dots\dots \ \sigma_n^2$

is the individual standard deviation of each comp.

And σ_t *is the total standard deviation* $\qquad\qquad (30)$

From equation **(29)**

$$\sigma = \frac{Tolerance \ t}{6} \qquad\qquad (31)$$

Then substituting equation **(31)** into equation **(30)**

$$\left(\frac{T_t}{6}\right)^2 = \left(\frac{T_1}{6}\right)^2 + \left(\frac{T_2}{6}\right)^2 + \left(\frac{T_3}{6}\right)^2 + \left(\frac{T_4}{6}\right)^2 + \ldots\ldots\ldots\ldots\left(\frac{T_n}{6}\right)^2 \quad \textbf{(32)}$$

Which can be simplified to

$$\left(\frac{T_t}{6}\right)^2 = \left(\frac{T_i}{6}\right)^2 * n \quad\quad \textbf{(33)}$$

or

$$T_i = T_t * \sqrt{\frac{1}{n}}$$

Where **(34)**

T_i = *The individual tolerance*
T_t = *The total tolerance*
n = *The number of items*

For the lamination example, the tolerance for each individual lamination is

$$T_i = 0.1 * \sqrt{\frac{1}{10}} = 0.032mm \quad\quad \textbf{(35)}$$

This tolerance (0.032mm) is obviously an improvement on the 0.01mm which was given by arithmetical tolerancing. Statistical tolerancing can provide cost and time savings - in the example the tolerance is now over three times larger, with probably no effect on the overall assembly performance.

There are, however, certain dangers with statistical tolerancing. The process needs to be capable, the process distribution needs to be normal, and vary equally around the mean. If these criteria are not met then there will be a detrimental effect on the statistical tolerance.

Following are some other examples of the application of statistical tolerancing.

The first example is of a hole and shaft. The clearance between the hole and the shaft needs to be 0.01 to 0.05mm. Sharing the arithmetical tolerance equally between the hole and shaft would mean that the hole and shaft tolerance would be 0.02mm each.

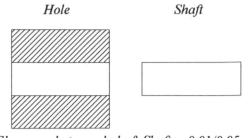

Hole   *Shaft*

Clearance between hole & Shaft = 0.01/0.05mm

Figure 96 Hole & Shaft

However if the statistical tolerancing equation is used then the tolerance becomes 0.028mm.

$$Individual\ tolerance\ T_i = 0.04 * \sqrt{\frac{1}{2}} = 0.028mm \qquad (36)$$

The second example is where a complete bar length is made up of three individual bars of various length and tolerance.

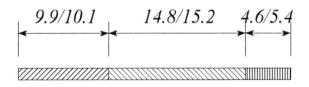

9.9/10.1   14.8/15.2   4.6/5.4

Bar length

Figure 97 Bar length

The arithmetical variation in bar length will be 0.2+0.4+0.8 = 1.4mm

The statistical variation in bar length will be:

$$\left(\frac{T_t}{6}\right)^2 = \left(\frac{0.2}{6}\right)^2 + \left(\frac{0.4}{6}\right)^2 + \left(\frac{0.8}{6}\right)^2 \qquad (37)$$

$$T_t = 0.92mm$$

As previously explained there are benefits to be gained from the use of statistical tolerancing but there are also dangers. It is important that the process is confirmed to be capable, otherwise the calculation may be in error.

Cost of Quality

Introduction

The Quality Department is often considered to be another cost burden on the company and not one that could make a positive contribution towards the company profitability. Nothing could be further from the truth and the quality function is capable of making essential contributions towards the financial performance of the company. Not only from the point of view of making a quality product

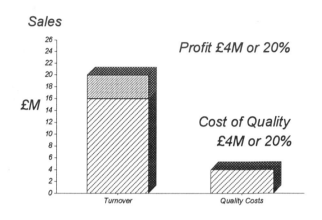

Figure 98 Typical cost of quality

that consequently would secure a strong position in the marketplace, but also by making significant savings in the overheads of the company.

Justification (Stage 1 - Sell)

It is essential to convince Management of the need to investigate the cost of quality in order to gain their commitment and active participation to the cost of quality programme. The method of convincing management could be based on the following:

Let us examine a company with sales of £20M and making profits of 20%. Investigations into the cost of quality at a number of companies has shown that the cost of quality will typically lie between 5 and 25% of the company's turnover. (See **Figure 98**).

Now say a 50% improvement in profits is targeted i.e. £6M. To achieve this new target then one approach could be to improve sales by a similar amount i.e. 50% providing the increased profit of £2M. (See **Figure 99**).

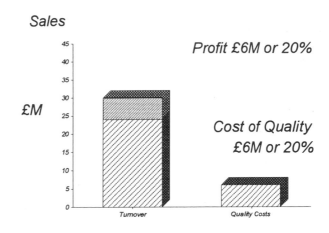

Figure 99 Sales improved by 50%

Using this approach to achieve the targeted £6M profit will involve large financial investment together with a major expansion programme, obviously involving considerable risks, particularly if it is set against a background of fierce market competition.

353

There is, however, another approach, that is to reduce the cost of quality by 50% this will produce the same effect; saving £2M and meeting the target figure of £6M. (See **Figure 100**). Now it is worth considering which is the easier to achieve a further 50% market penetration or to reduce the cost of quality by 50%. Which of these two exercises would require the greater

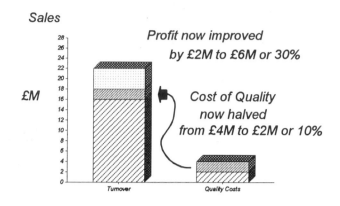

Figure 100 50% reduction in the cost of quality

resource to accomplish? The answer would largely depend on the industry involved, but this exercise does give an indication of the saving that can be made without resorting to a major expansion programme with all its inherent risks. In fact there are no risks involved in trying to reduce quality costs other than committing resources to achieve the objective. So the Quality Department can have a major impact on the profitability and performance of the company. The concept that is being suggested is that going for the avoidable quality costs can have major benefits without major risks. How do we undertake an attack on the avoidable quality costs?

There are a number of different approaches that can be adopted to establishing and reducing the cost of quality. E.g. a company or organisation wide approach, which involves the identification and detailing the total cost of quality for the organisation. Alternatively an individual department, process or task approach, where the process is analysed with the object to identify the conformance and non-conformance costs and to eliminate or reduce the non-conformance costs. Another approach may be to evaluate the relationship between profits and costs of an organisation. To determine a way in which these two factors can be altered to best effect.

The first approach described is the overall company wide approach (The Prevention, Appraisal, Failure Cost Model). On page 365 however, is described the process quality costs approach which can be used on a more departmental basis or in organisations where the more traditional Prevention, Appraisal, Failure cost model does not appear to work.

Table 61 describes a quality cost reduction programme that could be employed:

Prevention, Appraisal and Failure Model (PAF Model)

Cost of Quality Reduction Programme
Table 61

Stages in a Quality Cost Programme		
Stage	Name	Description
1	Sell	To establish whether it is viable to examine the cost of quality. Then to justify a programme to higher management to gain their commitment and agreement to provide allocation of resources.
2	Information	To find the key categories that go to make up the total quality cost.
3	Measurement	To assess the cost of each individual category and to decide how frequently the information should be gathered, together with establishing what resources should be allocated to gathering the data.
4	Analysis	To decide how the data will be analysed and when the results will be published and what form the results will take.
5	Action	To produce a programme that will effect a reduction in quality costs. Also to establish how this programme will be implemented and introduced including dates and targets.

Quality Cost Categories: (Stage 2 - Information)

What are the major factors that go to make up the total cost of quality? Well, basically there are four, **Table 62** below explains each of the factors.

Table 62 Cost of Quality - definition

Quality Cost Categories	
Prevention Cost	The cost of action taken to examine, avoid or reduce the number of defects and failures.
Appraisal Cost	The cost of assessing the achieved quality standard.
Failure Cost: The cost arising as a result of failing to achieve the required quality standard, which can be broken down into internal and external failure.	
Internal Failure Cost	Internal failure being within the organisation (e.g. scrap).
External Failure Cost	External failure being outside the organisation (e.g. warranty claims). This cost has often been found to be by far the largest expenditure and can be as high as 90% of the cost of quality.

The proportion shown in **Figure 101** typically reflects the expenditure or losses incurred against each category. The largest cost of quality is usually found to be failure costs, particularly warranty costs. The smallest cost of quality is usually prevention cost, the money spent on avoiding poor quality.

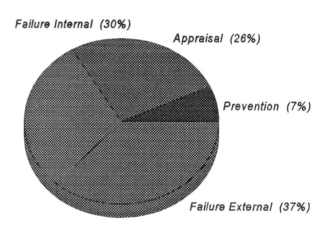

Figure 101 Cost of quality categories

The traditional approach to reducing the cost of quality was to attack the failure costs by increasing the appraisal costs (i.e. sorting the quality in). This would give the desired effect of stopping the customer receiving poor quality but has the knock on effect of increasing the internal failure costs (i.e. more scrap) and an increase in the appraisal costs (i.e. more inspectors). In order to break this cycle it is necessary to take preventive measures to stop the poor quality being produced in the first place, i.e. right first time.

So if we examine the cost of quality on the basis of prevention, appraisal and failure costs then this would assist in understanding the financial balance between these three factors. This information could be used in making judgements as to what the expenditure should be on prevention, appraisal and failure and to implement a cost reduction programme.

A typical company's cost of quality has been compiled. The break down of the costs can be seen in a spread sheet table. This table also shows some of the factors which are likely to make a contribution to the overall costs.

Data Collection (Stage 3 - Measurement)

The cost of each of these categories now needs to be established (see **Table 63**). To accomplish this task it is often wise to elicit the assistance of the company accountant to review the list of categories and to advise, and in certain cases, obtain the required data.

Some data may not be readily available and some means of data collection could become necessary or in certain circumstances accurate estimating may be appropriate, such as in establishing the cost of any quality planning carried out by the design department. (See Control of Non-Conforming Product and Corrective Action).

Some of the data could be already available but not in a suitable format, e.g.

- Staff and hourly paid payroll
- Scrap reports
- Rework reports
- Customer returns and field service data etc.
- Transport costs
- Design change notes

The pound rule: It is worth spending a little time examining the cost of change as this can constitute a considerable amount of the cost of quality. If the cost of change is examined at each stage in a project then it can be seen that after each stage the cost of change will increase. (See **Figure 102**) For example:

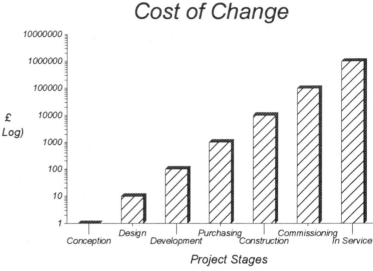

The change at the conceptual stage could only involve a few people and may require the rewriting of the functional specification - £1 (for an extremely simple change).

At the design stage a change could involve the redrawing of a number of drawings and possibly a rewrite to the specification - £10.

Figure 102 The pound rule

A change at the development stage could involve redrawing and further trials and tests - £100.

If the change occurs at the purchasing of equipment and material stage, this could involve extensive discussion with the supplier, changes to purchase orders and specification - £1000.

If construction or manufacturing has started and changes are required (possibly due to sub-assemblies not working or fitting together) then it can start to become extremely expensive, it may involve redesign and retesting of the new configuration - £10000.

At the commissioning stage changes may be required due to the product not passing the tests and trials. Man weeks of work may be required to resolve the problem of making the product work satisfactorily and to customer requirements. A large investment has been made which cannot be recouped as the customer will not pay until the product works properly. In the worse case there may be penalty clauses for late delivery - £100,000.

In service and under warranty, if the product requires recall or a campaign change then the costs can be dramatic to the extent that companies become insolvent because of these excessive costs. Possibly the classic case of the cost of change is the Shuttle Challenger - £1,000,000.

The pound rule indicates that a pound invested at the start of a project could provide savings by a factor of 10 for each subsequent stage of the project. Note, it may be considered that some of the estimated costs of change are very conservative.

Table 63 Spread Sheet showing the Cost of Quality

Cat No.	Cost Category	Company: QM&T Location GUILDFORD Year: 1994/5 Quarters				Total £K	Target £K	Diff £K
		Jan/Mar	Apr/Jun	Jul/Sep	Oct/Dec			
	PREVENTION COSTS							
P1	Quality Mg't & Sup'n	5031	5011	5039	5546	20.6	25	4.3
P2	Quality Engineering	4258	4227	3935	3988	16.4	16	-0.4
P3	Reliability Assessment	93	6	77	163	0.3	3	2.6
P4	Audit	500	500	500	500	2.0	2	0
P5	Supplier Assessment	636	590	424	16	1.7	3	1.3
P6	Quality Training	437	265	250	586	1.5	5	3.5
P7	Calibration	399	325	425	376	1.5	4	2.5
P8	Equip't (Engineering)	990	288	515	1217	3.0	3	0
	Total Prevention Costs	12344	11212	11165	12392	47.0	61	13.8
	APPRAISAL COSTS							
A1	Laboratory Test'g	48	52	16	463	0.6	1000	0.4
A2	In-Process Inspection	39336	39714	39201	39201	15.7	150	-7.4
A3	Insp'n & Test Equip't	2008	1916	776	402	0.5	12	6.9
A4	Goods Rec'g Inspect'n	4623	4590	4540	4548	18.3	20	1.7
A5	Product Quality Audit	609	600	636	636	2.4	3	0.5
	Total Appraisal Costs	46624	46872	45169	45250	37.5	1095	2.1
	INTERNAL FAILURE							
I1	Scrap	33981	31947	22515	25533	11.4	100	-14
I2	Rectification & Rework	14274	13056	12420	16695	56.4	50	-6.4
I3	Cost of Change	3636	429	183	69	4.3	0	-4.3
I4	Concessions	1530	348	135	42	20.5	0	-2.1
	Total Internal Failure	53421	45780	35253	42339	92.6	150	-26.8
	EXTERNAL FAILURE							
E1	Warranty Returns	31076	34471	34805	33212	133564	100	-33.5
E2	Complaints	3732	3258	3066	3318	13374	15	1.6
E3	Product Liability	15000	0	0	0	15000	15	0
E4	Warranty Spares	15040	15289	15746	15460	61535	50	-11.5
	Total External Failure	64848	53018	53617	51990	223473	180	-43.4
	TOTAL COST OF QUALITY	177237	156882	145204	151971	631.3	577	-54.3
	Sales Revenue	1004104	1001515	1002477	1001791	4009	3600	-410
	Manufacturing Costs	802575	810433	836565	835620	3285	4000	714.9
	Direct Labour Cost	195686	187006	186888	180452	750	1200	450
	% Cost of Quality/Sales	17.7%	15.7%	14.5%	15.2%	15.7%	16.0	
	% Scrap Cost/Manufactur'g	4.2%	3.9%	2.7%	3.1%	3.5%	2.5%	
	% Rectifi'n/Direct Labour	7.3%	7.0%	6.6%	9.3%	7.5%	4.2%	
	% Warranty Returns/Sales	3.1%	3.4%	3.5%	3.3%	3.3%	2.8%	
	% Warranty Spares/Sales	1.5%	1.5%	1.6%	1.5%	1.5%	1.4%	

Investigation (Stage 4 - Analysis)

Having identified the cost of each of the categories then these costs need to be analysed as a prelude to taking action to reduce the total cost. The analysis can be accomplished by various methods:

i) Comparison between prevention, appraisal and failure costs.

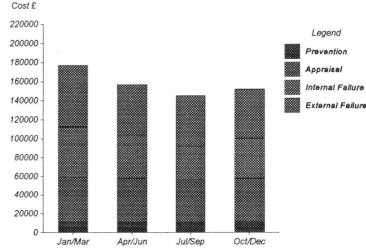

This provides the first snapshot of the way by which quality is organised and gives an initial guide as to whether the right balance is being maintained between prevention and appraisal. (See **Figure 103**).

Figure 103 Total Cost of Quality

ii) Comparison by time.

Analysis of quality cost data on the basis of time is essential in indicating trends, monitoring performance and to ascertain whether real improvements are being made, reducing the cost of quality.

iii) Comparison between products or departments.

The cost data can also be arranged by product or department to enable comparisons to be made between the relative performance of one product with another, or one department with another.

iv) Bases.

The cost figures by themselves indicate the expenditure on quality however, to establish a true and consistent guide as to the relative costs, it is necessary to relate the costs to different bases or indices. Some examples of quality cost indices can be:

a) Labour hours - Number of personnel involved in production or direct labour hours.

$$\% \ Rectification \ = \ \frac{Rectification \ Hours \ * \ 100\%}{Direct \ Labour \ Hours} \qquad \textbf{(38)}$$

The comparison of rectification hours is based on the time spent on rectifying bad products against the time spent on making good products. This comparison could be demonstrated graphically showing the year's percentage rectification performance.

$$\% \ Cost \ of \ Appraisal \ = \ \frac{Inspection \ Hours \ + \ Test \ Hours \ Hours \ * \ 100\%}{Direct \ Labour \ Hours} \qquad \textbf{(39)}$$

The cost of appraisal is a comparison of the time spent making the product against the time spent inspecting and testing the product.

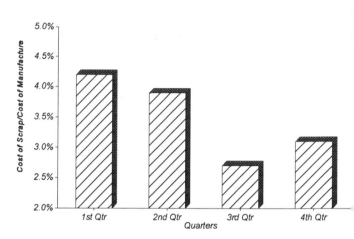

Figure 104 Percentage Scrap

b) Quantity - Number of components produced .

The percentage scrap calculation compares the number of bad components made against the number of good components made. (Sometimes referred to as yield). See **Figure 104**.

$$\% \ Scrap \ = \frac{Number \ of \ Components \ Scrapped \ * \ 100\%}{Number \ of \ Components \ Produced} \tag{40}$$

The calculation of percentage warranty compares the number of products returned faulty with the number of products sold and provides some indication of the changes in the proportion of warranty returns.

$$\% \ Warranty \ Returns \ = \frac{Number \ of \ Warranty \ Returns \ * \ 100\%}{Total \ Number \ of \ Products \ Sold} \tag{41}$$

c) Costs

    a.   Value of the output (unaffected by the fluctuation in sales).

    b.   Manufacturing cost (Labour + material costs)

    c.   Value of the sales

$$\% \ Total \ Cost \ of \ Quality = \frac{Total \ Cost \ of \ Quality \ * \ 100\%}{Value \ of \ the \ Output} \qquad \textbf{(42)}$$

The total cost of quality calculation compares the money spent on quality against the value of the output. Diagram **Figure 103** Total Cost of Quality shows the changes in the percentage total cost of quality throughout the year, together with the proportion of the costs spent on prevention, appraisal and failure. The diagram also shows the changes in the proportions of prevention, appraisal and failure.

Action (Stage 5)

Pareto Analysis Establishing the factors which together make up all the various causes of rejects, invariably means that a considerable number of problems are discovered. To tackle all these problems at one go would require enormous resources and in any case some of the problems may be trivial and not worth pursuing for the time being. A technique invaluable in singling out those problems which have the greatest influence on the total reject quantity is Pareto Analysis. Very often when this type of analysis is conducted the results show that when placed in order of importance, out of a given number of causes of non-conformance only a small percentage, usually around 20%, account for 80% of the total non-conformance problem. For this reason the concept is often known as the 80 - 20 rule, (see section Pareto Analysis).

Cause and Effect Diagrams The first stage in completing a cause and effect diagram is for the team to clearly define the problem. Having established the group's views on the most likely cause of the effect or problem, the team then needs to consider what, in their view, is the most likely cause or suspect. These suspects or causes can be ranked in order of most likely or most easy to eliminate from the investigations. Having prioritised the suspects an action plan or investigation plan can be completed and implemented. This plan would detail the suspect name, the method of evaluating the suspect's guilt and who is responsible for conducting the investigation. This stage would be repeated until the actual culprit was discovered - it may even be necessary for the team to reconstruct another cause and effect diagram to assist in identifying the culprit. (See section Cause and Effect Diagrams). In certain cases the problem may be so complex that more sophisticated statistical techniques may need to be employed (Taguchi Techniques). One of the reasons for employing Taguchi may be that there is no single factor or guilty party which is causing the problem but several factors interacting together.

Process Quality Costs Model

Stages in establishing and reducing the process quality costs are outlined in **Table 64**.

Table 64 Process Quality Cost Programme

Stages in a Process Quality Cost Programme		
Stage	Name	Description
1	Sell	To establish whether it is viable to examine the cost of quality. Then to justify a programme to higher management to gain their commitment and agreement to provide allocation of resources.
2	The Process	To identify the process to be analysed. Break the process down into discrete steps and tasks.
3	Process Analysis	To identify the inputs and outputs to the process. How the process is to be controlled and what resources are necessary for the process to work.
4	Process Quality Cost Reduction	To identify the costs associated with the process in terms of conformance and non-conformance costs and improve the process performance by the elimination of waste.

Justification   (Stage 1 - Sell) (See Justification Page 352)

This stage is the most important as without Management Commitment the Process Quality Cost programme cannot succeed.

Process Selection   (Stage 2 - The Process)

The process to be analysed needs to be identified. Once the process has been identified then the process can be broken down into each discrete task or step. Process flow charting is one way of describing the process, showing the sequence and sometimes feedback loops. During this first stage an analysis can be performed for the need for each task and agreement as to whether the sequence and tasks are correct.

Input/Output Analysis (Stage 3 - Process Analysis)

The inputs and outputs to the process need to be identified, how the process is controlled and what resources are necessary. This analysis can either be done by constructing a simple description of the inputs to the process, the activities associated with the process and the outputs from the process.

Process: All the activities or tasks necessary to convert the process inputs into the process outputs.

Inputs: The inputs to the process are all the materiel (material, equipment, data etc.) necessary, for the process to convert successfully into the output.

Output: The results of the process conversion. All the material, data etc. that the process generates.

Due to the complexity of some processes it is a good idea to restrict the analysis to a single process e.g. only material flow, paper work, information etc.

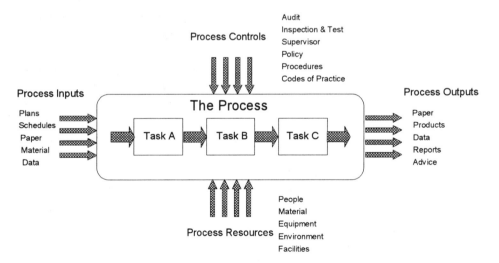

Figure 105 Process input/output

Alternatively (see **Figure 105**) the analysis can be quite complex not only detailing the inputs, activities and outputs but also the method of controlling the process (feedback mechanisms etc.) and the resources necessary for the process to take place.

Process controls: The method of controlling the process. How is the process controlled? inspection & test activities, supervision monitoring, audits, feedback of results etc.

Process resources: The items or people that facilitate the conversion process. Not the items that are converted but those items which make the conversion process possible e.g. people, equipment, data, information, facilities etc.

From this analysis it is possible to show how each of the tasks are linked together, the sequence and interdependence of the tasks. The diagram **Figure 105** can then be analysed to ensure that:

  o All the inputs must be available.

  o Each task must have an owner. (See Departmental Purpose Analysis)

  o All of the tasks must be of value. (See Non-Value Added Activities)

  o All of the outputs must go somewhere (if the outputs go nowhere - then they are unnecessary and should be deleted).

Due to the complexity of some processes it is sometimes a good idea to restrict the analysis to a single process e.g. material flow, paper work, information etc.

Some other techniques that can be usefully employed in understanding and analysing the process are Failure Mode and Effects Analysis (FMEA) and Quality Planning. FMEA can help to identify the failure modes of the process and force some decision regarding the action to take to eliminate any potential failures of the process. For example the failure mode could be misunderstanding of the customers' requirements or needs. The action may be to get the customers to write down their requirements. If the possible failure mode cannot be eliminated then action needs to be taken to avoid the likelihood of the failure modes occurring; in this case Quality Planning can be helpful as it forces a description of the quality controls that will be applied at each stage to ensure process conformity. Again, the example of misunderstanding the customer needs, it may not be possible for the customer to write down their needs or requirements (often the customer does not know what they want!). In this case Quality Planning may provide an approach, such as reviewing internally, with the key project personnel, the internally produced customer requirements.

Action (Stage 4 - Process Quality Cost Reduction)

367

Once the process is fully understood, it is then possible to evaluate the process to determine the necessary and unnecessary costs.

Completing a Failure Mode and Effects Analysis for the processes under investigation (see section Failure Mode and Effects Analysis) may help in determining the necessary and unnecessary costs. This is because part of the FMEA process is to identify possible and actual failure modes and their causes.

Necessary Costs: (Price of Conformance) Those activities and tasks associated with completing and getting the process right.

Unnecessary Costs: (Price of Non-Conformance) Those activities as a result of getting the activity or task wrong (unnecessary costs - the task necessary as a result of failure).

Table 65 Process Quality Costs - for the Purchasing Department

Process Name: Purchasing Department				Process Owner: Buyer			Date	
#	Description	Necessary Tasks	Time (min)	£	Unnecessary Tasks	Time (min)	%Occur rence	£
1	Receive Purchase Requisitions	Reviewing/accepting the Purchase Requisition and up dating the purchase ledger.	2	0.3	Rejected purchase requisitions. Dealing with queries regarding order processing.	10	5%	0.08
2	Identify supplier	Searching appropriate databases for an adequate supplier.	10	1.7	Failing to identify a supplier or no unqualified acceptance of the terms and conditions. Reordering in the event of a change of requirements or wrong information.	30	1%	0.05
3	Complete the Purchase Order	Completing the Purchase Order (including gaining approval). Updating the Purchase Ledger.	5	0.8	Inadequate or incorrect information on the purchase requisition.	20	5%	0.17
4	Liaise with Suppliers	Liaison and building up a good working relationship with the supplier.	5	0.8	Inadequate or incorrect information sent to the supplier. Additions, omissions or changes to the order. Chasing the status of the purchase order.	30	4%	0.20
5	Receive purchased material	Goods Receiving and Inspection & testing.	15	2.5	Late delivery, rejection, poor service, defects, shortages, reconciliation of any discrepancies etc.	40	3%	0.20
		Total	37	6.1	Total	130		0.70

Table 65 shows a Process Cost Model for the purchasing department. The table consists of:

Cost of Quality

Column 1	The task number
Column 2	The task description
Column 3	The necessary tasks - Those activities necessary to complete the tasks correctly
Column 4	The time to complete the necessary tasks
Column 5	The cost of completing the necessary tasks i.e. time to complete * the labour rate e.g. 6 min/60 (hours) * £10/hour = £1
Column 6	If any unnecessary task occurs the time to complete the unnecessary tasks - Those activities necessary as a result of a task being incorrectly performed
Column 7	The time to complete the unnecessary tasks
Column 8	The likelihood of an unnecessary task occurring e.g. The average number of orders with incorrect information is usually about 5 in a hundred orders or 5%
Column 9	The average cost of completing an unnecessary task i.e. time to complete * the likelihood of occurrence * labour rate e.g. When an incorrect information on an order occurs, it usually takes 20 minutes to resolve, but an incorrect order will only happen in about 5 in a hundred orders. Therefore, the cost will be: (Time to resolve) 20 min/60 (hours) * (Likelihood of happening) 5% * (labour Rate) £10/hour = £0.17

Comparison of the Total Cost of Quality with Process Quality Cost

The advantage of the Total Cost of Quality (TCQ) over the Process Quality Cost (PQC) approach is that the cost of quality for the whole organisation will be established whereas only the cost of quality for particular processes will be determined with the PQC approach. This tends to suggest that the TCQ approach is the best, unfortunately this is not always the case. For certain organisations it is very difficult to use the TCQ model as it does not fit the way the organisation works. E.g. a service organisation servicing and repairing equipment or a construction company does not fit the traditional TCQ model. Determining the internal and external costs is very difficult. However, analysing each individual service or design process in turn can expose the true hidden costs of quality. With design organisations, is project planning or design reviews a quality task or part of the normal design activities and therefore part of the design costs and not a quality cost at all.

It is important to note that this is not an "either or" situation; employing both techniques can be successful, possibly using the PQC model first to obtain and establish the individual process quality cost data, then collating all the information into the organisation's overall TCQ model.

Problems with Cost of Quality Analysis & Data Collection

There are certain issues that need to be considered when compiling the Cost of Quality Data. Namely, there is a considerable amount of effort associated with collection of the data which is wasted if the data is not used or acted on. The frequency of data collection can vary but often is between quarterly to yearly. Monthly is generally too frequent. It is important to gather the data to confirm that improvements and savings are being made. If the wrong data is gathered or false information is collected this can give a false picture of the Costs of Quality. Care needs to be taken with the targets set for Costs of Quality as over-confident figures and conversely over-cautious targets will create a falsely optimistic picture of the future for the company.

Profit/Cost Model

Introduction

Whilst the PAF and PQC models are the more widely accepted methods of evaluating the costs of quality for organisations, there are other approaches which are just as effective, namely the profit/cost model.

The two previously described models tend to focus on identifying the areas where the failure or non-conformance costs are high and taking steps to reduce these costs. A different approach may be to evaluate the cost of production or delivering a service, with the aim of reducing the conformance costs, together with identifying ways in which to maximise the profitability of an organisation.

The relationship under investigation is the Profit/Cost ratio. The object being to improve the ratio by identifying the means of increasing profit and/or reducing costs.

$$Improving \ the \ Profit/Cost \ Ratio \ = \ \frac{Increasing \ the \ Profits}{Reducing \ the \ Costs} \qquad \textbf{(43)}$$

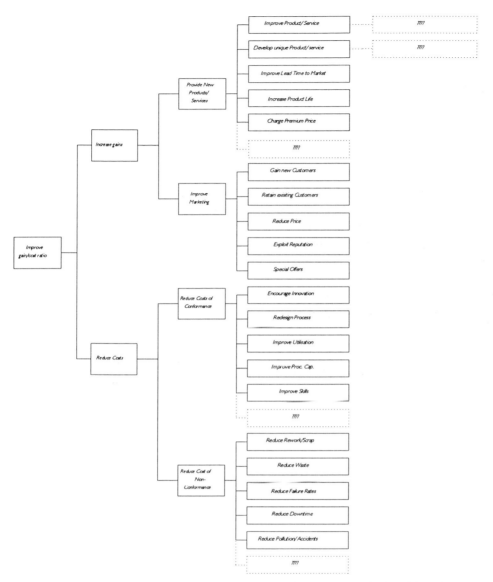

Figure 106 Relationship Diagram

For non-profit making organisations the profit aspect maybe considered to be underspend on the organisation's budget without detrimentally affecting the quality of the delivered service or product.

Some more astute readers may have noticed a basic conflict with this ratio and TQM. *The primary purpose of a TQM organisation is not to make a profit but to satisfy the customer. Satisfying the customer will consequentially provide a profit!* Whether this statement is accurate or not, can be safely left to the TQM philosopher. Those from the school of - *if it works use it* - may still like to evaluate this approach.

Guidelines

The method of conducting the analysis is initially the same as with the other Quality Cost models - *justification*. It is pointless to embark on a Quality Cost exercise without the active and visible support of the management team.

Next the factors which affect the profitability and costs need to be established. One of the methods that can be used is a relationship diagram shown in **Figure 106** (similar to a cause and effect diagram).

The left-hand side of the diagram shows the objective - improving the profit/costs ratio. To the right are the means of achieving this objective. Firstly increasing profit and reducing costs and so on. At the extreme right of the diagram are some question marks (????). This is deliberate to show how the diagram can be extended. For example, in the top box marked ???? could be - Better Guarantee or Individualise the Product or Service. Other ideas could be generated on how to improve the Product or Service branch of the diagram.

Exercise - Cost of Quality

The section Cost of Quality refers to three methods of determining the quality costs: the Prevention, Appraisal and Failure method (PAF Model), the Process Cost Model and the Profit/Cost model.

Using the above models, obtain sufficient data to apply each of these methodologies to an organisation and process of your choice.

a.   The output of the PAF methodology should be:
     i.   A Cost of Quality Spread Sheet
     ii.   Identification of the key cost of quality elements
     iii.   A brief action plan that would result in real reduction of the cost of quality for the organisation to which the exercise has been applied

b.   The output of the Process Cost Model should be:
     i.   A completed Process Quality Cost table (including both actual and synthetic costs)
     ii.   Identification of the key non-conformance costs
     iii.   A brief action plan which would result in real reduction of the cost of operating the process selected

c.   The output of the Profit/Cost Model should be:
     i.   A completed Profit/Cost Model relationship diagram
     ii.   A brief action plan that would result in real reduction of the cost of quality for the organisation to which the profit/cost model has been applied

Quality Assurance and the Law

The law has always been concerned with quality by specifying what standard should be set and by providing means of enforcement. Legal attention has now widened to the process or system of controlling quality and the overall responsibility of management to provide safe, high-quality goods and services.

The relevance of the law to Quality Assurance is twofold. Firstly, everything happens according to law and as a corollary there is no such thing as an accident. In fact the systematic approach of QA is an acknowledgement of that very truth. Secondly, and more conventionally, the law establishes a system by which duties and responsibilities may be identified and enforced.

The Criminal Law is a means of protecting society from the dangers of poor quality and deterring or punishing those who fail to achieve their public duty. Civil Law is a means of enforcing private responsibilities and recompensing those who suffer damage as a consequence.

Thus the law concerns us all, for whatever our situation, at work or outside, we need to rely on the safety and reliability of other people's designs, products and services.

It is well known that ignorance of the law is no defence, and today it seems that inaction is no defence either. Society is not prepared to accept failures in quality or safety, as witnessed by public reaction to recent tragedies, for example in rail, sea and air transport. More and more the individuals concerned and the companies for which they work are being held responsible and liable by the courts. At the same time there is a continual stream of new laws, regulations, codes and directives, which seek to protect society and indeed improve the quality of our lives.

Criminal Law

Statutes or Acts of Parliament, may establish a criminal responsibility as a deterrent or punishment for bad quality. Penalties may include fines, the loss of a trading licence or even imprisonment. It is a crime to sell certain goods, which are not approved by an Independent agency and marked by them, e.g. Hall-marking, or other products which are not marked as conforming to British Standards, e.g. crash helmets. Offences may be committed under the Weights and Measures Acts, Food and Drugs legislation and the Trade Descriptions Acts. It is a defence under the last mentioned Acts to have taken reasonable precautions and exercised due diligence to avoid committing an offence. In

1989 one company pleaded this defence and cited its QA system and BS5750 registration as proof. However the prosecution was successful, thus indicating that the British Standard assessment may fall short of what the law requires.

The Health and Safety at Work Act, 1974, laid down duties on the designers, manufacturers, importers and suppliers of substances and articles for use at work. Since 1988 these duties have been extended to include liability for the misuse of items where that was foreseeable. Chairs and tables are often used to stand on and screwdrivers are commonly employed to open tins of paint! Another amendment means that producers and suppliers now have an extended duty under the Act. There is a continuing duty to revise information and warnings about a product when anything gives rise to a serious risk to health and safety. Responsibilities are ongoing, and there is no simple answer as to when, if ever, they cease. Executives can be personally liable under the Act if consent, connivance or neglect is proved against them. The possibility of a manslaughter charge is no idle threat today.

Since the Consumer Protection Act 1987 it is now a criminal offence "to supply consumer goods which are not reasonably safe having regard to all the circumstances". One defence would be compliance with an approved standard. Trading Standards Officers have been given greater powers of investigation, testing, seizure and prohibition, in the interest of public safety.

More recently, new regulations have been introduced to control the quality of the work environment, namely the Control of Substances Hazardous to Health, Noise at Work and Electricity at Work Regulations. Other E.C. Directives also cover the Safety of the workplace, and work equipment. A common feature in all these Regulations and Directives is the need for a systematic approach to ensure assets, materials and services are assessed, evaluated and maintained properly. In short the risks involved must be well managed.

Civil Law

There are three areas of civil law which are concerned with the quality of goods and services. They are the law of Contract, Negligence and Strict Liability. These laws apply whether or not any criminal offence has occurred.

The Law of Contract

A contract is a legally binding agreement, whether in writing or not, by which the parties acquire rights and undertake responsibilities. The quality of the subject matter may be expressly stated in a specification. There may even be an insistence that a particular QA system is in operation. Terms as to quality may also be implied by custom or by statute. The Sale of Goods Act 1979 implies the following terms into business contracts:

(1)   Goods must fit their description. This may refer to quantity, quality, size, measurement, packing, labelling and so on.

(2)   Goods must accord with their sample.

(3)   Goods must be of merchantable quality. This term is being replaced now by "acceptable quality".

(4)   Goods must be fit for the purposes requested.

One question that often arises is: for how long should quality last? Case law may provide some guidance. In **Crowther & Shannon (1975)** the dealer was still liable for the engine seizure of a second-hand Jaguar that he sold - with 80,000 miles on the clock.

Terms as to the quality of a service are implied by The Supply of Goods and Services Act 1982. In the absence of specific terms a service should be to a reasonable quality, at a reasonable price and performed within a reasonable time. The definition of reasonableness is what could be expected according to the circumstances of the particular case. Ultimately it may require an arbitrator or judge to decide.

Legislation has also been found necessary to stop parties contracting out of their responsibilities by the use of exclusion clauses or disclaimers. Under the Unfair Contract Terms Act 1977, such clauses must pass the test of "reasonableness". As between businesses it is possible to exclude liability via specially agreed non-standard terms, for example, that an item is not warranted as suitable for incorporation into some other assembly.

Contractual Chains. This inter-relationship between contracts merits further consideration. The diagram **Figure 107** Contractual Chain illustrates how many parties may be involved in the quality of an item from its initial conception through to its use or even misuse. Links in the contractual chain can be identified at various stages. Each party therefore has legal responsibilities towards its immediate partner.

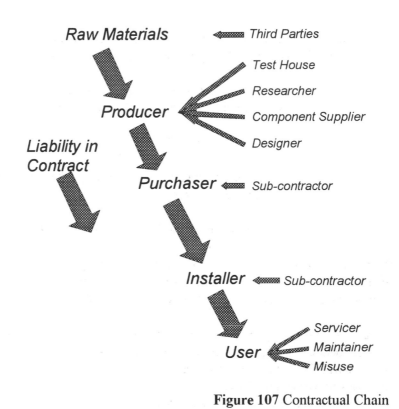

Figure 107 Contractual Chain

However, the advent of Product Liability (see section The Law of Strict Liability) has increased the exposure of all these parties to legal redress. Not only can the 'chain' be short-circuited with a direct action by anyone suffering damage, but as the liability is now 'joint and several' one party may be answerable for the liability of another, who, for example, has become insolvent. The contractual device that is now being used is to obtain an indemnity in the contract to prevent that liability being transferred. This in turn necessitates an insurance obligation to ensure the party responsible is able to pay. Concern about the capability, financial or otherwise, of a trading partner, has been a key factor in the development of QA itself.

The Law of Negligence

In the diagram "Contractual Chain" reference is made to "Third Parties", who are outside the "contractual chain". Without a remedy in law - Contract third parties can only sue for damages under the Tort of Negligence. A "tort" is simply a civil wrong. To be successful a victim has to prove that he is owed a duty of care, that the duty was broken, and that the resultant damage caused his injury. This is well illustrated by the famous case of **Donoghue v Stevenson**, in 1932, when the non-purchaser of a bottle of ginger ale was made ill by the drink which also contained the remains of a snail. It is interesting to note that the retailer of the drink was not liable because he could not inspect the opaque, sealed bottles. Hence it was the manufacturer who was negligent in not having an adequate system for production and quality control.

The duty of care under Negligence can be very far reaching. Anyone involved in the design, production, inspection and marketing of a product or service may be liable. The Tort of Negligence has evolved to include liability for careless statements, even negligent certification of the quality of a product. After a recent Chinook helicopter crash in the U.S.A. both the Boeing inspector and the F.A.A. representative were charged with negligence. A QA system is evidence that an organisation is attempting to fulfil its duty of care. On the other hand it may be easier to point out a failure by reference to such a system. So it may be a two-edged sword with the advent of more professional organisations seeking to be quality assured, warnings have been sounded again. An engineer's duty of care is based on reasonable skill and care, but the public may be entitled to a higher standard if the engineer is certified. However QA is evidence of the 'state of the art', and unless there was an alternative equivalent system, that might be evidence of a breach of duty too.

The apparent ease of suing in negligence is however tempered by the need to prove fault. Without such proof the defendant is not liable. This difficulty reached a high-water mark with the Thalidomide tragedy. The drug manufacturers pleaded that they were not at fault in failing to foresee the consequences of the product they developed. In turn this tragedy precipitated a movement to introduce No-fault Liability, more accurately termed: Strict Liability.

The Law of Strict Liability

An E.C. Directive gave rise to the Consumer Protection Act 1987, which introduced into the U.K. a system of strict liability for products. Now any person injured by a defect in a product may sue any person responsible for its production or supply (including importers and 'own branders') and without the need to prove fault. Therefore the onus is thus on the party sued to prove who else was responsible for the defect if they are to escape liability. Furthermore, as the liability is joint and several one party's inability to pay may render another liable for the whole damage. This was referred to earlier as the cause for indemnity and insurance terms in contracts. It illustrates the importance of quality in procurement, servicing, maintenance and so on.

As victims had discovered to their cost before, it is not easy to prove that another party is to blame. One prerequisite is to be able to trace the product origin, hence traceability and accurate record systems are essential, and these records may be required for up to twenty-five years after initial circulation. Traceability will be vital too if a dangerous product has to be recalled. Recent examples involving baby food and mineral water show the importance of emergency recall procedures which should be laid down, rehearsed and fully effective. The damage to business reputation here is verging on the irrecoverable.

Under the new law it is still incumbent upon the claimant to prove that there was a defect in the product. However the definition of a defective product is quite wide, i.e. "where the safety of the product is not such as persons generally are entitled to expect". It is not the expectation of the designer, producer or marketing manager nor the user. Thus, if people expect screwdrivers not to fracture when opening tins of paint, that indicates a defect in the screwdriver and cannot be dismissed as misuse. This has given rise to a few surprising cases on 'reasonable misuse', (although not as bizarre as several American equivalents). It is not unreasonable to stand on a packing case, nor to crawl across a ladder suspended across some open floor joists. The warnings and instructions for product use take on added significance here, for they are deemed to be part of the product. Such literature must be in the appropriate languages, unambiguous, and be to hand even long after initial circulation. For all these points the importance of feedback, via prototype testing, market research, customer complaints, records of accidents and near-misses assume added significance.

The so-called "defect" may also manifest itself in the handling, storage, packaging or delivery of an item. Nor are these stages limited to the control of the producer or supplier, for the user may need to be warned too. This is another example of the continuing responsibility even long after handover which was referred to under the Health and Safety at Work Act (See section Criminal Law - Health and Safety

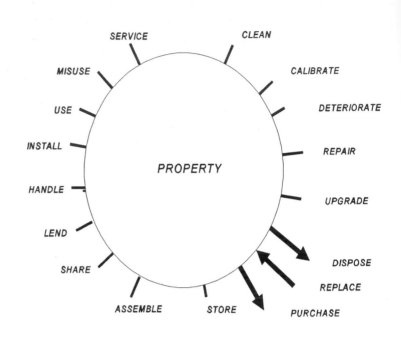

Figure 108 Product Life Cycle (After Sale)

at Work) . In fact a product in its life "may play many parts", as illustrated by **Figure 108** Product Life Cycle (after sale). At any of the stages on the circle a defect may arise for which the designer, producer or supplier could be sued. The onus is then on them to prove otherwise. It should be noted that this potential liability may continue and include the safe disposal of the product. Designers of buildings may be liable if decommissioning cannot be carried out safely. Under another E.C. Directive, which was implemented in 1991, strict liability applies to anyone who produces, stores, transports or disposes of waste. A QA system would seem to be indispensable.

The law is becoming more involved in how goods are processed or services are provided rather than just being concerned with the quality of the end product. It seems right to look at the causes not just the effects. It will also mean a safer workplace and environment for the staff and the community. The principle is that prevention of the harm is better than the cure and QA helps to achieve both. Lately management systems have come in for heavy criticism whenever tragic accidents have occurred. Public opinion demands more accountability and the punishment of companies and individuals who fail in their duties. Individual claims for damages can now even exceed £1M. The consequences for the reputation, even survival, of a business are immense. It is no accident that Insurance Companies are offering premium reductions to firms that can show evidence of the assessed capability of their Quality Assurance Systems.

CE Marking

Introduction

The European Union (EU) or E.C. has a series of Directives on General Safety and Product Liability. These Directives were agreed by all Member States and will affect all businesses that design, manufacture or export into the European Union. The purpose of these directives is to:

CE

Figure 109
The CE Mark

o   Create a legal requirement for all the Member States to adopt these agreed, common and harmonised technical standards.

o   Prohibit the supply of goods which do not conform to these technical standards. The CE mark is shown in the diagram **Figure 109** and is used to declare that a product complies with all relevant standards.

o   Promote free trade within the EU by removing local or national technical standards that may have been a barrier to free trade. The CE mark is the guarantee that the product will not be challenged at national boundaries.

Listed in **Table 66** are the Directives adopted since the resolution of May 1985.

Table 66 EU Directives

Title	Directive
Acoustics	90/270/EEC
Active Implantable Medical Devices	90/385/EEC
Appliances Burning Gaseous Fuels	90/396/EEC
Cable-Way Installations	94/C70/07
CE Labels	91/C160/07
Construction Products	89/106/EEC
Electrical Equipment designed for use within certain voltage limits	73/23/EEC

Title	Directive
Electromagnetic Compatibility	89/336/EEC
Machinery	89/392/EEC
Medical Devices	93/42/EEC
New Hot-Water Boilers fired with Liquid or Gaseous Fuels	92/42/EEC
Non-automatic Weight Instruments	89/384/EEC
Personal Protective Equipment	89/686/EEC
Pressure Equipment	93/C246/10
Recreational Craft	92/C123/07
Safety of Toys	88/378/EEC
Satellite Earth Stations	3/97/EEC
Simple Pressure Vessels	87/404/EEC
Telecommunications Terminal Equipment	91/263/EEC
VDU Ergonomics	90/270/EEC 91/2303

It is a criminal act to supply goods which do not conform to the harmonised standard and consequently the penalties are quite severe. They include the supplier being required to remove all similar products from the EU. The persons found guilty will have a criminal record and can be imprisoned for up to three months and fined £5,000 per offence.

Outlined below are some typical steps necessary to ensure designs and products meet the CE marking requirements and any other appropriate national or international regulations and directives. There are some reference documents which include:

> Outline Technical Construction File Contents
> Outline Declaration of Conformance
> Outline Declaration of Incorporation

The procedure below, embraces the sequence of events necessary to ensure compliance with Directives or Regulations. (This needs to include both new or modified product or production equipment and other modified purposes such as production.) The procedure also needs to include the steps necessary when incorporating other suppliers equipment into a company's own products.

There may be a need to review existing Purchasing and Goods Inwards Inspection Procedures to ensure that they adequately cover the CE marking requirements and do not need enhancement.

CE Marking Procedure Guidelines

Introduction: **Figure 110** CE Marking Overview indicates the general shape to addressing the CE mark requirements. CE marking is self-certification and does not usually involve third party registration. In other words the supplier is claiming compliance with a particular requirement as supported by their own checks, tests, approvals etc.

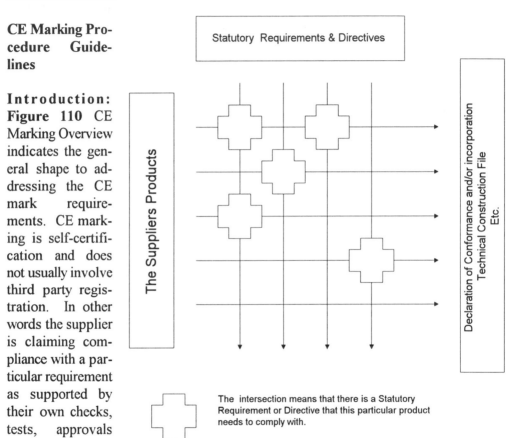

The intersection means that there is a Statutory Requirement or Directive that this particular product needs to comply with.

Figure 110 CE Marking Overview

The left-hand side is a list of all of the supplier's products. At the top is a list of any applicable requirements, regulations or directive. The output from this analysis will be the central matrix showing where a Product or Design needs to show compliance with a requirement, then certain documentation will need to be produced. Namely the creation of a design Technical Construction File which provides evidence of compliance with the necessary requirements. Together with the Declaration of Conformance and/or Incorporation (in the case of the suppliers products being incorporated in another product). I.e. documentation that goes with the product to show compliance.

Input to the CE Marking Process: A current, new product[28] or significant design change to a new product must be reviewed to ensure that it complies with all current directives and regulations. Any modification to production or other types of equipment will also need to be reviewed to ensure compliance with all directives and regulations. Reviews will need to include any new directives or where the directives have become mandatory[29] i.e. the transition period has ended.

---

[28]   A product referred to here is a generic product not an individual variation. I.e. the individual product variation does not impact on the essential requirements of a directive or is not covered in an existing Technical Construction File.

[29]   The technical expression is *Transition Ends* - the period between in force and mandatory.

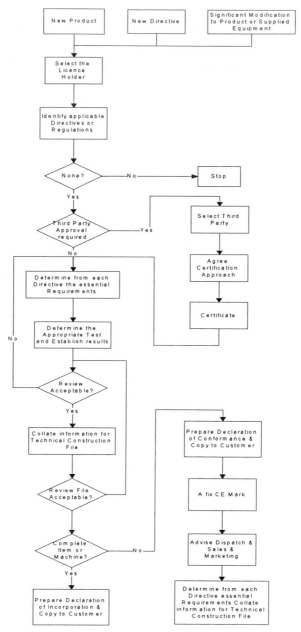

Figure 111 CE Marking Sequence

CE Marking Sequence: See **Figure 111**. Firstly it is necessary to identify a Product Licence Holder[30]. Once the person has been established, then a review can take place.

REVIEW 1: Identify any directives or regulations which are applicable. E.g. Electrical Equipment, Simple Pressure Vessels, Electromagnetic Compatibility and Machinery. Taking due account of any directives which are in force and transition has ended. See **Table 66** for guidance.

If Third Party Certification[31] is required (only as a result of the directive) e.g. Pressure Vessels, then the certification body will need to be selected. Next the test standard and certification approach[32] will need to be agreed with the certification body.

Having established the appropriate directives then each of the requirements needs to have been addressed. One way in ensuring complete coverage of the directives' requirements is by copying[33] the Directive, then adding and completing three columns, headed; Requirements, Test and Results. The following table shows the Directives Requirements (in normal print) and adjacent to each requirement (in script) the tests carried out to confirm compliance, together with the test results.

---

30   The person responsible for compliance

31   A Notified Body such as BSI can provide an E.C. type examination certificate

32   Samples Tested by an Independent Testing Body, Audit by an Independent Body, Testing by the suppliers etc.

33   Copying is acceptable

Table 67 Typical example of part of a completed Directive Review

Requirement	Test	Result
The suppliers Designed Items		
1.1.4 Light Suitable	*Visual*	*OK*
1.2.1 Safety & Reliability of the Controls	*Visual* *Enclosure Test*	*OK* *OK*
Subcontract Sourced Items		
1.5.1 Electrical Supply	*Add Declaration of Incorporation required from Suppliers to Purchase Order*	*Added Declaration of Incorporation Provided*

REVIEW 2: The above information is then examined by the Licence Holder and possibly the Department Head and if appropriate the Buyer. If acceptable the last page could be signed by the Licence Holder.

The information detailed in the Table of Contents for the Technical Construction File can then be compiled. See Appendix Technical Construction File Contents List.

REVIEW 3: All of the information in the Technical Construction File can then be examined reviewed by the Licence Holder and the Departmental Manager. If the same person then a peer. If acceptable then archive information for a minimum of ten years after cessation of manufacture. If the product is a complete machine then a Declaration of Conformity needs to be completed and a copy sent to the customer. A CE mark can then be added to the machine (usually adjacent to the rating plate). Sales & Marketing can be advised that the sales literature can be updated to indicate that the product conforms to specified directives. The dispatch documentation will usually need to carry the same information.

If the product is not a complete item (e.g. a sub-assembly) then a declaration of incorporation can be produced and a copy sent to the customer.

Note: Every piece of equipment that is to be sold for use in the European Community must be affixed with a CE mark. This mark must be affixed to one or more of the following:

(1)	The equipment
(2)	The equipment packaging
(3)	The equipment instructions for use
(4)	The equipment guarantee certificate.

Typical Technical Construction File Contents List:

1	Contents List
2	Copy of Directive which includes the tests and results essential to show compliant with the directive
3	Drawing List (including issue status) and Drawings
4	Calculation List and Calculations
5	Manuals (User, Operation, Maintenance, Installation, Commissioning etc.)
6	Any Quality Plans or ISO9000 records
7	Copy of the Declaration of Conformance or Certificate of Adequacy of equipment supplied
8	Bibliography of the Standard Used

Computer Aided Quality Assurance

The computer has now become a common place, relatively low cost item of equipment which can have dramatic effects on productivity, particularly in the handling and manipulation of data. One of the largest activities of the Quality Department is the handling and manipulation of data and it is for this reason that the computer has been quickly adopted in the Quality Assurance environment.

Some of the reasons why the computer has been used in the quality assurance environment are:

Information	o	the sheer volume of information that the quality department handles
Expediency	o	it is much more efficient and time saving to employ a computer to perform data processing
Data collation	o	the manipulation and presentation of data
Archiving	o	data can be stored and retrieved, sorted and selected much more quickly.
Communication	o	the use of electronic mail can improve the speed and accuracy of information transferred between locations

There are various types of computer available although the distinction between the different types is becoming much less clear. Main/mini frame, multi-tasking and multi-user computer systems. E.g. Vax, Prime, Digital etc. Personal computers. E.g. I.B.M., Olivetti, Apple Macintosh etc. These computers can also vary in terms of the operating systems employed e.g. MS DOS, Unix, OS2, Windows etc. Sometimes, because of the various operating systems, communication between each type of machine can be difficult.

Types of Software available

Word Processor Packages - e.g. WordStar, Word Perfect, Microsoft Word, etc.

Word processor packages are commercially available software programs for the production of documentation. These programs are generally Menu based for "User Friendliness" and have help facilities available, i.e. they display the various options available to the user when compiling documents. Many of the word processor packages are capable of processing graphics as well as text, so can be useful for presentations. These graphical capabilities can also be used to make the Quality Manual presentation more acceptable and easier to use. Control of issue and amendment of the Quality Manual can be enhanced by

392

the use of a word processor. Repetitive or similar documents are easier to produce (e.g. quotations, procedures etc.), with more effective archiving, retrieval and data storage etc.

Desktop publishing or Graphics packages - e.g. Harvard Graphics, Ventura, Fleet Street Editor etc.

Desktop publishing packages are commercially available software programs that are a highly sophisticated extension to a word processor. These software packages enable documents such as reports and material for presentations etc. to be compiled or presented in a sophisticated way which emulates the quality of magazines and books. Most word processor packages are now capable of performing many of the operations that were the exclusive province of the Desktop Package.

Database packages - e.g. dBASE, DataEase, Fox Pro, Access

Processing of information and data is one of the principal activities of the Quality Department. The data processing usually involves these basic steps: data input (paper-work), storage and retrieval system (files), processing or manipulation of data and finally an output or report.

With manual systems data manipulation can be difficult to achieve, especially if the data is required to be analysed in a different or new manner, e.g. obtaining from the calibration control system the total cost of all the measuring equipment. It can be done, but it may be a lengthy process.

Flexibility is just one of the advantages that can be gained by the application of a database program, there are many others like reduction in cost, ease of writing reports, speed of data processing etc.

What are Databases? A database is a file containing all the relevant information pertaining to a particular record. In everyday life this could be analogous to an address book, telephone book or price list. On the computer this could be a file containing information and records of all the measuring equipment in a factory.

One of the fundamental requirements of a database is to arrange data in a specific order. With a telephone directory this would be alphabetical - name, initial and then address. With a manual calibration database the usual order would be by equipment number. Having the data on a computer means that it is a relatively simple task to alter the data into numerous different sequences. For example, calibration date, withdrawal date, equipment cost, equipment name, equipment supplier etc.

This information can be sent to a printer to provide a printout of equipment records. To get the information into a database the data must be structured. See **Figure 112**. Each discrete piece of information is given a field such as equipment name, recall frequency, location etc. The FIELD-HEADER is the prompt on the computer screen when the computer is expecting a response to a question, e.g. Equipment No.

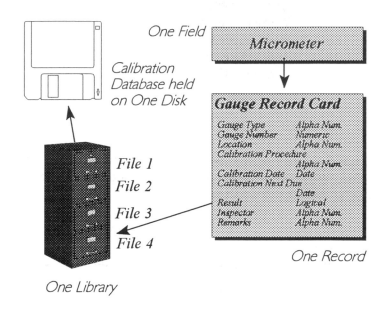

Figure 112 Database for Calibration

A set of fields relating to a particular individual entity, such as an equipment type, equipment name etc. is called a **record**.

A collection of records is called a **file**, such as all the equipment in one department or all the equipments of one type (e.g. micrometers).

A collection of files is called a **library**, such as all the equipment in a factory.

Possible Database Applications

There are numerous applications within the Quality Department for a computer database. Below are listed just some applications that have been identified which may require a considerable amount of data manipulation.

- o   Calibration Control
- o   Vendor Rating or Supplier Management
- o   Product Recall System
- o   Customer Complaints Analysis

o   Quality Problems
o   Warranty Reports
o   Audit Reports
o   Training Records
o   Document Control

Spread Sheet packages

A spread sheet program is a general purpose software package. Such a software package provides a relatively simple means of modelling certain calculations on a computer by electronic representation of calculation paper.

A spread sheet takes the form of a large sheet of paper divided into columns (usually identified by a letter) and rows (usually identified by a number). Each cell can be identified by its column and row coordinate, (Cell Address). Each cell can contain information such as: letters, numbers or instructions. See **Figure 113**.

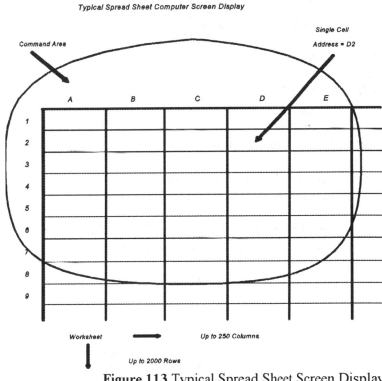

Figure 113 Typical Spread Sheet Screen Display

Letters: Can be headers for each column or row, or labels used as a guide to the contents of a cell. E.g. Prevention Cost.

Numbers: The basic raw data or value that is going to be used in the spread sheet. E.g. amounts of money spent on prevention for a particular month.

Instructions: or formulae are used to carry out calculations or the manipulation of the data. E.g. sums all the values in column E. Possibly the total cost of quality for a particular month

This sheet can be viewed on a monitor screen, but if the spread sheet is of any size then the whole sheet could not be displayed at the same time. The monitor screen acts as a window displaying only a section of the spread sheet at any one time. This window can be moved over the spread sheet by using the cursor control keys.

The section on the Cost of Quality includes a spread sheet showing the cost break down on a quarter by quarter basis. The graphs in the section Cost of Quality were produced from the cost of quality data using a spread sheet package.

Application for such programs could be: budgets, cash flow plans and forecasts, cost allocation, ad hoc calculations, statistical analysis and quality cost analysis. Examples of commercially available spread sheet programs for the IBM PC include: Lotus 123, Quattro Supercalc and Excel.

Before entering data into the spread sheet it is often wise to consider the most appropriate screen layout and what information to place in the spread sheet. The spread sheet can be preprogrammed so that after the data to be processed has been entered the computer will automatically calculate all the necessary factors, plot the graphs and print out the results in a report format.

Processing of Statistical Quality Control Data

Statistical Quality Control (SQC) is very easily adapted for use on the computer, this is because a considerable number of calculations are necessary in order to calculate the statistics or data required. E.g. mean and standard deviation.

Programs are now available which can calculate process capability, standard deviations etc. They can establish whether the process is capable of producing to a required specification. Subsequently, when the particular process is running, the software can calculate the data for the average and range charts and determine the position of the control limits for variable charts or the proportion of defects and control limits for attribute charts. These charts can then be displayed graphically on the computer screen and a 'hard copy' obtained from the printer for a permanent record.

The results obtained can be displayed graphically on the screen and the computer can give timely warnings of any trends which could result in material not meeting specification, for example trends which, if continued, could mean the data going outside of control limits or any other non-random or special cause of variation which is above or below the mean. (See Statistical Quality Control).

The SQC software has the ability to spot these non-random factors and draw them to the attention of the computer user. The way in which the software could be used may involve the inspector collecting the data (possibly in hand written form), returning to the computer and feeding the data into the computer. Alternatively electronic equipment is available which may be data linked to gauging which feed directly into the computer and therefore remove the necessity for manual measurement recording. This provides the ability to continuously monitor processes with immediate graphic interpretation of the data being collected.

This is obviously a vast improvement over the old methods of collecting data which had tended to rely on a detective approach to Quality Assurance. With the application of computers then a new preventive type of approach can be adopted by closely monitoring the process. The likelihood of defects being produced at some future time can be predicted so that timely corrective action can be taken.

There are a number of excellent share ware programmes available to perform statistical analysis of data, these include SPCPro and SPCEx.

Although this is a great advantage there are some major disadvantages. Where a number of different features need to be monitored then the cost of attaching electronic measuring equipment to all of these features may be prohibitively expensive. This is particularly so, where a product has a number of different features or where small batch quantities are produced. Also, the whole philosophy behind SQC is towards operator quality control. The use of an inspector and a computer removes the operator involvement. The emphasis with computer control SQC is for the inspector to gather the data, or for the inspector to do the interpretation of the graphical results. This runs totally contrary to the concepts of operators being responsible for the quality of the work they produce. Controlling the processes by means of plotting and monitoring the data, provides the operator with the opportunity for active participation in the monitoring of the quality of the work. With the computer in the quality control system, the inspection department becomes the controlling factor, shifting the emphasis and possibly responsibility for quality from production to the quality department.

Bespoke software

Bespoke software is generally a customised program that is used to manipulate data into a format that is "recognised" by a commercial package. I.e. It is a pre-processing program.

Management Information Systems

A Management Information System (MIS) enables real time manufacturing data to be available to management for monitoring such things as processes, progress, and defects. To process this raw data the system may utilise all or some of the above.

Special Purpose Software

There are numerous readily available database packages which have been specially adapted to provide the Quality Department with ready to use software. Using a database package such as DBASE these programs require the database to be set up or programmed. This may be quite daunting for people not experienced in programming or setting up databases. In this case these readily available packages may be useful. The main problem will be that these specially designed databases are generally of a fixed standard or nature. The Quality Department's system will have to be changed to suit the software rather than the software changed to suit the system.

Other special purpose software includes programs for:

Failure analysis   Failure Mode and Effects Analysis and Fault Tree Analysis to standards such as MIL-STD-1629A.

Reliability modelling	Reliability Calculation and Mean Time Between Failure using European and USA Standards such as HRD-5/CNET/RDF or MIL-HDBK-472, Reliability Block Diagrams.

Computer Controlled Equipment

CNC - Computer Numerical Control: CNC machines are computer controlled equipment generally used for the production of complicated, tight tolerance machined parts. CNC is normally used for low to medium volume production due to the programming time required. The advantages of these machines is that once programmed they will produce the same component on a highly repeatable basis.

CNC machines frequently employ multi-headed 'tool posts' (e.g. chucks) which once loaded up hold every tool required for that operation or series of operations, i.e. can reduce the number of tools and jigs required etc. Examples of CNC equipment are lathes, drilling and milling machines.

The effect of using these machines is to put the emphasis for quality control on the programming and first off inspection. It is important to ensure that the first component produced conforms to specification. Thereafter it should only be necessary to monitor for tool breakage and wear. Next time the job is run the first off inspection on the computer programme has been completed and it may be possible to perform a much reduced inspection. Often when new computer controlled manufacturing equipment is employed it is soon discovered that much of the new equipment's time is spent in waiting for inspection from the quality department. To overcome such delays a computer aided measuring machine can be employed, reducing inspection time and improving the productivity of the computer controlled manufacturing equipment. However, what is not always appreciated is that considerable engineering support is supplied to introducing the computer aided manufacturing equipment but the same effort and support is not always given to the computer aided measuring machine; the result being that full benefit is not derived from the computer aided measuring machine.

The type of engineering support which could be provided could include: programming the measuring machine at the same time as the manufacturing machine (although there may be certain dangers with this approach - making the same programming mistake twice), provision of special purpose fixtures from holding the components, basically planning the inspection and test activities with the same diligence as the manufacturing activities (Quality Planning).

Automatic Test Equipment - ATE: ATE equipment is computer controlled test equipment which is frequently used for the testing of (electronic) assemblies and sub-assemblies.

Typically these types of machines have either an 'in circuit' or a 'functional' test capability (or a combination of these).

'In circuit' testing really confirms that a circuit board has been manufactured correctly (i.e. finds short circuits, open circuits and components that are outside tolerance limits). The in circuit tester usually interfaces with the unit under test (UUT) via a bed of nails fixture that has one pin for every electrical node. This allows measuring of characteristics between any electrical connections (e.g. across each component).

'Functional' testing interfaces to the UUT either via a few pins in a bed of nails fixture (e.g. maybe one pin per 100 connections) or by way of flying leads. This means of testing could be used for a printed circuit board or a whole assembly. A 'good' functional test will find any manufacturing defects plus any parameters that are not within design specifications.

Functional testing is quick to highlight a failure whereas in circuit testing it is quicker to pin-point where the failure lies, i.e. identifies the fault location down to component level.

ATE is typically used for medium to high volume production or where high level technology, such as the space industry, is used.

The use of automatic testing ensures that all the assemblies are tested to within predefined tolerances. The testing becomes objective as opposed to subjective. The QA personnel would need to ensure that the preselected tolerances are correct. Once proven, this method of testing provides a very high degree of repeatability plus the availability of automatically logged test results for use in SQC and real time fault analysis (RTFA).

Material Requirements Planning (MRP 1) & Manufacturing Resource Planning (MRP 2)

Collectively MRP defines the total resources required to manufacture a product and in what time scale and when to order any materials to meet any such time scales.

The aim of these systems is to maximise profit and performance by having all the resources planned prior to commencement of a works order and by monitoring its progress throughout the company.

As each order (both customer and supplier) is logged it is possible to use this system to keep records of traceability, i.e. which orders were for which jobs, when they came in, if there were any returns etc. There can then be traceability from raw material to finished product.

Provided the quality of the installed system and database is initially good and is accurately and completely maintained, then the information it contains includes all the procedures and requirements for manufacture of a given product.

Index